Airplane Flight Dynamics and Automatic Flight Controls

Jan Roskam
Ackers Distinguished Professor of Aerospace Engineering
The University of Kansas, Lawrence

Part II

2003

DARcorporation
Design • Analysis • Research

1440 Wakarusa Drive, Suite 500 • Lawrence, Kansas 66049, U.S.A.

PUBLISHED BY

Design, Analysis and Research Corporation (*DARcorporation*)
1440 Wakarusa Drive, Suite 500
Lawrence, KS 66049
U.S.A.
Phone: (785) 832-0434
Fax: (785) 832-0524
info@darcorp.com
www.darcorp.com

Library of Congress Catalog Card Number: 94-83444

ISBN 1-884885-18-7

In all countries, sold and distributed by
Design, Analysis and Research Corporation
1440 Wakarusa Drive, Suite 500
Lawrence, KS 66049
U.S.A.

TABLE OF CONTENTS TO PARTS I AND II

PART I

SYMBOLS AND ACRONYMS (PART I)   vii

INTRODUCTION   1

1. EQUATIONS OF MOTION AND AXIS SYSTEMS   3

    1.1   COORDINATE SYSTEMS AND EXTERNAL FORCES   3
    1.2   DERIVATION OF THE EQUATIONS OF MOTION   3
    1.3   EFFECT OF SPINNING ROTORS   13
    1.4   ORIENTATION OF THE AIRPLANE RELATIVE TO THE EARTH
            FIXED COORDINATE SYSTEM X'Y'Z'   14
    1.5   THE AIRPLANE FLIGHT PATH RELATIVE TO THE EARTH   15
    1.6   THE COMPONENTS OF THE GRAVITATIONAL FORCE   20
    1.7   REVIEW OF THE EQUATIONS OF MOTION   21
    1.8   STEADY STATE EQUATIONS OF MOTION   24
          1.8.1   CASE 1: Equations of motion for steady state rectilinear flight   25
          1.8.2   CASE 2: Equations of motion for steady state turning flight   26
          1.8.3   CASE 3: Equations of motion for steady symmetrical pull–up   26
    1.9   PERTURBED STATE EQUATIONS OF MOTION   27
    1.10   SUMMARY FOR CHAPTER !   32
    1.11   PROBLEMS FOR CHAPTER 1   33
    1.12   REFERENCES FOR CHAPTER 1   34

2. REVIEW OF AERODYNAMIC FUNDAMENTALS   35

    2.1   DEFINITION OF AIRFOIL PARAMETERS   35
    2.2   AIRFOIL AERODYNAMIC CHARACTERISTICS   35
          2.2.1   Airfoil aerodynamic center   38
          2.2.2   Airfoil lift curve slope   41
    2.3   PLANFORM PARAMETERS   42
    2.4   COEFFICIENTS AND REFERENCE GEOMETRIES   44
    2.5   AERODYNAMIC CHARACTERISTICS OF PLANFORMS AND FUSELAGE   45
          2.5.1   Lift–curve slope   45
          2.5.2   Aerodynamic center   47
          2.5.3   Zero–lift angle of attack   49
          2.5.4   Moment coefficient about the aerodynamic center   50
          2.5.5   Down–wash, up–wash and dynamic pressure ratio   51
          2.5.6   Effect of the fuselage on wing aerodynamic center   56

2.6   EFFECTIVENESS OF CONTROL SURFACES   59

2.7   MODERN AIRFOILS COMPARED TO NACA AIRFOILS   62

2.8   SUMMARY FOR CHAPTER 2   62

2.9   PROBLEMS FOR CHAPTER 2   63

2.10   REFERENCES FOR CHAPTER 2   64

3.   AERODYNAMIC AND THRUST FORCES AND MOMENTS   65

3.1 STEADY STATE FORCES AND MOMENTS   67

    3.1.1   Longitudinal aerodynamic forces and moments   71

    3.1.2   Airplane drag   71

    3.1.3   Airplane lift   77

    3.1.4   Airplane aerodynamic pitching moment   80

    3.1.5   Longitudinal thrust forces and moments   90

    3.1.6   Assembling the steady state longitudinal forces and moments 93

    3.1.7   Lateral–directional aerodynamic forces and moments   94

    3.1.8   Airplane aerodynamic rolling moment   95

    3.1.9   Airplane aerodynamic side force   109

    3.1.10   Airplane aerodynamic yawing moment   114

    3.1.11   Lateral–directional thrust forces and moments   122

    3.1.12   Assembling the steady state lateral–directional forces and moments 123

3.2 PERTURBED STATE FORCES AND MOMENTS   125

    3.2.1   Perturbed state, longitudinal aerodynamic forces and moments 131

    3.2.2   Aerodynamic force and moment derivatives with respect to forward speed 132

    3.2.3   Aerodynamic force and moment derivatives with respect to angle of attack 137

    3.2.4   Aerodynamic force and moment derivatives with respect to angle of attack rate 140

    3.2.5   Aerodynamic force and moment derivatives with respect to pitch rate 143

    3.2.6   Aerodynamic force and moment derivatives with respect to control surface and flap deflections 145

    3.2.7   Assembling the perturbed, longitudinal aerodynamic forces and moments 147

    3.2.8   Perturbed state, lateral–directional aerodynamic forces and moments 148

    3.2.9   Aerodynamic force and moment derivatives with respect to sideslip 148

    3.2.10   Aerodynamic force and moment derivatives with respect to sideslip rate 148

    3.2.11   Aerodynamic force and moment derivatives with respect to roll rate 149

    3.2.12   Aerodynamic force and moment derivatives with respect to yaw rate 157

    3.2.13   Aerodynamic force and moment derivatives with respect to lateral–directional control surface deflections 160

    3.2.14   Assembling the perturbed, lateral–directional aerodynamic forces and moments 162

    3.2.15   Perturbed state longitudinal and lateral–directional thrust forces and moments 162

    3.2.16   Thrust force and moment derivatives with respect to forward speed 163

    3.2.17   Thrust force and moment derivatives with respect to angle of attack 168

    3.2.18   Thrust force and moment derivatives with respect to angle of sideslip 172

3.2.19   Assembling the perturbed state longitudinal and lateral–directional thrust forces
and moments   174

3.2.17   REVIEW OF IMPORTANT SIGN CONVENTIONS

3.3   OVERVIEW OF USUAL SIGNS FOR AERODYNAMIC COEFFICIENTS
AND DERIVATIVES   175

3.4   SUMMARY FOR CHAPTER 3   175

3.5   PROBLEMS FOR CHAPTER 3   180

3.6   REFERENCES FOR CHAPTER 3   182

4. STABILITY AND CONTROL DURING STEADY STATE FLIGHT   183

4.1   INTRODUCTION TO STATIC STABILITY AND ITS CRITERIA   184

4.1.1   Static stability criteria for velocity perturbations   186

4.1.2   Static stability criteria for angle of attack and sideslip perturbations   191

4.1.3   Static stability criteria for angular velocity perturbations   193

4.1.4   Discussion of pitching moment due to forward speed and rolling moment due to
sideslip stability   195

4.2   STABILITY AND CONTROL CHARACTERISTICS FOR STEADY STATE,
STRAIGHT LINE FLIGHT   197

4.2.1   Longitudinal stability and control characteristics for steady state, straight line flight   198

4.2.2   The airplane trim diagram   205

4.2.3   Stable and unstable pitch breaks   212

4.2.4   Use of windtunnel data in determining dε/dα 214

4.2.5   Effect of thrust in the trim diagram   214

4.2.6   lateral–directional stability and control characteristics for steady state, straight
line flight   216

4.3   STABILITY AND CONTROL CHARACTERISTICS FOR STEADY STATE,
MANEUVERING FLIGHT   224

4.3.1   Stability and control characteristics for steady state, turning flight   224

4.3.2   Stability and control characteristics for steady state, symmetrical pull–up
(push–over) flight   231

4.4   TRIM COMPARISONS FOR CONVENTIONAL, CANARD AND THREE–
SURFACE CONFIGURATIONS   234

4.4.1   Trim of a conventional configuration   234

4.4.2   Trim of a canard configuration   235

4.4.3   Trim of a three–surface configuration   236

4.5   EFFECTS OF THE FLIGHT CONTROL SYSTEM ON STABILITY AND
CONTROL IN STEADY STATE FLIGHT   238

4.5.1   Variation of stick–force and stick–force–speed gradient   239

4.5.2   Effect of control surface reversibility on static longitudinal stability   251

4.5.3   Another look at the stick–force–versus–speed gradient   253

4.5.4   Calculation of stick–force–per–'g'   254

4.5.5	Effect of control surface tabs, down–spring and bob–weight	257
	4.5.5.1 Effect of trim tabs	257
	4.5.5.2 Effect of balance or geared tabs	259
	4.5.5.3 Effect of a blow–down tab	261
	4.5.5.4 effect of a down–spring	264
	4.5.5.5 Effect of a bob–weight	266
4.6	LATERAL–DIRECTIONAL COCKPIT CONTROL FORCES	267
4.6.1	Rudder pedal control forces	267
4.6.2	Pedal–free directional stability, pedal forces in sideslip and rudder lock	268
4.6.3	Aileron wheel (stick) control forces	270
	4.6.3.1 Steady state roll rate	272
	4.6.3.2 Steady state, straight line flight	274
4.7	A MATRIX APPROACH TO THE GENERAL LONGITUDINAL TRIM PROBLEM	275
4.8	A MATRIX APPROACH TO THE GENERAL LATERAL–DIRECTIONAL TRIM PROBLEM	283
4.9	THE TAKEOFF ROTATION PROBLEM	288
4.10	INTRODUCTION TO IRREVERSIBLE FLIGHT CONTROL SYSTEMS	293
4.11	SUMMARY FOR CHAPTER 4	295
4.12	PROBLEMS FOR CHAPTER 4	299
4.13	REFERENCES FOR CHAPTER 4	301

5. STABILITY AND CONTROL DURING PERTURBED STATE FLIGHT — 303

5.1	DYNAMIC STABILITY AND RESPONSE BEHAVIOR OF A SPRING–MASS–DAMPER SYSTEM AND ITS STABILITY CRITERIA	309
5.2	LONGITUDINAL, DYNAMIC STABILITY AND RESPONSE	318
5.2.1	Longitudinal equations and transfer functions	318
5.2.2	Longitudinal characteristic equation roots and their connection to dynamic stability	325
5.2.3	Connection between dynamic and static longitudinal stability	328
5.2.4	Examples of longitudinal transfer functions	329
5.2.5	The short period approximation	333
5.2.6	The phugoid approximation	338
5.2.7	Response to an elevator step input	340
5.2.8	Standard format for the longitudinal transfer functions	341
5.2.9	The longitudinal mode shapes	341
5.3	LATERAL–DIRECTIONAL, DYNAMIC STABILITY AND RESPONSE	346
5.3.1	Lateral–directional equations and transfer functions	346
5.3.2	Lateral–directional characteristic equation roots and their connection to dynamic stability	355
5.3.3	Connection between dynamic and static lateral–directional stability	356
5.3.4	Examples of lateral–directional transfer functions	356
5.3.5	The dutch roll approximation	363

5.3.6	The spiral approximation	365
5.3.7	The roll approximation	367
5.3.8	Response to aileron and rudder step inputs	371
5.3.9	Standard format for the lateral–directional transfer functions	372
5.3.10	The lateral–directional mode shapes	372
5.4	CENTER–OF–GRAVITY AND DERIVATIVE ROOT–LOCI AND THE ROLE OF SENSITIVITY ANALYSES	378
5.4.1	Effect of center–of–gravity and mass distribution on longitudinal dynamic stability	378
5.4.2	Effect of stability derivatives on longitudinal dynamic stability	380
5.4.3	Effect of center–of–gravity and mass distribution on lateral–directional dynamic stability	383
5.4.4	Effect of stability derivatives on lateral–directional dynamic stability	386
5.5	EQUIVALENT STABILITY DERIVATIVES, STABILITY AUGMENTATION AND DEPENDENCE ON CONTROL POWER	395
5.5.1	Equivalent pitch damping derivative	395
5.5.2	Equivalent yaw damping derivative	397
5.5.3	Equivalent longitudinal stability derivative	398
5.6	INERTIAL COUPLING DUE TO ROLL RATE AND PITCH RATE	400
5.6.1	Inertial coupling due to roll rate	400
5.6.2	Inertial coupling due to pitch rate	407
5.7	SUMMARY FOR CHAPTER 5	409
5.8	PROBLEMS FOR CHAPTER 5	409
5.9	REFERENCES FOR CHAPTER 5	411
6.	FLYING QUALITIES AND PILOT RATINGS, REGULATIONS AND APPLICATIONS	413
6.1	FLYING QUALITIES AND PILOT RATINGS	413
6.2	MILITARY AND CIVILIAN FLYING QUALITY REQUIREMENTS: INTRODUCTION AND DEFINITIONS	415
6.2.1	Definition of airplane classes	417
6.2.2	Definition of mission flight phases	417
6.2.3	Definition of flying quality levels and allowable failure probabilities	417
6.3	LONGITUDINAL FLYING QUALITY REQUIREMENTS	423
6.3.1	Longitudinal control forces	423
6.3.1.1	Control forces in maneuvering flight	423
6.3.1.2	Control forces in steady state flight	423
6.3.1.3	Control forces in takeoff and landing	426
6.3.1.4	Control forces in dives	426
6.3.2	Phugoid stability	427
6.3.3	Flight path stability	427
6.3.4	Short period frequency and damping	428

  6.3.5   Control anticipation parameter ... 431
6.4   LATERAL–DIRECTIONAL FLYING QUALITY REQUIREMENTS ... 434
  6.4.1   Lateral–directional control forces ... 434
    6.4.1.1 Roll control forces ... 434
    6.4.1.2 Directional control forces with asymmetric loadings ... 435
    6.4.1.3 Directional and roll control forces with one engine inoperative ... 435
  6.4.2   Dutch roll frequency and damping ... 436
  6.4.3   Spiral stability ... 437
  6.4.4   Coupled roll–spiral (=lateral phugoid) stability ... 437
  6.4.5   Roll mode time constant ... 438
  6.4.6   Roll control effectiveness ... 439
  6.4.7   Yawing moments in steady sideslips ... 439
  6.4.8   Side forces in steady sideslips ... 442
  6.4.9   Rolling moments in steady sideslips ... 442
6.5   CHARACTERISTICS OF THE FLIGHT CONTROL SYSTEM ... 443
6.6   RELATION BETWEEN FLYING QUALITY REQUIREMENTS AND DESIGN ... 445
  6.6.1   Design for roll control effectiveness ... 445
  6.6.2   Design for inherent spiral and dutch roll stability ... 446
  6.6.3   Design for augmented static and dynamic stability in pitch ... 451
    6.6.3.1 Effect of horizontal tail size on longitudinal stability and control derivatives ... 451
    6.6.3.2 Stability augmentation by angle–of–attack and pitch–rate feedback ... 455
    6.6.3.3 Effect of horizontal tail area on controllability in gust and on maneuvering ... 456
    6.6.3.4 Effect of horizontal tail area on trim ... 457
6.7   SUMMARY FOR CHAPTER 6 ... 459
6.8   PROBLEMS FOR CHAPTER 6 ... 459
6.9   REFERENCES FOR CHAPTER 6 ... 460

APPENDIX A: DESCRIPTION OF THE ADVANCED AIRCRAFT ANALYSIS (AAA) PROGRAM ... 461
A1   GENERAL CAPABILITIES OF THE AAA PROGRAM ... 461
A2   BRIEF DESCRIPTION OF AAA PROGRAM MODULES ... 461
A3   STABILITY AND CONTROL CAPABILITIES OF THE AAA PROGRAM ... 464
A4   REFERENCES FOR APPENDIX A ... 466

APPENDIX B: AIRPLANE DATA ... 479

APPENDIX C: SUMMARY OF LAPLACE TRANSFORM PROPERTIES ... 551

APPENDIX D   ON THE EFFECT OF FREE, REVERSIBLE FLIGHT CONTROLS ON AIRPLANE DYNAMIC STABILITY ... 555

INDEX TO PART I ... 561

PART II

SYMBOLS AND ACRONYMS (PARTS I AND II)   xiii

INTRODUCTION   577

7. EFFECTS OF AEROELASTICITY ON STABILITY AND CONTROL   579

    7.1   EXAMPLES OF AEROELASTIC BEHAVIOR   579
         7.1.1   Aileron Reversal   579
         7.1.2   Wing Divergence   582
         7.1.3   Elevator Control Power Reduction due to Aft Fuselage Bending   583
    7.2   INTRODUCTION TO AERODYNAMIC AND STRUCTURAL INFLUENCE
         COEFFICIENT MATRICES   586
         7.2.1   Aerodynamic Influence Coefficients for Rigid Airplanes   587
         7.2.2   Structural Influence Coefficients for Elastic Airplanes   590
    7.3   STABILITY AND CONTROL CHARACTERISTICS OF ELASTIC AIRPLANES
         IN STEADY STATE FLIGHT   593
    7.4   STABILITY AND CONTROL CHARACTERISTICS OF ELASTIC AIRPLANES
         IN PERTURBED STATE FLIGHT   597
         7.4.1   Derivation of Elastic Airplane Stability Derivatives for Perturbed State Flight   597
         7.4.2   Interpretation and Use of Elastic Airplane Stability Derivatives   602
    7.5   DETERMINING THE JIG SHAPE OF ELASTIC AIRPLANES   608
         7.5.1   Determining the Jig Shape   608
         7.5.2   Determining the Equilibrium Angle of Attack Distribution   609
    7.6   DETERMINING LATERAL–DIRECTIONAL DERIVATIVES FOR ELASTIC AIRPLANES   611
         7.6.1   Determination of the Roll Damping Derivative for an Elastic Airplane   611
         7.6.2   Determination of the Directional Stability Derivative for an Elastic Airplane   613
    7.7   NUMERICAL EXAMPLES OF ELASTIC AIRPLANE STABILITY AND
         CONTROL DERIVATIVES   615
         7.7.1   Numerical Examples: Longitudinal Stability Derivatives   615
         7.7.2   Numerical Examples: Lateral–Directional Stability Derivatives   615
    7.8   SUMMARY FOR CHAPTER 7   622
    7.9   PROBLEMS FOR CHAPTER 7   623
    7.10   REFERENCES FOR CHAPTER 7   625

8. THEORY AND APPLICATIONS OF BODE PLOTS   627

    8.1   INTRODUCTION TO THE FREQUENCY RESPONSE OF LINEAR SYSTEMS   629
    8.2   DETERMINATION OF THE FREQUENCY RESPONSE OF LINEAR SYSTEMS
         DIRECTLY FROM THE SYSTEM OPEN LOOP TRANSFER FUNCTION   637
    8.3   ASYMPTOTIC APPROXIMATIONS TO REAL FREQUENCY RESPONSE

		OF TRANSFER FUNCTIONS	645
	8.3.1	Differentiators and Integrators	645
	8.3.2	First Order Lead and Lag Transfer Functions	648
	8.3.3	Second Order Lead and Lag Transfer Functions	653
	8.3.4	Summary of Amplitude and Phase Angle Properties of First and Second Transfer Functions	657
8.4		APPLICATIONS OF BODE PLOTS TO AIRPLANES	659
	8.4.1	Bode Plots for Speed, Angle of Attack and Pitch Attitude Angle Response to Elevator Inputs	662
	8.4.2	Bode Plots for Sideslip Angle, Bank Angle and Heading Angle Response to Aileron and Rudder Inputs	668
8.5		AN INVERSE APPLICATION OF BODE PLOTS	678
8.6		SUMMARY FOR CHAPTER 8	683
8.7		PROBLEMS FOR CHAPTER 8	683
8.8		REFERENCES FOR CHAPTER 8	684

9. CLASSICAL CONTROL THEORY WITH APPLICATIONS TO AIRPLANES — 685

9.1		EXAMPLE OF THE POTENTIAL OF FEEDBACK CONTROL	688
9.2		BASIC RELATIONSHIPS AND DEFINITIONS USED IN FEEDBACK CONTROL SYSTEMS	692
9.3		THE ROOT LOCUS METHOD	696
	9.3.1	Root Locus Fundamentals	696
	9.3.2	Root Locus Asymptotes	703
	9.3.3	Breakaway Angle from a Complex Pole	706
	9.3.4	Step–by–Step Construction of a Root Locus Diagram	707
9.4		APPLICATION OF THE THE BODE PLOT METHOD TO CONTROL SYSTEM ANALYSIS	711
9.5		CONNECTION BETWEEN THE FREQUENCY DOMAIN AND THE TIME DOMAIN	715
9.6		SYSTEM PERFORMANCE SPECIFICATIONS	725
	9.6.1	Frequency Domain Specifications	725
	9.6.2	Time Domain Specifications	728
	9.6.3	Error and Error Constant Specifications	730
		9.6.3.1 Error characteristics of unity negative feedback systems	731
		9.6.3.2 Error characteristics of general systems	734
	9.6.4	System Sensitivity	737
9.7		SOME FEEDBACK CONTROL SYSTEM DESIGN APPLICATIONS	738
	9.7.1	A Multiple Feedback Loop System: Pole Assignment	738
	9.7.2	Setting System Gain to Achieve a Specified Damping Ratio	742
	9.7.3	Setting Gain to Achieve a Specified Gain Margin and Position Error Constant	743
	9.7.4	Finding Lag Compensation to Alter the Breakaway Angle from Complex Poles	744
	9.7.5	Finding a Lead–Lag Compensator to Increase System Gain Margin	746

	9.7.6	Using Cancellation Compensation to Achieve Better Closed Loop Characteristics	750
	9.7.7	Root Contours for Variable Poles	753
	9.7.8	Root Contours for Variable Zeros	756
9.8	SUMMARY FOR CHAPTER 9		759
9.9	PROBLEMS FOR CHAPTER 9		759
9.10	REFERENCES FOR CHAPTER 9		761

10. ANALYSIS OF AIRPLANE PLUS PILOT AS A CLOSED LOOP CONTROL SYSTEM — 763

10.1	THE HUMAN PILOT TRANSFER FUNCTION	763
10.2	PILOT CONTROL OF BANK ANGLE	768
10.2	PILOT CONTROL OF PITCH ATTITUDE ANGLE	774
10.4	SUMMARY FOR CHAPTER 10	777
10.5	PROBLEMS FOR CHAPTER 10	777
10.6	REFERENCES FOR CHAPTER 10	777

11. STABILITY AUGMENTATION AND AUTOMATIC FLIGHT CONTROL SYSTEMS — 779

11.1	YAW DAMPERS		780
11.2	PITCH DAMPERS		789
11.3	STATIC STABILITY AUGMENTATION SYSTEMS		793
	11.3.1	Angle–of–attack Feedback to the Longitudinal Controls	793
	11.3.2	Load Factor Feedback to the Longitudinal Controls	794
	11.3.3	Sideslip Feedback to the Directional Controls	797
11.4	BASIC AUTOPILOT SYSTEMS		801
11.5	BASIC LONGITUDINAL AUTOPILOT MODES		804
	11.5.1	Pitch Attitude Hold Mode	804
	11.5.2	Altitude Hold Mode	813
	11.5.3	Airspeed or Mach Number Hold Mode	816
		11.5.3.1 Airspeed hold mode using autothrottles	817
		11.5.3.2 Airspeed hold mode using speedbrakes	819
		11.5.3.3 Mach hold using the elevator	823
		11.5.3.4 Mach tuck control (Mach trim)	824
	11.5.4	Control Wheel Steering Mode	828
11.6	BASIC LATERAL–DIRECTIONAL AUTOPILOT MODES		833
	11.6.1	Bank Angle Hold Mode	833
	11.6.2	Heading Angle Hold Mode	836
	11.6.3	Turn Rate Mode at Constant Speed and Altitude	838
	11.6.4	Turn Coordination (Zero Lateral Acceleration)	839
11.7	LONGITUDINAL NAVIGATION MODES		841

11.7.1	Approach Categories and Guidance	841
11.7.2	Glideslope Hold Mode	843
11.7.3	Automatic Flare Mode	852
11.8	LATERAL–DIRECTIONAL NAVIGATION MODES	857
11.8.1	Localizer Hold Mode	857
11.8.2	V.O.R. Hold Mode	866
11.9	MULTIPLE LOOP, MULTIPLE VARIABLE CONTROL SYSTEMS	868
11.10	SEPARATE SURFACE CONTROL SYSTEMS	873
11.10.1	Introduction and Definitions	873
11.10.2	Closed Loop Analysis of Separate Surface Control Systems	874
11.11	SUMMARY FOR CHAPTER 11	879
11.12	PROBLEMS FOR CHAPTER 11	879
11.13	REFERENCES FOR CHAPTER 11	880

12. FUNDAMENTALS OF DIGITAL CONTROL SYSTEM ANALYSIS — 881

12.1	INTRODUCTION TO SIGNAL SAMPLING	881
12.2	LAPLACE TRANSFORMS AND SAMPLED DATA SYSTEMS	884
12.2.1	The Uniqueness Problem	884
12.2.2	The Laplace Transform of the Sampled Unit Step	885
12.2.3	The Laplace Transform of the Sampled Function: e^{-t}	885
12.2.4	On the Periodicity of: $\varepsilon^*(s)$	886
12.3	RECONSTRUCTION OF ANALOG DATA FROM SAMPLED DATA	886
12.3.1	Introductory Observations	886
12.3.2	The Zero Order Hold	888
12.3.3	The First Order Hold	890
12.4	FUNDAMENTALS OF Z–TRANSFORM THEORY	893
12.4.1	Definition and Derivation of Z–Transforms	893
12.4.2	Mapping of the s–Plane into the z–Plane	899
12.4.3	Mapping of Constant Damping Loci	901
12.4.4	Mapping of Constant Frequency Loci	901
12.4.5	Mapping of Constant Damping Ratio Loci	903
12.4.6	Mapping of Constant Undamped Natural Frequency Loci	904
12.4.7	Inverse z–Transforms	906
12.4.8	Important z–Transform Properties	908
12.5	AN APPLICATION OF Z–TRANSFORMS	911
12.5.1	The Pulse Transfer Function of Sampled Data Systems	911
12.5.2	Closed Loop Sampled Data Systems	915
12.5.3	A Simple Bank Angle Control System	917
12.6	EFFECT OF SAMPLING FREQUENCY ON THE STABILITY OF DIGITAL SYSTEMS	924
12.6.1	Jury's Test	924
12.6.2	Routh–Hurwitz Criterion	927

   12.6.3 The Root–Locus Method   929

 12.7 RELATIONS BETWEEN THE S–, Z– AND TIME DOMAINS 929

 12.8 SUMMARY FOR CHAPTER 12   931

 12.9 PROBLEMS FOR CHAPTER 12   931

 12.10 REFERENCES FOR CHAPTER 12   932

APPENDIX E: HARDWARE ASPECTS OF AUTOPILOT SYSTEMS 933

 E1 AUTOPILOT AND SENSOR FUNDAMENTALS   933

   E1.1 Pitch Attitude Angle, θ and Bank Angle, ϕ 933

   E1.2 Heading Angle, ψ 933

   E1.3 Angular Rates Such As: $d\psi/dt$, $d\theta/dt$ and $d\phi/dt$ 936

 E2 AUTOPILOT MODES   936

 E3 REFERENCES   938

INDEX TO PARTS I AND II   939

SYMBOLS AND ACRONYMS (PARTS I AND II)

Symbol	Description	Unit(s)
Regular		
a_{bw}	Moment arm of bobweight (see Figure 4.41)	ft
a_{ds}	Moment arm of downspring (see Figure 4.41)	ft
a_i	Element of control surface distribution matrix	———
a_t	Tab spring moment arm	ft
A	Aspect ratio, also a combination function of hingemoment coefficients: see Eqn (4.160)	———
A, B, C, D	Coefficients for control surface hingemoment rates	———
A_i	Inlet area	ft^2
A_i	Also: input amplitude	———
A_0	Output amplitude	———
A_1	Coefficient in denominator of longitudinal transfer function	ft/sec
A_2	Coefficient in denominator of lateral–directional transfer function	ft/sec
A_{ij}	Element of the aerodynamic influence coefficient matrix	ft^2/rad
A_α	Coefficient in numerator of angle–of–attack–to–elevator transfer function	ft/sec^2
A_β	Coefficient in numerator of angle–of–sideslip to aileron or rudder transfer function	ft/sec^2
A_u	Coefficient in numerator of speed–to–elevator transfer function	ft^2/sec^3
A_θ	Coefficient in numerator of pitch–attitude–to–elevator transfer function	ft/sec^3
A_ϕ	Coefficient in numerator of bank–angle to aileron or rudder transfer function	ft/sec^3
A_ψ	Coefficient in numerator of heading–angle to aileron or rudder transfer function	ft/sec^3
$[A]$	System matrix as defined in Eqn (4.228)	See Eqn (4.228)
$\{B\}$	Column matrix as defined in Eqn (4.228)	See Eqn (4.228)

Symbol	**Description**	**Unit(s)**
Regular (Continued)		
$[B]$	Matrix as defined in Eqn (7.52)	——
b	Span	ft
B_1	Coefficient in denominator of longitudinal transfer function	ft/sec^2
B_2	Coefficient in denominator of lateral–directional transfer function	ft/sec^2
B_α	Coefficient in numerator of angle–of–attack–to–elevator transfer function	ft/sec^3
B_β	Coefficient in numerator of angle–of–sideslip to aileron or rudder transfer function	ft/sec^3
B_u	Coefficient in numerator of speed–to–elevator transfer function	ft^2/sec^4
B_θ	Coefficient in numerator of pitch–attitude–to–elevator transfer function	ft/sec^4
B_ϕ	Coefficient in numerator of bank–angle to aileron or rudder	ft/sec^4
B_ψ	Coefficient in numerator of heading–angle to aileron or rudder	ft/sec^4
c	chord	ft
c	viscous damping constant	lbs/ft/sec
$\overline{c}$	Mean geometric chord	ft
c_d	Section drag coefficient	——
c_f	Flap or control surface chord	ft
$C(s)$	Laplace transform of system output	——
C_1	Coefficient in denominator of longitudinal transfer function	ft/sec^3
C_1	Inertia ratio defined by Eqn (5.180)	
C_2	Coefficient in denominator of lateral–directional transfer function	ft/sec^3
C_{ij}	Element of the structural influence coefficient matrix	rad/lbs
C_α	Coefficient in numerator of angle–of–attack–to–elevator transfer function	ft/sec^4
C_β	Coefficient in numerator of angle–of–sideslip to aileron or rudder	ft/sec^4

Symbol	Description	Unit(s)

Regular (Continued)

Symbol	Description	Unit(s)
C_u	Coefficient in numerator of speed–to–elevator transfer function	ft^2/sec^5
C_θ	Coefficient in numerator of pitch–attitude–to–elevator transfer function	ft/sec^5
C_ϕ	Coefficient in numerator of bank–angle to aileron or rudder	ft/sec^5
C_ψ	Coefficient in numerator of heading–angle to aileron or rudder	ft/sec^5
C_D	Drag coefficient (airplane)	——
C_{D_0}	Drag coefficient (airplane) for zero angle of attack	——
$\overline{C}_{D_0}$	Drag coefficient (airplane) for zero lift coefficient	——
$C_{D_\alpha} = \partial C_D/\partial\alpha$	Variation of airplane drag coefficient with angle of attack	1/rad
$C_{D_{\dot\alpha}} = \partial C_D/\partial(\dot\alpha\bar{c}/2U_1)$	Variation of airplane drag coefficient with dimensionless rate of change of angle of attack	1/rad
$C_{D_{i_h}} = \partial C_D/\partial i_h$	Variation of airplane drag coefficient with stabilizer incidence angle	1/rad
$C_{D_{\delta_e}} = \partial C_D/\partial\delta_e$	Variation of airplane drag coefficient with elevator deflection angle	1/rad
$C_{D_q} = \partial C_D/\partial(q\bar{c}/2U_1)$	Variation of airplane drag coefficient with dimensionless pitch rate	1/rad
$C_{D_u} = \partial C_D/\partial(u/U_1)$	Variation of airplane drag coefficient with dimensionless speed	1/rad
C_f	Airplane equivalent skin friction coefficient	——
C_h	Control surface hingemoment coefficient	——
$C_{h_\alpha} = \partial C_h/\partial\alpha$	Variation of control surface hingemoment coefficient with angle of attack	1/rad
$C_{h_{\beta_v}} = \partial C_{h_r}/\partial\beta$	Variation of rudder hingemoment coefficient with angle of sideslip	1/rad
$C_{h_\delta} = \partial C_h/\partial\delta$	Variation of control surface hingemoment coefficient with control surface deflection	1/rad
$C_{h_{\delta_t}} = \partial C_h/\partial\delta_t$	Variation of control surface hingemoment coefficient with control surface tab deflection	1/rad
$C^t_{h_{\delta_t}} = \partial C_{h_t}/\partial\delta_t$	Variation of control surface tab hingemoment coef–cient about the tab hingeline with respect to tab deflection	1/rad

Symbol	Description	Unit(s)

Regular (Continued)

Symbol	Description	Unit(s)
$C_{h_u} = \partial C_h / \partial(u/U_1)$	Variation of control surface hingemoment coefficient with respect to speed	———
$C_{h_q} = \partial C_h / \partial(q\bar{c}/2U_1)$	Variation of control surface hingemoment coefficient with respect to pitch rate	1/rad
$C_{h_{\delta_e}} = \partial C_h / \partial(\dot{\delta}_e \bar{c}_e / 2U_1)$	Variation of elevator hingemoment coefficient with respect to elevator rate	1/rad
$C_{h_{\delta_r}} = \partial C_h / \partial(\dot{\delta}_r b_e / 2U_1)$	Variation of rudder hingemoment coefficient with respect to rudder rate	1/rad
c_l	Section lift coefficient	———
$c_{l_\alpha} = \partial c_l / \partial\alpha$	Variation of section lift coefficient with angle of attack	1/rad
$c_{l_\delta} = \partial c_l / \partial\delta$	Variation of section lift coefficient with control control surface deflection angle	1/rad
C_l	Rolling moment coefficient (airplane)	———
C_{l_0}	Rolling moment coefficient for zero sideslip angle and zero control surface deflections	———
$C_{l_\beta} = \partial C_l / \partial\beta$	Variation of airplane rolling moment coefficient with angle of sideslip	1/rad
$\overline{C}_{l_\beta} = \partial\overline{C}_l / \partial\beta$	Variation of airplane component rolling moment coefficient with sideslip angle, but based on component reference geometry	1/rad
$C_{l_{\dot{\beta}}} = \partial C_l / \partial(\dot{\beta}b/2U_1)$	Variation of airplane rolling moment coefficient with dimensionless rate of change of angle of sideslip	———
$C_{l_{\delta_a}} = \partial C_l / \partial\delta_a$	Variation of airplane rolling moment coefficient with aileron deflection angle	1/rad
$C_{l_{\delta_r}} = \partial C_l / \partial\delta_r$	Variation of airplane rolling moment coefficient with rudder deflection angle	1/rad
$C_{l_{i_h}} = \partial C_l / \partial i_h$	Variation of airplane rolling moment coefficient with differential stabilizer angle	1/rad
$C_{l_p} = \partial C_l / \partial(pb/2U_1)$	Variation of airplane rolling moment coefficient with dimensionless rate of change of roll rate	1/rad
$C_{l_r} = \partial C_l / \partial(rb/2U_1)$	Variation of airplane rolling moment coefficient with dimensionless rate of change of yaw rate	1/rad
$C_{l_{T_\beta}} = \partial C_{l_T} / \partial\beta$	Variation of airplane rolling moment coefficient due to thrust with sideslip angle	1/rad

Symbol	**Description**	**Unit(s)**
Regular (Continued)		
C_L	Lift coefficient (airplane)	——
C_{L_0}	Lift coefficient (airplane) for zero angle of attack	——
$\partial C_L / \partial n$	Variation of airplane lift coefficient with load factor	——
$C_{L_\alpha} = \partial C_L / \partial \alpha$	Variation of airplane lift coefficient with angle of attack	1/rad
$C_{L_{\dot{\alpha}}} = \partial C_L / \partial (\dot{\alpha}\bar{c}/2U_1)$	Variation of airplane lift coefficient with dimensionless rate of change of angle of attack	1/rad
$C_{L_{i_h}} = \partial C_L / \partial i_h$	Variation of airplane lift coefficient with stabilizer incidence angle	1/rad
$C_{L_{\delta_e}} = \partial C_L / \partial \delta_e$	Variation of airplane lift coefficient with elevator deflection angle	1/rad
$C_{L_q} = \partial C_L / \partial (q\bar{c}/2U_1)$	Variation of airplane lift coefficient with dimensionless pitch rate	1/rad
$C_{L_u} = \partial C_L / \partial (u/U_1)$	Variation of airplane lift coefficient with dimensionless speed	——
c_m	Section pitching moment coefficient	——
$c_{m_{ac}}$	Section pitching moment coefficient about the a.c.	——
c_{m_0}	Section pitching moment coefficient at zero angle of attack	——
$\bar{c}_{m_0}$	Section pitching moment coefficient at zero lift	——
$c_{m_\alpha} = \partial c_m / \partial \alpha$	Variation of section pitching moment coefficient with angle of attack	1/rad
C_m	Pitching moment coefficient (airplane)	——
C_{m_0}	Pitching moment coefficient (airplane) for zero angle of attack	——
$\bar{C}_{m_0}$	Pitching moment coefficient (airplane) for zero lift	——
$\partial C_m / \partial n$	Variation of airplane pitching moment coefficient load factor	——
$C_{m_\alpha} = \partial C_m / \partial \alpha$	Variation of airplane pitching moment coefficient with angle of attack	1/rad
$C_{m_{\dot{\alpha}}} = \partial C_m / \partial (\dot{\alpha}\bar{c}/2U_1)$	Variation of airplane pitching moment coefficient with dimensionless rate of change of angle of attack	1/rad

Symbol	Description	Unit(s)

Regular (Continued)

Symbol	Description	Unit(s)
$C_{m_{i_h}} = \partial C_m/\partial i_h$	Variation of airplane pitching moment coefficient with stabilizer incidence angle	1/rad
$C_{m_{\delta_e}} = \partial C_m/\partial \delta_e$	Variation of airplane pitching moment coefficient with elevator deflection angle	1/rad
C_{m_T}	Pitching moment coefficient due to thrust	——
$C_{m_{T_{N_p}}}$	Pitching moment coefficient due to propeller normal force coefficient	——
$C_{m_q} = \partial C_m/\partial(q\bar{c}/2U_1)$	Variation of airplane pitching moment coefficient with pitch rate	1/rad
$C_{m_u} = \partial C_m/\partial(u/U_1)$	Variation of airplane pitching moment coefficient with dimensionless speed	——
$C_{m_{T_\alpha}} = \partial C_{m_T}/\partial\alpha$	Variation of airplane pitching moment coefficient due to thrust with angle of attack	1/rad
$C_{m_{T_u}} = \partial C_{m_T}/\partial(u/U_1)$	Variation of airplane pitching moment coefficient due to thrust with dimensionless speed	——
C_n	Yawing moment coefficient (airplane)	——
C_{n_0}	Yawing moment coefficient for zero sideslip angle and zero control surface deflections	1/rad
C_{N_p}	Propeller normal force coefficient	
$C_{n_\beta} = \partial C_n/\partial\beta$	Variation of airplane yawing moment coefficient with angle of sideslip	1/rad
$C_{n_{\dot\beta}} = \partial C_n/\partial(\dot\beta b/2U_1)$	Variation of airplane yawing moment coefficient with dimensionless rate of change of angle of sideslip	1/rad
$C_{n_{\delta_a}} = \partial C_n/\partial\delta_a$	Variation of airplane yawing moment coefficient with aileron deflection angle	1/rad
$C_{n_{\delta_{r_{drag}}}} = \partial C_n/\partial\delta_{r_{drag}}$	Variation of airplane yawing moment coefficient with drag rudder deflection angle	1/rad
$C_{n_{i_h}} = \partial C_n/\partial i_h$	Variation of airplane yawing moment coefficient with differential stabilizer angle	1/rad
$C_{n_{\delta_r}} = \partial C_n/\partial\delta_r$	Variation of airplane yawing moment coefficient with rudder deflection angle	1/rad
$C_{n_{\delta_s}} = \partial C_n/\partial\delta_s$	Variation of airplane yawing moment coefficient with spoiler deflection angle	1/rad

Symbol	Description	Unit(s)

Regular (Continued)

$C_{n_p} = \partial C_n / \partial(pb/2U_1)$ — Variation of airplane yawing moment coefficient with dimensionless rate of change of roll rate — 1/rad

$C_{n_r} = \partial C_n / \partial(rb/2U_1)$ — Variation of airplane yawing moment coefficient with dimensionless rate of change of yaw rate — 1/rad

$C_{n_{T_\beta}} = \partial C_{n_T} / \partial\beta$ — Variation of airplane yawing moment coefficient due to thrust with sideslip angle — 1/rad

C_T — Thrust coefficient — _____

$C_{T_{x_u}} = \partial C_{T_x} / \partial(u/U_1)$ — Variation of airplane thrust coefficient in the X–axis direction w.r.t. dimensionless speed — _____

$C_{T_{x_\alpha}} = \partial C_{T_x} / \partial\alpha$ — Variation of airplane thrust coefficient in the X–axis direction with angle of attack — 1/rad

$C_{T_{x,y \text{ or } z}}$ — Thrust coefficient component in the X,Y or Z axis direction

$C_{T_{z_u}} = \partial C_{T_z} / \partial(u/U_1)$ — Variation of airplane thrust coefficient in the Z–axis direction w.r.t. dimensionless speed — _____

$C_{T_{z_\alpha}} = \partial C_{T_z} / \partial\alpha$ — Variation of airplane thrust coefficient in the Z–axis direction with angle of attack — 1/rad

$C_{T_{y_\beta}} = \partial C_{T_y} / \partial\beta$ — Variation of airplane thrust coefficient in the Y–axis direction with sideslip angle — 1/rad

C_x — Force coefficient along the stability X–axis — _____

$C_{x_\alpha} = \partial C_x / \partial\alpha$ — Variation of airplane X–axis force coefficient with angle of attack — 1/rad

$C_{x_q} = \partial C_x / \partial(q\bar{c}/2U_1)$ — Variation of airplane X–axis force coefficient with dimensionless pitch rate — 1/rad

$C_{x_u} = \partial C_x / \partial(u/U_1)$ — Variation of airplane X–axis force coefficient with dimensionless speed — _____

C_y — Side force coefficient (airplane) — _____

C_{y_0} — Side force coefficient for zero sideslip angle and zero control surface deflections — _____

$C_{y_\beta} = \partial C_y / \partial\beta$ — Variation of airplane side force coefficient with sideslip angle — 1/rad

$C_{y_{\dot\beta}} = \partial C_y / \partial(\dot\beta b/2U_1)$ — Variation of airplane side force coefficient with dimensionless rate of change of angle of sideslip — 1/rad

$C_{y_{\delta_a}} = \partial C_y / \partial\delta_a$ — Variation of airplane side force coefficient with aileron angle — 1/rad

Symbol	Description	Unit(s)
Regular (Continued)		
$C_{y_{\delta_r}} = \partial C_y / \partial \delta_r$	Variation of airplane side force coefficient with rudder angle	1/rad
$C_{y_p} = \partial C_y / \partial(pb/2U_1)$	Variation of airplane side force coefficient with dimensionless rate of change of roll rate	1/rad
$C_{y_r} = \partial C_y / \partial(rb/2U_1)$	Variation of airplane side force coefficient with dimensionless rate of change of yaw rate	1/rad
C_x	Force coefficient along the stability Z–axis	——
$C_{z_{\dot{\alpha}}} = \partial C_z / \partial(\dot{\alpha}\bar{c}/2U_1)$	Variation of airplane Z–axis force coefficient with dimensionless rate of change of angle of attack	1/rad
$C_{z_q} = \partial C_z / \partial(q\bar{c}/2U_1)$	Variation of airplane Z–axis force coefficient with dimensionless pitch rate	1/rad
$C_{z_u} = \partial C_z / \partial(u/U_1)$	Variation of airplane Z–axis force coefficient dimensionless speed	——
dm	Airplane mass element	slugs
D_1	Coefficient in denominator of longitudinal transfer function	ft/sec4
D_1	Inertia ratio defined by Eqn (5.180)	——
D_2	Coefficient in denominator of lateral–directional transfer function	ft/sec4
D_α	Coefficient in numerator of angle–of–attack–to elevator transfer function	ft/sec5
D_β	Coefficient in numerator of angle–of–sideslip to aileron or rudder transfer function	ft/sec5
D_u	Coefficient in numerator of speed–to–elevator transfer function	ft2/sec6
D_ψ	Coefficient in numerator of heading–angle to aileron or rudder	ft2/sec6
D	Drag (airplane)	lbs
$\overline{D}_1$	Denominator of longitudinal transfer functions	ftrad4/sec5
$\overline{D}_2$	Denominator of lateral–directional transfer functions	ftrad5/sec6
D_p	Propeller diameter	ft
ds	Airplane surface area element	ft2

Symbol	Description	Unit(s)
Regular (Continued)		
d_T	Distance of a thrust line projection onto the XZ–plane to the c.g.	ft
dv	Airplane volume element	ft^3
$e = 2.7183$	Napierian logarithm constant	———
e	Oswald's efficiency factor	———
e	Also: Factor defined in Figure 7.1	———
E	Factor defined in Figure 7.1	———
E_1	Coefficient in denominator of longitudinal transfer function	ft/sec^5
E_2	Coefficient in denominator of lateral–directional transfer function	ft/sec^5
f	Equivalent parasite area of the airplane	ft^2
f(t)	Function of time	lbs
f_{pl}	Preload of downspring	lbs
$\vec{F}$	Force per unit area (aerodynamic and/or thrust)	lbs/ft^2
$\vec{F}_A$	Total aerodynamic force vector	lbs
f_{A_x} , f_{A_y} , f_{A_z}	Perturbed values of F_{A_x} , F_{A_y} and F_{A_z}	lbs
f_{g_i}	Perturbed value of gravity forces	lbs
f_{I_i}	Perturbed value of inertial forces	lbs
F_{A_x} , F_{A_y} , F_{A_z}	Aerodynamic force components along XYZ	lbs
F_{OEI}	Factor which accounts for drag induced yawing moment	———
F_a	Aileron wheel or stick force	lbs
F_r	Rudder pedal force	lbs
F_s	Stick force (or wheel force)	lbs

Symbol	Description	Unit(s)
Regular (Continued)		
f_{T_x} , f_{T_y} , f_{T_z}	Perturbed values of F_{T_x} , F_{T_y} and F_{T_z}	lbs
F_{T_x} , F_{T_y} , F_{T_z}	Thrust force components along XYZ	lbs
$\vec{F}_T$	Total thrust force vector	lbs
$\vec{g}$	Acceleration of gravity	ft/sec^2
g_x , g_y , g_z	Acceleration of gravity components along XYZ	ft/sec^2
G	Gearing ratio for a flight control surface	rad/ft
GM	Gain margin	db
G(s)	Open loop transfer function	varies
G(s)	Open loop transfer function (forward path)	varies
h	Altitude	ft
h_{flare}	Altitude at which flare is initiated	ft
$\vec{h}$	Angular momentum vector for spinning rotor(s)	slugft^2/sec
h_x , h_y , h_z	Components of $\vec{h}$ along XYZ	slugft^2/sec
H(s)	Open loop transfer function (feedback path)	varies
HM	Hinge moment about control surface hingeline	ftlbs
i_c	Canard incidence angle	deg or rad
i_h	Horizontal tail (stabilizer) incidence angle	deg or rad
i_v	Vertical tail (stabilizer) incidence angle	deg or rad
i , j , k	Unit vectors along XYZ	———
I_{xx} , I_{yy} , I_{zz}	Airplane moments of inertia about XYZ	slugsft^2
I_{xy} , I_{yz} , I_{xz}	Airplane products of inertia about XYZ	slugsft^2
I_R	Rotor moment of inertia about its spin axis	slugsft^2

<u>Symbol</u>	<u>Description</u>	<u>Unit(s)</u>

<u>Regular (Continued)</u>

$J = U/nD_p$	Propeller advance ratio	——

k	Spring constant	lbs/ft
k_α , k_q	Feedback gain constant w.r.t. angle–of–attack or pitch rate	deg/deg
K	Feedback gain constant	varies
$K_{1\ through\ 7}$	Constants used in Eqn (4.225) or (4.239) or (4.240)	see Eqns
$K_{sw\ or\ sw}$	Gearing constant between cockpit control wheel or stick and aileron or spoiler deflection	rad/ft
K_{ds}	Downspring constant	lbs/ft
K_α	Angle–of–attack–to–elevator feedback gain	rad/rad
K_c	Coupler gain	varies
K_h	Altitude–to–elevator feedback gain	rad/ft
K_α	Also: wing torsional stiffness constant	ftlbs/rad
K_q	Pitch–rate–to–elevator feedback gain	rad/rad/sec
K_r	Yaw–rate–to–rudder feedback gain	rad/rad/sec
K_t	Tab spring constant	lbs/ft
K_u	Speed–to–elevator feedback gain	rad/ft/sec
K_A	Acceleration error constant	——
K_p	Pilot gain	varies
K_P	Position error constant	——
K_T	Engine–to–throttle gain	varies
K_V	Velocity error constant	——
$K_{\alpha_{\delta_e}}$	Zero frequency gain in the angle–of–attack–to elevator transfer function	——
$K_{u_{\delta_e}}$	Zero frequency gain in the speed–to–elevator transfer function	ft/sec

Symbol	Description	Unit(s)
Regular (Continued)		
$K_{\theta_{\delta_e}}$	Zero frequency gain in the pitch–attitude–to–elevator transfer function	———
$K_{\beta_{\delta_{a\ or\ r}}}$	Zero frequency gain in the angle–of–sideslip to aileron or rudder transfer function	———
$K_{\phi_{\delta_{a\ or\ r}}}$	Zero frequency gain in the bank–angle to aileron or rudder transfer function	———
$K_{\psi_{\delta_{a\ or\ r}}}$	Zero frequency gain in the heading–angle to aileron or rudder transfer function	———
l	Characteristic length	ft
l_A , m_A , n_A	Perturbed values of L_A , M_A and N_A	ftlbs
l_c	Distance from the canard a.c. to the c.g.	ft
l_h	Distance from hor. tail a.c. to the c.g.	ft
l_s	Moment arm of stick (see Figure 4.41)	ft
L	Lift	lbs
L	also: overall airplane length	ft
L'	Lift per unit span	lbs/ft
L_A , M_A , N_A	Aerodynamic moment components about XYZ	ftlbs
$L_\beta = \dfrac{\overline{q}_1 Sb C_{l_\beta}}{I_{xx}}$	Roll angular acceleration per unit sideslip angle	rad/sec²/rad
$L_p = \dfrac{\overline{q}_1 Sb^2 C_{l_p}}{2 I_{xx} U_1}$	Roll angular acceleration per unit roll rate	1/sec
$L_r = \dfrac{\overline{q}_1 Sb^2 C_{l_r}}{2 I_{xx} U_1}$	Roll angular acceleration per unit yaw rate	1/sec
$L_{\delta_a} = \dfrac{\overline{q}_1 Sb C_{l_{\delta_a}}}{I_{xx}}$	Roll angular acceleration per unit aileron angle	rad/sec²/rad
$L_{\delta_r} = \dfrac{\overline{q}_1 Sb C_{l_{\delta_r}}}{I_{xx}}$	Roll angular acceleration per unit rudder angle	rad/sec²/rad
l_T , m_T , n_T	Perturbed values of L_T , M_T and N_T	ftlbs
L_T , M_T , N_T	Thrust moment components about XYZ	ftlbs

Symbol	**Description**	**Unit(s)**
Regular (Continued)		
m	Airplane mass (or just mass)	slugs
m_i	Mass associated with element i	slugs
$\dot{m}'$	Mass flow rate through an engine	slugs/sec
M	Mach number	-----
M	Also: amplitude ratio	-----
M'	Pitching moment per unit span	ftlbs/ft
MM	Maneuver margin	fraction m.g.c.
MP	Maneuver point	fraction m.g.c.
$M_\alpha = \dfrac{\overline{q}_1 S \overline{c} C_{m_\alpha}}{I_{yy}}$	Pitch angular acceleration per unit angle of attack	$1/\text{sec}^2$
$M_{T_\alpha} = \dfrac{\overline{q}_1 S \overline{c} C_{m_{T_\alpha}}}{I_{yy}}$	Pitch angular acceleration per unit angle of attack (due to thrust)	$1/\text{sec}^2$
$M_u = \dfrac{\overline{q}_1 S \overline{c}(C_{m_u} + 2C_{m_1})}{I_{yy}U_1}$	Pitch angular acceleration per unit change in speed	rad/sec/ft
$M_{T_u} = \dfrac{\overline{q}_1 S \overline{c}(C_{m_{T_u}} + 2C_{m_{T_1}})}{I_{yy}U_1}$	Pitch angular acceleration per unit change in speed (due to thrust)	rad/sec/ft
$M_{\dot{\alpha}} = \dfrac{\overline{q}_1 S \overline{c}^2 C_{m_{\dot{\alpha}}}}{2I_{yy}U_1}$	Pitch angular acceleration per unit change of angle of attack	1/sec
$M_q = \dfrac{\overline{q}_1 S \overline{c}^2 C_{m_q}}{2I_{yy}U_1}$	Pitch angular acceleration per unit pitch rate	1/sec
$M_{\delta_e} = \dfrac{\overline{q}_1 S \overline{c} C_{m_{\delta_e}}}{I_{yy}}$	Pitch angular acceleration per unit elevator angle	$1/\text{sec}^2$
M_A	Aerodynamic moment scalar	ftlbs
$\vec{M}_A$	Total aerodynamic moment vector	ftlbs
M_{pl}	Moment about tab hingeline due to spring pre-load	ftlbs
$\vec{M}_T$	Total thrust moment vector	ftlbs
M_{tab}	Tab moment about its own hingeline	ftlbs

Symbol	Description	Unit(s)
Regular (Continued)		
n	Real part of complex root	1/sec
n	Also: load factor	——
n	Fraction number, also load factor, $n = L/W$	——
n_{limit}	Limit load factor	——
$\bar{n}$	Quantity defined in Eqn (4.218)	——
$\hat{n}$	Quantity defined on page 283	——
$n_\alpha = n/\alpha = \frac{\partial n}{\partial \alpha}$	Variation of load factor with angle of attack	1/rad
n_j	Number of jet engines per airplane	——
n_p	Number of propellers per airplane	——
n_{prpm}	Propeller r.p.m.	1/min
n_{prps}	Propeller r.p.s.	1/sec
N_D	Drag induced yawing moment due to O.E.I.	ftlbs
NP	Neutral point	fraction m.g.c.
N_j	Inlet normal force	lbs
N_p	Propeller normal force	lbs
N_u	Numerator of speed–to–elevator transfer function	ft^2rad^2/sec^6
N_α	Numerator of angle–of–attack–to–elevator transfer function	$ftrad^2/sec^5$
N_β	Numerator of sideslip to aileron or rudder transfer function	$ftrad^3/sec^6$
N_θ	Numerator of pitch–attitude–to–elevator transfer function	$ftrad^2/sec^5$
N_ϕ	Numerator of bank angle to aileron or rudder transfer function	$ftrad^3/sec^6$
N_ψ	Numerator of heading angle to aileron or rudder transfer function	$ftrad^3/sec^6$
$N_\beta = \dfrac{\bar{q}_1 S b C_{n_\beta}}{I_{zz}}$	Yaw angular acceleration per unit sideslip angle	$rad/sec^2/rad$

Symbol	Description	Unit(s)

Regular (Continued)

Symbol	Description	Unit(s)
$N_{T_\beta} = \dfrac{\overline{q}_1 S b C_{n_{T_\beta}}}{I_{zz}}$	Yaw angular acceleration per unit sideslip angle (due to thrust)	rad/sec2/rad
$N_p = \dfrac{\overline{q}_1 S b^2 C_{n_p}}{2 I_{zz} U_1}$	Yaw angular acceleration per unit roll rate	1/sec
$N_r = \dfrac{\overline{q}_1 S b^2 C_{n_r}}{2 I_{zz} U_1}$	Yaw angular acceleration per unit yaw rate	1/sec
$N_{\delta_a} = \dfrac{\overline{q}_1 S b C_{n_{\delta_a}}}{I_{zz}}$	Yaw angular acceleration per unit aileron angle	rad/sec2/rad
$N_{\delta_r} = \dfrac{\overline{q}_1 S b C_{n_{\delta_r}}}{I_{zz}}$	Yaw angular acceleration per unit rudder angle	rad/sec2/rad
PM	Phase margin	deg
p , q , r	Perturbed values of P, Q and R	rad/sec
P , Q , R	Airplane angular velocity components about XYZ	rad/sec
$\overline{q} = 0.5 \varrho V_P^2 = 1,482 \delta M^2$	Airplane dynamic pressure	lbs/ft2
$\vec{r}$	Vector which connects the c.g. with a mass element	ft
$\vec{r}'$	Vector which connects the origin of X'Y'Z' with an airplane mass element	ft
$\vec{r}_P{}'$	Vector which connects the origin of X'Y'Z' with airplane c.g.	ft
R	Electrical resistance	Ohm
R also :	Slant range	ft
R(s)	Laplace transform of system input	———
$R_N = \dfrac{\varrho V_P l}{\mu}$	Reynolds number	———
$\overline{R}_y$	Dimensionless radius of gyration about the Y–axis	———

Symbol	Description	Unit(s)

Regular (Continued)

Symbol	Description	Unit(s)
s	Laplace domain variable	rad/sec
S	Area	ft²
SM	Static margin	fraction mgc
S_p	Propeller disk area	ft²
S_{w_f}	Flapped wing area	ft²
S_{wet}	Airplane wetted area	ft²

Symbol	Description	Unit(s)
t	Thickness	ft
T	Thrust	lbs
T also:	Sampling time	sec
$T_{1/2}$	Time to half amplitude	sec
T_2	Time to double amplitude	sec
T_{lag}	Pilot lag time constant	sec
T_{lead}	Pilot lead time constant	sec
T_n	Pilot neuromuscular time constant	sec
T_s , T_r	Time constant of spiral and roll mode respectively	sec
$T_n = 2\pi/\omega_n$	Normalized time	sec
$(t/c)_{max}$	Maximum thickness ratio	———

Symbol	Description	Unit(s)
u , v , w	Perturbed value of U, V and W	ft/sec
u	Also: nondimensional frequency	———
$\dot{u}$, $\dot{v}$, $\dot{w}$	Accelerations in X,Y and Z directions	ft/sec²
U , V , W	Components of $\vec{V}_p$ along XYZ	ft/sec
$\dot{U}$	Forward acceleration along the ground	ft/sec²
U(s)	Laplace transform of system external disturbance input	—

Symbol	Description	Unit(s)
Regular (Continued)		
$\overline{V}_{h \text{ or } v}$	Horizontal or vertical tail volume coefficient	——
V_{mc}	Minimum control speed (engine out)	ft/sec
$\vec{V}_P$	Airplane velocity (true airspeed)	ft/sec
V_s	Stall speed	ft/sec
$V_{s_{OEI}}$	Stall speed with one engine inoperative	ft/sec
w	w–Domain transform	——
W	Airplane weight	lbs
W(s)	Closed loop system transfer function	varies
W_{bw}	Weight of bobweight	lbs
x , y , z	Components of $\vec{r}$ along XYZ	ft
$\dot{x}'$, $\dot{y}'$, $\dot{z}'$	Components of $\vec{V}_P$ along X'Y'Z'	ft/sec
x_{ac}	A.C. location relative to l.e. of chord	ft
$\overline{x}_{ac}$	Aerodynamic center location as fraction of mgc	——
$\overline{x}_{cp}$	C.P. location relative to l.e. of chord	ft
x_h	Distance from the 3/4 mgc point on the wing to the horizontal tail a.c.	ft
x_j	Distance from the inlet normal force to the c.g. measured along the X–stability axis	ft
$x_{ac_{h_g}}$	Distance defined in Figure 4.51	ft
$x_{ac_{wf_g}}$	Distance defined in Figure 4.51	ft
x_{cg_g}	Distance defined in Figure 4.51	ft
x_{mg_g}	Distance defined in Figure 4.51	ft
x_p	Distance from the propeller normal force to the c.g. measured along the X–stability axis	ft
x_T	Distance from a thrust line attachment point to the c.g. measured along the stability X–axis	ft

Symbol	Description	Unit(s)
Regular (Continued)		
$\overline{x}_{ac_A}$	Aerodynamic center location as a fraction of the mgc and measured from the leading edge of the mgc, positive aft	————
$\overline{x}_{cg}$	Center of gravity location as a fraction of the mgc and measured from the leading edge of the mgc, positive aft	————
$\overline{x}_{ref}$	Reference point location relative to l.e. of chord	ft
x_{v_s}	Distance between the vertical tail a.c. and the c.g. measured along the stability x–axis	ft
$X_\alpha = \dfrac{-\,\overline{q}_1 S(C_{D_\alpha} - C_{L_1})}{m}$	Forward acceleration per unit angle of attack	ft/sec^2/rad
$X_u = \dfrac{-\,\overline{q}_1 S(C_{D_u} + 2C_{D_1})}{mU_1}$	Forward acceleration per unit change in speed	1/sec
$X_{T_u} = \dfrac{\overline{q}_1 S(C_{T_{x_u}} + 2C_{T_{x_1}})}{mU_1}$	Forward acceleration per unit change in speed (due to thrust)	1/sec
$X_{\delta_e} = \dfrac{-\,\overline{q}_1 SC_{D_{\delta_e}}}{m}$	Forward acceleration per unit elevator angle	ft/sec^2/rad
y_a	Distance from aileron center of load to the airplane centerline	ft
y_{dr}	Distance between the drag rudder c.p. and the c.g. measured along the stability y–axis	ft
y_T	Distance from a thrust line attachment point to the c.g. measured along the stability Y–axis	ft
$Y_\beta = \dfrac{-\,\overline{q}_1 SC_{y_\beta}}{m}$	Lateral acceleration per unit sideslip angle	ft/sec^2/rad
$Y_p = \dfrac{-\,\overline{q}_1 SbC_{y_p}}{2mU_1}$	Lateral acceleration per unit roll rate	ft/sec/rad
Y_p also :	Human pilot transfer function	————
$Y_r = \dfrac{-\,\overline{q}_1 SbC_{y_r}}{2mU_1}$	Lateral acceleration per unit yaw rate	ft/sec/rad
$Y_{\delta_a} = \dfrac{-\,\overline{q}_1 SC_{y_{\delta_a}}}{m}$	Lateral acceleration per unit aileron angle	ft/sec^2/rad
$Y_{\delta_r} = \dfrac{-\,\overline{q}_1 SC_{y_{\delta_r}}}{m}$	Lateral acceleration per unit rudder angle	ft/sec^2/rad

Symbol	Description	Unit(s)
Regular (Continued)		
z	Z–domain transform	———
z_{cg_g}	Distance defined in Figure 4.51	ft
z_{D_g}	Distance defined in Figure 4.51	ft
z_{mg_g}	Distance defined in Figure 4.51	ft
z_{T_g}	Distance defined in Figure 4.51	ft
z_{v_s}	Distance between the vertical tail a.c. and the stability x–axis	ft
$Z_\alpha = \dfrac{-\bar{q}_1 S(C_{L_\alpha} + C_{D_1})}{m}$	Vertical acceleration per unit angle of attack	ft/sec2/rad
$Z_u = \dfrac{-\bar{q}_1 S(C_{L_u} + 2C_{L_1})}{mU_1}$	Vertical acceleration per unit change in speed	1/sec
$Z_{\dot{\alpha}} = \dfrac{-\bar{q}_1 S\bar{c} C_{L_{\dot{\alpha}}}}{2mU_1}$	Vertical acceleration per unit rate of change of angle of attack	ft/sec/rad
$Z_q = \dfrac{-\bar{q}_1 S\bar{c} C_{L_q}}{2mU_1}$	Vertical acceleration per unit pitch rate	ft/sec/rad
$Z_{\delta_e} = \dfrac{-\bar{q}_1 S C_{L_{\delta_e}}}{m}$	Vertical acceleration per unit elevator angle	ft/sec2/rad

Greek

Symbol	Description	Unit(s)
α	Angle of attack	deg or rad
$\dot{\alpha}$	Rate of change of angle of attack	rad/sec
α_0	Angle of attack at zero lift (section)	deg or rad
α_{0_L}	Angle of attack at zero lift (planform or airplane)	deg or rad
α_{tilt}	Tilt angle of a rate gyro: positive aft	deg or rad
$\alpha*$	Angle of attack value at end of linear range	deg or rad
$\alpha_\delta = \partial\alpha/\partial\delta$	Angle of attack effectiveness derivative	———
$\alpha_{c_{l_{max}}}$	Angle of attack at maximum lift coefficient	deg or rad
β	Angle of sideslip	deg or rad

Symbol	Description	Unit(s)
Greek (Continued)		
γ	Flight path angle	deg or rad
Γ	Geometric dihedral angle	deg or rad
Γ also :	Glideslope error angle	deg or rad
δ	Control surface deflection angle	deg or rad
δ_t	Control surface tab deflection angle	deg or rad
δ_{t_0}	Control surface tab deflection angle when up against a mechanical stop	deg or rad
Δ	Determinant of a matrix or increment of a parameter	———
$\Delta\overline{x}_{ac_{fus}}$	Shift in wing+fuselage aerodynamic center from the wing aerodynamic center in fractions of the m.g.c.	———
Δy	Leading edge shape parameter	———
ε	Downwash angle	deg or rad
$\varepsilon(s)$	Laplace transform of system error	varies
$\varepsilon^*(s)$	Pulse Laplace transform of $\varepsilon(s)$	varies
$\varepsilon(t)$	Time domain function	varies
ε_0	Downwash angle at zero angle of attack	deg or rad
ε_j	Upwash angle at inlet	deg or rad
ε_p	Upwash angle at propeller disk	deg or rad
ε_T	Twist angle	deg or rad
η	Spanwise station in fraction of b/2	———
η_h, η_v, η_c	Dynamic pressure ratio at h.t., v.t. or canard resp.	———
η_p	Propeller efficiency	———
θ	Perturbed value of Θ	rad
Θ	Airplane pitch attitude angle (See Figure 1.6)	rad
Θ	Angle in s–plane, see Fig. 5.7	rad

Symbol	Description	Unit(s)
Greek (Continued)		
λ	Taper ratio	———
λ	Root of characteristic equation	1/sec
λ also :	Localizer error angle	deg or rad
Λ	Sweep angle	deg or rad
μ	Coefficient of viscosity	lbs–sec/ft^2
μ_g	Wheel–to–ground friction coefficient	1/lbs
ζ	Damping ratio	———
ζ_α	Damping ratio of an airplane free to oscillate in pitch only	———
ζ_β	Damping ratio of an airplane free to oscillate in yaw only	———
π	3.14	———
ϱ	Air density	slugs/ft^3
ϱ_A	Airplane mass density	slugs/ft^3
ϱ_i	Air density in inlet	slugs/ft^3
σ	Sidewash angle	deg or rad
τ	Pilot reaction time delay constant	sec
τ also :	Washout circuit time constant	sec
$\tau_{e\ or\ r} = \partial\alpha/\partial\delta_{e\ or\ r}$	Angle of attack effectiveness factor	
ϕ	Perturbed value of Φ	rad
ϕ_{TE}	Trailing edge angle	deg
Φ	Airplane bank angle (See Figure 1.6)	rad
ϕ_T	Thrust line inclination angle w.r.t. YX–plane	rad
$\phi(\omega)$	Phase angle at frequency ω	rad
ψ	Perturbed value of Ψ	rad

Symbol	Description	Unit(s)

Greek (Continued)

Symbol	Description	Unit(s)
Ψ	Airplane heading angle (See Figure 1.6)	rad
ψ_T	Inclination angle of the projection of a thrust line on the XZ–plane w.r.t the XY–plane	rad
$\vec{\omega}$	Airplane angular velocity vector	rad/sec
ω	Frequency	rad/sec
ω_n	Undamped natural frequency	rad/sec
ω_{n_α}	Undamped natural frequency of an airplane free to oscillate in pitch only	rad/sec
ω_{n_β}	Undamped natural frequency of an airplane free to oscillate in yaw only	rad/sec
$\vec{\omega}_R$	Angular velocity of rotor about its spin axis	rad/sec
ω_s	Sampling frequency	rad/sec

Subscripts

Note: A, S, b and $\bar{c}$ without a subscript indicates a wing property!

1	Steady state quantity
a	Aileron
ac or a.c. or A.C.	Aerodynamic center
artificial	Quantity obtained artificially (for example, in control forces)
A	Aerodynamic or airplane
B	Body–fixed axes
c	Canard
cg	Center of gravity
c/4	Relative to the quarter chord
cp or c.p. or C.P.	Center of pressure
CAP	Control anticipation parameter
d	Dutch roll
dr	Drag rudder
e	Elevator
E	Elastic
e.a.	Elastic axis

Subscripts (Continued)

f	Fuselage
FOH	First order hold
ff	Fowler flap
fix	Stick (or controls) fixed
fk	Krueger flap
free	Stick (or controls) free
fus	Fuselage
g	Gust, also: gravity
ground	Quantity determined in ground effect
h	Horizontal tail
i	Item number i
I	Inertial
i_h	Horizontal tail (stabilizer) incidence angle
inb'd	Inboard
j	Jet
J	Jig shape
max	Maximum
mcf	Magnitude crossover frequency
mg	Main gear, about or relative to main gear
min	Minimum
l	Left
L	Landing
LE	Leading edge
M	At some Mach number
M=0	At zero Mach number
MP	Maneuver point
n	Normal to
outb'd	Outboard
OWE	Operating weight empty
p	Pylon, also: propeller
pcf	Phase crossover frequency
ph	Phugoid
PA	Powered Approach
r	Right or rudder
reqd	Required
t	Tip or tab
trim	trimmed
T	Thrust
r	Root or rudder or roll
rs	Roll–spiral

s	Spiral, store or spoiler or stability axes
sp	Short period
ss	Steady state
TO	Takeoff
v	Vertical tail
w	Wing
wf	Wing+fuselage
x, y or z	In the x, y or z–direction

Acronyms

ac or a.c. or A.C.	Aerodynamic center
AD	Analog to digital
AFCS	Automatic flight control system
APU	Auxiliary power unit
BPR	Bypass ratio
c.g.	Center of gravity
cp or c.p. or C.P.	Center of pressure
CSS	Control stick steering
CWS	Control wheel steering
DA	Digital to analog
EMP	Electromagnetic pulse
FAA	Federal aviation administration
FBL	Fly–by–light
FBW	Fly–by–wire
GPS	Global positioning system
HDG	Heading
h.t.	Horizontal tail
irrev.	Irreversible
ILS	Instrument landing system
l.e.	Leading edge
l.e.r.	Leading edge radius (ft)
l.h.s.	Left hand side
mgc or MGC	Mean geometric chord (ft)
MM	Maneuver margin
NP	Neutral point
O.E.I.	One engine inoperative
P.F.C.S.	Primary flight control system
r.h.s.	Right hand side
r.p.s.	Rotations per second
S.A.S.	Stability augmentation system

Acronyms (Continued)

SM	Static margin
SSSA	Separate surface stability augmentation
TFF	Transfer function
VOR	Very high frequency omnidirectional range
v.t.	Vertical tail
w.r.t.	With respect to
YD	Yaw damper
ZOH	Zero order hold

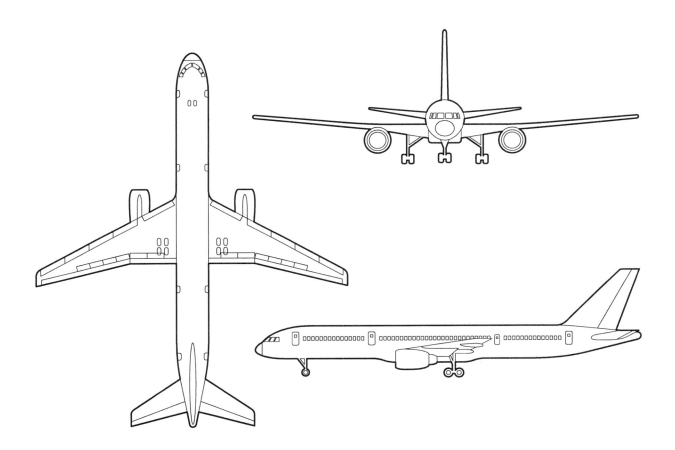

INTRODUCTION

In this two–part textbook, methods are presented for analysis and synthesis of the steady state and perturbed state (open and closed loop) stability and control of fixed wing aircraft.

Part I contains Chapters 1–6 and Appendices A–D. Part II contains Chapters 7–12 as well as Appendix E.

The book is aimed at junior, senior and first level graduate students of aeronautical engineering. Aeronautical engineers working in the aircraft industry will also find this book useful.

Throughout this text the practical (design) applications of the theory are stressed with many examples. Aircraft stability and control characteristics are all heavily regulated by civil as well as by military airworthiness authorities for reasons of safety. The role of these safety regulations in the application of the theory is therefore stressed throughout.

Many of the examples used to illustrate the application of the theory were generated with the help of a computer program called: AAA (Advanced Aircraft Analysis). This program is compatible with most Apollo, Sun, Silicon Graphics, IBM and DEC work–stations as well as with certain types of personal computers. The AAA program can be purchased from DARCorporation, 120 East Ninth Street, Suite 2, Lawrence, Kansas 66044, USA.

In Chapter 1 the general equations of motion are developed for a rigid airplane. These equations are then specialized into sets which apply to steady state and perturbed state flight conditions respectively. Before these equations can be used to help in the analysis and design of airplanes it is necessary to develop mathematical models for the aerodynamic and thrust forces and moments which act on an airplane.

Chapter 2 provides an overview of aerodynamic fundamentals needed to understand and use aerodynamic force and moment models. Several important properties of airfoils and lifting surfaces are reviewed. The effect of the fuselage on aerodynamic center is discussed and some fundamental aspects of control surface and flap characteristics are covered.

The actual modelling of aerodynamic and thrust forces and moments is discussed in Chapter 3. The reader is introduced to the concept and use of stability and control derivatives. Physical explanations and examples of signs and magnitudes of these derivatives are given.

Chapter 4 contains a discussion of the steady state equations of motion of airplanes. Solutions and applications are presented particularly from a viewpoint of how this material is used in airplane analysis and design. The relationship to handling quality regulations is pointed out. The airplane trim problem, take–off rotation problem and engine–out control problem are given significant emphasis.

In Chapter 5 the perturbed equations of motion of airplanes are discussed. The reader is introduced to the concept of airplane open loop transfer functions. The fundamental dynamic modes of airplanes (phugoid, short period, roll, spiral and dutch roll) are analyzed. Approximations to these modes are derived and typical 'drivers' of good and bad dynamic stability properties are identified. The idea of equivalent stability derivatives is introduced and the relation to automatic control of unstable airplanes is pointed out. Derivative sensitivity analyses are also discussed.

In Chapter 6 an introduction is given to the subject of airplane flying qualities. The reader is introduced to the Cooper–Harper scale and to various civil and military regulations for flying qualities. The relationship to airplane design is pointed out.

The subject of elastic airplane stability and control is taken up in Chapter 7 (in Part II). Finite element methods are used to determine stability and control coefficients and derivatives for elastic airplanes. A method for determining the equilibrium and jig (i.e. manufacturing) shape of an elastic airplane is also presented. Several numerical examples of the effect of aeroelasticity on stability and control derivatives are given for a subsonic and for a supersonic transport.

Chapter 8 presents an introduction to the construction and interpretation of Bode plots with open and closed loop airplane applications. An important inverse application is also given.

In Chapter 9 an overview is given of so–called classical control theory. The use of the root–locus method and the Bode method are illustrated with examples.

It is shown in Chapter 10 that classical control theory can be used to predict whether or not an airplane can be controlled by a human pilot. This is done with the aid of human pilot transfer functions for compensatory situations.

In Chapter 11 the reader is introduced to various aspects of automatic control of airplanes. It is shown why certain airplanes require stability augmentation. Pitch dampers, yaw dampers and roll dampers are discussed. The reader is familiarized with the basic synthesis concepts of automatic flight control modes such as: control–stick steering, various auto–pilot hold modes, speed control, navigation modes and automatic landing modes. Applications to various airplane types are also included.

In Chapter 12 a brief introduction to digital control systems using classical control theory is provided. Applications of the Z–transformation method are also included.

CHAPTER 7:   EFFECTS OF AEROELASTICITY ON STABILITY AND CONTROL

In this chapter, the effects of aeroelasticty on the stability and control of an airplane are discussed from a finite element viewpoint. In Section 7.1 several examples of aeroelastic behavior are presented with a simple mathematical model to illustrate the major problems. In Section 7.2 the reader is introduced to a finite element model which employs influence coefficient matrices. The resulting aerodynamic and structural influence coefficient matrices are then used in the development of closed form solutions for the longitudinal stability and control derivatives of elastic airplanes. This is done in Sections 7.3 and 7.4 for steady state and perturbed state applications respectively. Applications of these derivatives to various airplane performance, stability and control problems are also discussed.

Elastic airplanes must be manufactured to a shape different than the intended design cruise shape. How the manufacturing shape (called the jig–shape) can be determined from a desired (known) cruise shape to produce a given cruise lift–to–drag ratio is discussed in Section 7.5.

Applications of the influence coefficient method to lateral–directional derivatives are presented in Section 7.6. Numerical examples of elastic airplane derivatives (longitudinal and lateral–directional) are given in Section 7.7.

7.1   EXAMPLES OF AEROELASTIC BEHAVIOR

In this section, three examples of aeroelastic behavior are discussed:

* Aileron reversal

* Wing divergence

* Loss of longitudinal control power due to aft fuselage bending

7.1.1   AILERON REVERSAL

Figure 7.1 shows a cross section of an unswept wing taken at one of the aileron wing stations.

When the aileron is deflected downward, an upward lift is created. This lift in turn will cause a moment about the elastic axis. That moment will rotate the wing section in a nose–down direction. In turn, this elastic rotation will induce a down lift on the wing section. The question is: will the commanded up–lift (due to the aileron deflection) exceed the down–lift due to the aeroelastic rotation? If that happens, the aileron is said to have reversed. Clearly, such aileron reversal is not acceptable within the normal flight envelope of an airplane.

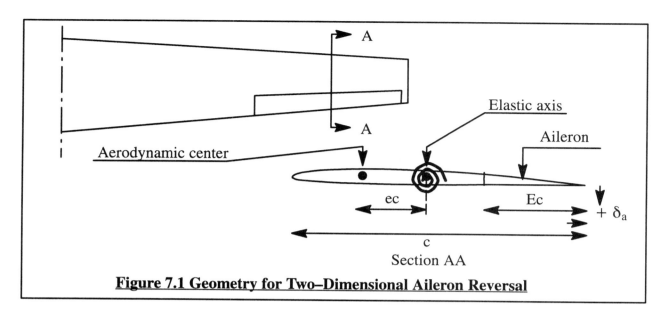

Figure 7.1 Geometry for Two–Dimensional Aileron Reversal

The following simple analysis shows how the dynamic pressure at which aileron reversal occurs can be predicted for an unswept, slender wing.

Section values for the incremental lift and pitching moment coefficients can be expressed as follows:

$$c_l = c_{l_\alpha}\alpha_E + c_{l_{\delta_a}}\delta_a \qquad (7.1)$$

$$c_{m_{\text{about the a.c.}}} = c_{m_o} + c_{m_{\delta_a}}\delta_a \qquad (7.2)$$

where: α_E is the elastic twist angle

δ_a is the aileron deflection angle

For a two–dimensional airfoil in incompressible flow, it can be shown that the following expressions hold for the sectional lift coefficient and pitching moment coefficient due to aileron derivatives:

$$c_{l_{\delta_a}} = \frac{c_{l_\alpha}}{\pi}\left\{\arccos(1 - 2E) + 2\sqrt{E(1 - E)}\right\} \qquad (7.3)$$

$$c_{m_{\delta_a}} = -\frac{c_{l_\alpha}}{\pi}(1 - E)\sqrt{E(1 - E)} \qquad (7.4)$$

where: E is defined in Figure 7.1.

Per unit length of span, the incremental lift can be written as:

$$L' = \bar{q}c(c_{l_\alpha}\alpha_E + c_{l_{\delta_a}}\delta_a) \qquad (7.5)$$

At the reversal speed this incremental lift will be equal to zero:

$$L' = 0 = \bar{q}_{\text{reversal}}c(c_{l_\alpha}\alpha_E + c_{l_{\delta_a}}\delta_a) \qquad (7.6)$$

From this result it follows that at the reversal speed the following relation holds between the elastic twist angle and the aileron deflection angle:

$$\frac{\partial \alpha_E}{\partial \delta_a} = - c_{l_{\delta_a}}/c_{l_\alpha} \tag{7.7}$$

Because of the aileron deflection, δ_a, and the lift which acts at the aerodynamic center, the wing will experience a pitching moment (= torsion moment) about its elastic axis equal to:

$$M' = \overline{q}c^2(ec_l + c_{m_{\delta_a}}\delta_a + c_{m_o}) \tag{7.8}$$

The wing torsional stiffness is assumed to be represented by a torsional spring with stiffness constant, K_α. As a result, the wing will resist any torsional deformation, α_E, about the elastic axis by an elastic restoring moment equal to: $\alpha_E K_\alpha$. At equilibrium (i.e. at the reversal dynamic pressure) the elastic restoring moment will equal the aerodynamic moment:

$$\alpha_E K_\alpha = \overline{q}_{reversal}c^2(ec_{l_\alpha}\alpha_E + ec_{l_{\delta_a}}\delta_a + c_{m_{\delta_a}}\delta_a + c_{m_o}) \tag{7.9}$$

In writing this equation, use was made of Eqn (7.1). Differentiation of Eqn (7.9) with respect to the aileron angle, δ_a, results in:

$$K_\alpha \frac{\partial \alpha_E}{\partial \delta_a} = \overline{q}_{reversal}c^2(ec_{l_\alpha}\frac{\partial \alpha_E}{\partial \delta_a} + ec_{l_{\delta_a}} + c_{m_{\delta_a}}) \tag{7.10}$$

Substitution of Eqn (7.7) into Eqn (7.10) yields:

$$- K_\alpha \frac{c_{l_{\delta_a}}}{c_{l_\alpha}} = \overline{q}_{reversal}c^2(- ec_{l_{\delta_a}} + ec_{l_{\delta_a}} + c_{m_{\delta_a}}) = \overline{q}_{reversal}c^2(c_{m_{\delta_a}}) \tag{7.11}$$

Therefore, the reversal dynamic pressure can be expressed as:

$$\overline{q}_{reversal} = \frac{c_{l_{\delta_a}}K_\alpha}{c_{l_\alpha}c^2}(- c_{m_{\delta_a}})^{-1} \tag{7.12}$$

As expected, the dynamic pressure at reversal will be large if the torsional stiffness, K_α, is large. An unexpected result is that the dynamic pressure at reversal is NOT dependent on the distance, ec, between the elastic axis and the aerodynamic center. This result is correct only for unswept wings. For swept wings, the dynamic pressure at reversal depends significantly on the quantity ec.

Note that the size of the aileron, Ec, does have an effect on the dynamic pressure at reversal: Ec is a factor in both aileron derivatives, $c_{l_{\delta_a}}$ and $c_{m_{\delta_a}}$.

An example of aileron control power degradation due to aeroelasticity is shown in Figure 7.2 for a swept wing transport. Note, that at a typical cruise flight condition (point A) the ailerons have lost much of their effectiveness! At lower altitudes this problem is seen to get worse. This is why outboard ailerons are frequently 'locked in place' during cruise in several jet transports.

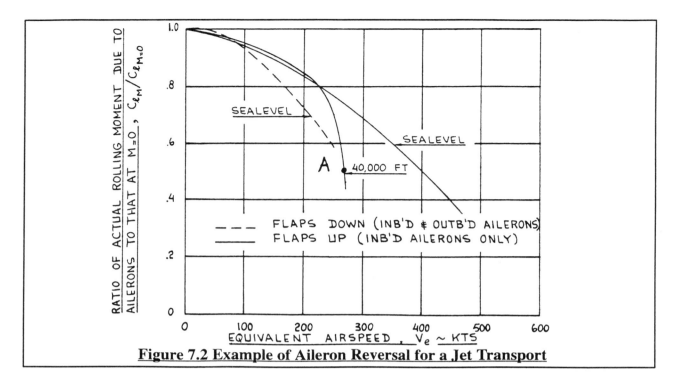

Figure 7.2 Example of Aileron Reversal for a Jet Transport

7.1.2 WING DIVERGENCE

The phenomenon of wing divergence is a design problem which tends to occur either in unswept or in swept forward wings. Figure 7.3 shows a cross section of an unswept wing taken at one outboard wing station. When the wing is flying at an angle of attack, α, the lift vector which acts at the aerodynamic center will cause a nose–up pitching moment. This in turn will cause an elastic deformation angle, α_E. The torsional stiffness of the wing as expressed by the constant, K_α, will attempt to resist this deformation. If the wing has insufficient torsional stiffness, it will diverge.

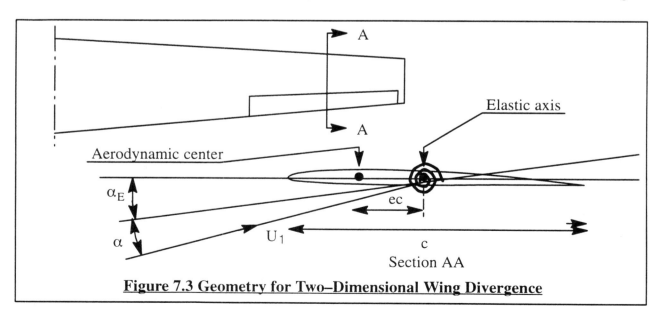

Figure 7.3 Geometry for Two–Dimensional Wing Divergence

To start the analysis of this wing divergence phenomenon, consider the lift per unit span:

$$L' = c_l \overline{q} c = \overline{q} c c_{l_\alpha} (\alpha + \alpha_E) \tag{7.13}$$

Next, consider the pitching moment (per unit span) about the aerodynamic center:

$$M'_{ac} = c_{m_{ac}} \overline{q} c^2 \tag{7.14}$$

The torsion moment about the elastic axis can now be written as:

$$M'_{e.a.} = M'_{ac} + L'ec = \overline{q} c^2 \left\{ c_{m_{ac}} + e c_{l_\alpha} (\alpha + \alpha_E) \right\} \tag{7.15}$$

This applied torsion moment is resisted by the torsional stiffness so that:

$$K_\alpha \alpha_E = \overline{q} c^2 \left\{ c_{m_{ac}} + e c_{l_\alpha} (\alpha + \alpha_E) \right\} \tag{7.16}$$

This equation can be solved for the equilibrium elastic twist angle:

$$\alpha_E = \frac{\overline{q} c^2 \left(c_{m_{ac}} + e c_{l_\alpha} \alpha \right)}{K_\alpha - \overline{q} c^2 e c_{l_\alpha}} \tag{7.17}$$

It is seen that a finite solution for the equilibrium twist angle, α_E, does not exist when the denominator of Eqn (7.17) approaches zero. That occurs at the dynamic pressure for wing divergence which is found by setting the denominator of Eqn (7.17) equal to zero:

$$\overline{q}_{divergence} = \frac{K_\alpha}{c^2 e c_{l_\alpha}} \tag{7.18}$$

As expected, if the stiffness K_α is high, the divergence dynamic pressure is high. Also, the divergence dynamic pressure is high if the distance, ec, between the aerodynamic center and the elastic axis is small. Clearly, the dynamic pressure for wing divergence must be well outside the normal flight envelope of an airplane.

The analysis presented here rests on the so–called "rigid clamp" assumption: the wing is assumed to be clamped to the fuselage which in turn is assumed to stay "put" in inertial space.

In the real world, airplanes will start to accelerate up if wing divergence sets in. The result is a coupling of wing divergence into the so–called "rigid body degrees of freedom". A phenomenon called wing–body–freedom flutter then sets in. The current analysis is only a crude approximation for wing divergence.

7.1.3 ELEVATOR CONTROL POWER REDUCTION DUE TO AFT FUSELAGE BENDING

As a final example of aeroelastic effects, consider Figure 7.4 where the aft fuselage of an airplane is considered to be a flexible beam, clamped at the wing–fuselage intersection.

If the horizontal tail experiences an up load, L_h, the fuselage will bend upward such that an

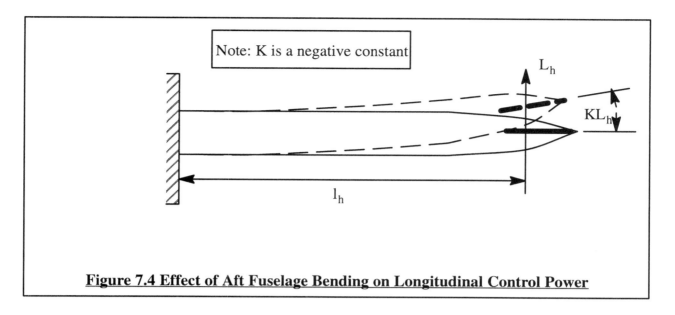

Figure 7.4 Effect of Aft Fuselage Bending on Longitudinal Control Power

elastically induced angular deflection, KL_h, is produced. As shown in Figure 7.4, the structural flexibility constant, K, is negative. This means that an up load on the tail will produce a negative change in tail angle of attack. The total aerodynamic load on the horizontal tail may be written as:

$$L_h = C_{L_{\alpha_h}}(\alpha_w + i_h - \varepsilon + \tau_e\delta_e + KL_h)\overline{q}S \qquad (7.19)$$

Note that the tail load, L_h, is a function of itself. That is a typical feature of nearly all steady state, aeroelastic problems. Solving Eqn (7.19) for the tail load and rearranging:

$$L_h = \frac{C_{L_{\alpha_h}}(\alpha_w + i_h - \varepsilon + \tau_e\delta_e)\overline{q}S}{(1 - C_{L_{\alpha_h}}K\overline{q}S)} \qquad (7.20)$$

Because K is a negative number, the denominator cannot become zero. However, at high dynamic pressure, the denominator will grow very large so that the tail load will diminish. To obtain the pitching moment coefficient contribution of the tail it is necessary to multiply Eqn (7.20) by the tail moment arm, l_h , and divide by $\overline{q}S\overline{c}$. This yields:

$$C_{m_h} = \frac{- C_{L_{\alpha_h}}(\alpha_w + i_h - \varepsilon + \tau_e\delta_e)l_h}{(1 - C_{L_{\alpha_h}}K\overline{q}S)\overline{c}} \qquad (7.21)$$

Differentiation with respect to the elevator deflection, δ_e , yields the elevator control power derivative for the elastic airplane:

$$C_{m_{\delta_e}} = \frac{- C_{L_{\alpha_h}}\tau_e l_h}{(1 - C_{L_{\alpha_h}}K\overline{q}S)\overline{c}} \qquad (7.22)$$

As the dynamic pressure increases, the control power derivative will decrease. Figure 7.5 shows an example of this effect for a subsonic jet transport. Observe, that at the cruise condition, point P, about 50% of the 'rigid airplane' control power has been lost due to fuselage bending!

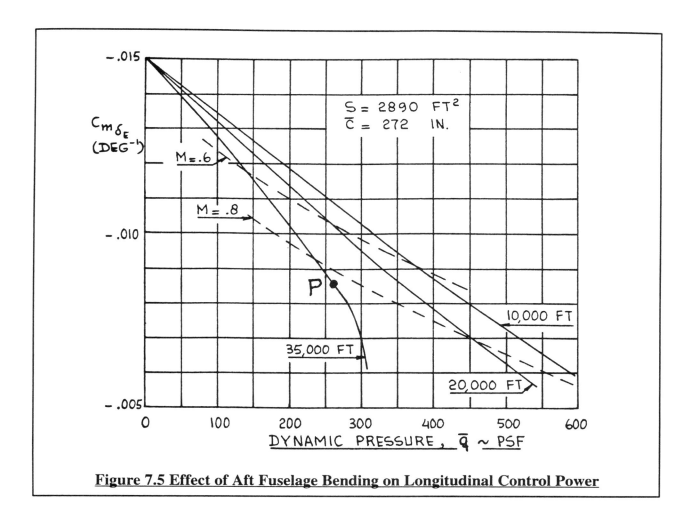

Figure 7.5 Effect of Aft Fuselage Bending on Longitudinal Control Power

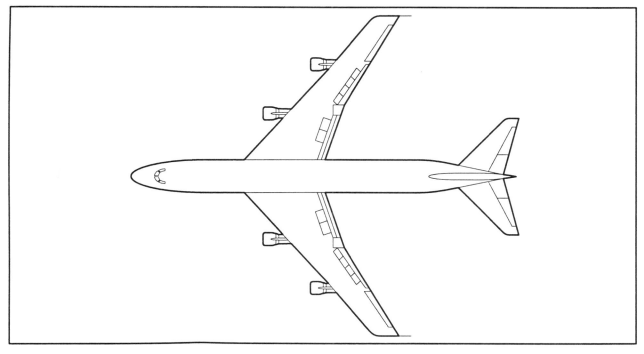

7.2 INTRODUCTION TO AERODYNAMIC AND STRUCTURAL INFLUENCE COEFFICIENT MATRICES

Before discussing the meaning and use of aerodynamic and structural influence coefficients, it is desirable to point out several aspects of the equilibrium state of highly elastic airplanes.

Consider first Figure 7.6. In this figure an exaggerated view is given of an elastic airplane in an equilibrium state. Observe that the center of gravity (Point P?) does not necessarily correspond to a specific point on the structure of the airplane. The reader will remember that the center of gravity was used until now to draw a body–fixed coordinate system (XYZ) in which the airplane equations of motion were derived. As long as P is not a fixed point on the structure this represents a problem.

To solve this problem the idea of undeformed shape (also called jig shape) is introduced.

In Figure 7.6 the airplane is held in its elastic equilibrium shape by an equilibrium load distribution which consists of the sum of all forces and moments which act on the airplane. The moments about the center of gravity are assumed to be zero in the equilibrium state. The forces are assumed to consist of gravity forces, aerodynamic forces and thrust forces. It is also assumed that the airplane is elastically deformed in its equilibrium state. That means that a certain amount of strain energy is "pent up" in its structure. According to Newton's Laws, when a system of equilibrium loads is removed from an elastically deformed airplane two things happen:

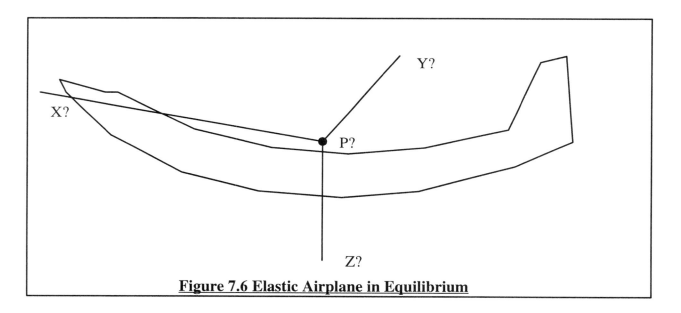

Figure 7.6 Elastic Airplane in Equilibrium

1) the center of gravity continues its motion in space without change
2) the airplane shape "springs back" into its undeformed shape

After the system of equilibrium loads has been removed from the airplane the situation depicted in Figure 7.7 prevails. Note that the center of gravity (point P) is now a fixed point on the structure of the airplane in its undeformed (or jig) shape. In the deformed shape, point P simply becomes point P_0. The axis system in which the equations of motion are written is now $X_0Y_0Z_0$.

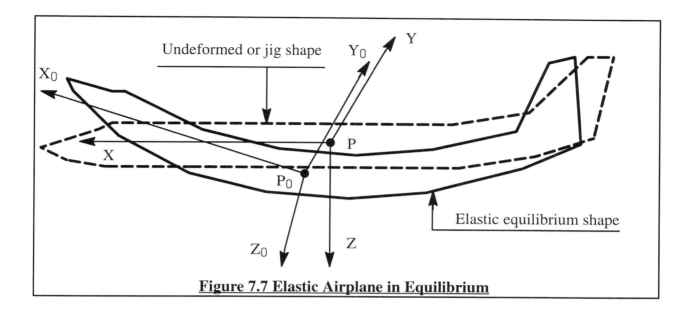

Figure 7.7 Elastic Airplane in Equilibrium

7.2.1 AERODYNAMIC INFLUENCE COEFFICIENTS FOR RIGID AIRPLANES

Figure 7.8 shows an example of a panelled airplane. At each panel a control point is assumed to exist. The panel is assumed to be sufficiently small so that the net aerodynamic pressure force which acts perpendicular to each panel also acts at the control point with no net moment about the control point. The coordinate system XYZ is the usual body–fixed coordinate system introduced in Figure 1.1 of Chapter 1. The panels in Figure 7.8 will be numbered from 1 to n. The aerodynamic force acting on panel i is called F_{A_i}.

Figure 7.9 shows a cut through the airplane of Figure 7.8 parallel to its XZ plane. The significance of the various angles and other quantities in Figure 7.9 will now be explained.

α_J is the airplane angle of attack, normally called α. The subscript J is included to indicate that this is associated with the airplane jig shape.

θ_J is the airplane pitch attitude angle, normally called θ. The subscript J is included to indicate that this is associated with the airplane jig shape.

γ is the airplane flight path angle. As usual: $\gamma + \theta_J = \alpha_J = \alpha_{ref}$.

θ_{J_i} is the so–called jig shape of the airplane. θ_{J_i} represents the camber/twist distribution which is "built into" the airplane in its assembly jigs.

δ_e is the control surface deflection angle required to trim the airplane.

a_i is an element of the (nx1) so–called control surface distribution matrix, $\{a_i\}$. If panel i is part of a control surface, the numerical value of the corresponding element of $\{a_i\}$ will be 1.0. If panel i is not part of a control surface, the value of the corresponding element of $\{a_i\}$ will be zero. The column matrix $\{a_i\}$ is usually filled with zeros except for those elements which are part of the control surface.

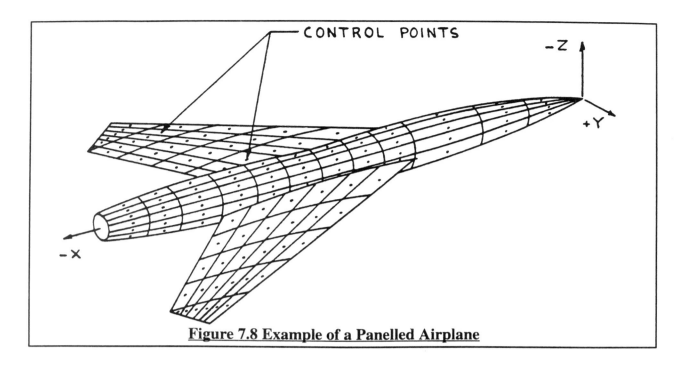

Figure 7.8 Example of a Panelled Airplane

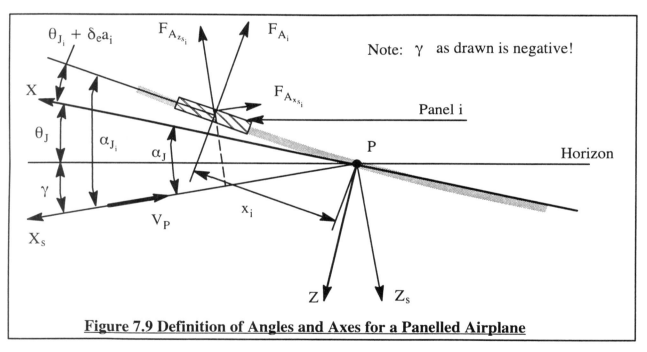

Figure 7.9 Definition of Angles and Axes for a Panelled Airplane

α_{J_i} is the angle of attack of panel i. It differs from α_J by the sum of $a_i\delta_{e_i}$ and θ_{J_i}.

x_i is the moment arm of panel i about the Y–axis.

F_{A_i} is the aerodynamic pressure force which acts on panel i at its control point.

$F_{A_{x_{S_i}}}$ is the component of F_{A_i} in the stability X–axis direction.

$F_{A_{z_{S_i}}}$ is the component of F_{A_i} in the stability Z–axis direction.

The aerodynamic influence coefficient matrix $[A_{ij}]$ is defined as a nxn matrix with elements a_{ij}. Each element has the following physical meaning: a_{ij} represents the aerodynamic force induced on panel i as a result of a unit change in angle of attack on panel j. With this definition the following equation relates the column matrix of aerodynamic forces $\{F_{A_i}\}$ to the aerodynamic influence coefficient matrix $[A_{ij}]$ and the airplane angle of attack distribution as represented by the column matrix $\{\alpha_{J_i}\}$:

$$\{F_{A_i}\} = \overline{q}[A_{ij}]\{\alpha_{J_i}\} \tag{7.23}$$

The reader is asked to show that the elements of the aerodynamic influence coefficient matrix, A_{ij} have the physical unit of ft2 /rad. One way of interpreting this is to think of A_{ij} as the product of local panel lift–curve–slope and local panel area! A discussion of methods for calculating the numerical magnitudes of the elements of the aerodynamic influence coefficient matrix, A_{ij}, is beyond the scope of this text. Such methods are considered part of the theory and application of computational aerodynamics. It will be assumed here that a computer program for evaluating the elements A_{ij} at any Mach number and for any reasonable panelling scheme is available. Reference 7.1 provides an example of one method for determining aerodynamic influence coefficients.

It will now be shown how Eqn (7.23) can be used as the cornerstone for determining longitudinal stability and control derivatives for a rigid airplane. After introducing the idea of structural influence coefficients in Sub–section 7.2.2 it will be shown in Sections 7.3 and 7.4 that the method is easily extended to the calculation of elastic airplane stability and control derivatives.

If an airplane is in a steady state maneuvering flight condition, the angle of attack column matrix, α_{J_i}, can be written as follows:

$$\{\alpha_{J_i}\} = \left\{ \gamma + \theta_J + \theta_{J_i} + \delta_e a_i + Q_1 \frac{x_i}{V_{P_1}} \right\} \tag{7.24}$$

where: Q_1 is the steady state pitch rate.

Substituting Eqn (7.24) into Eqn (7.23) yields:

$$\{F_{A_i}\} = \overline{q}[A_{ij}]\left\{ \gamma + \theta_J + \theta_{J_i} + \delta_e a_i + Q_1 \frac{x_i}{V_{P_1}} \right\} \tag{7.24a}$$

By using Eqn (7.23) and taking the components in the stability X and Z axis directions while also taking the moments about point P, it follows that:

$$\{F_{A_{xs_i}}\} = -\overline{q}[A_{ij}]\left\lceil \sin \alpha_{J_i} \right\rfloor \{\alpha_{J_i}\} \tag{7.25}$$

$$\{F_{A_{zs_i}}\} = -\overline{q}[A_{ij}]\left\lceil \cos \alpha_{J_i} \right\rfloor \{\alpha_{J_i}\} \tag{7.26}$$

$$\left\{ M_{A_{ys_i}} \right\} = \overline{q} \left[\diagdown x_i \diagdown \right] \left[A_{ij} \right] \left\{ \alpha_{J_i} \right\} \tag{7.27}$$

In the expression for the pitching moment, it has been assumed that the forces F_{A_i} are essentially perpendicular to the stability X–axis (small angle assumption).

The drag, lift and pitching moment acting on the airplane can be written as:

$$D = C_D \overline{q} S = -F_{A_{x_s}} = \overline{q} \{1\}^T [A_{ij}] \left[\diagdown \sin \alpha_{J_i} \diagdown \right] \left\{ \alpha_{J_i} \right\} \tag{7.28}$$

$$L = C_L \overline{q} S = -F_{A_{z_s}} = \overline{q} \{1\}^T [A_{ij}] \left[\diagdown \cos \alpha_{J_i} \diagdown \right] \left\{ \alpha_{J_i} \right\} \tag{7.29}$$

$$M_A = C_m \overline{q} S \overline{c} = \overline{q} \{x_i\}^T [A_{ij}] \left\{ \alpha_{J_i} \right\} \tag{7.30}$$

By substituting Eqn (7.24) into Eqns (7.28) through (7.30) and partial differentiation the steady state coefficients and derivatives of Table 7.1 can be found. The subscript 1 in Table 7.1 indicates that the coefficients and derivatives have been evaluated in the steady state. The steady state angle of attack distribution, $\left\{ \alpha_{J_{i_1}} \right\}$, is defined by analogy to Eqn (7.24) as:

$$\left\{ \alpha_{J_{i_1}} \right\} = \left\{ \alpha_{J_1} + \theta_{J_i} + \delta_{e_1} a_i + Q_1 \frac{x_i}{V_{P_1}} \right\} \tag{7.31}$$

The reader is asked to verify that the Equations (7.33) through (7.44) in Table 7.1 are correct. To assist in carrying out the differentiation process, the following sequence shows how Eqn (7.32) was derived. Starting with Eqn (7.28):

$$C_{D_\alpha} = \frac{1}{S} \{1\}^T [A_{ij}] \left[\diagdown 1 \diagdown \right] \left\{ \alpha_{J_{i_1}} \right\} + \frac{1}{S} \{1\}^T [A_{ij}] \left[\diagdown \sin \alpha_{J_i} \diagdown \right] \{1\} =$$
$$= \frac{2}{S} \{1\}^T [A_{ij}] \left\{ \alpha_{J_{i_1}} \right\} \tag{7.32}$$

It is well known that particularly wing camber and twist distributions have a significant effect on the sign and magnitude of the coefficients C_{L_0} and C_{m_0}. Equations (7.37) and (7.41) in Table 7.1 reflect this clearly because of the presence of the matrix θ_{J_i} which represents the total airplane camber and twist distribution!

7.2.2 STRUCTURAL INFLUENCE COEFFICIENTS FOR ELASTIC AIRPLANES

In the following it will be assumed that a linear relationship exists between a force acting at some control point j on the airplane structure and the linear or angular deflection at some other control point i on the structure. Figure 7.10 illustrates this property for co–located points in terms of the relationship between force and linear deflection. The coefficient C is called a structural influence coefficient. Figure 7.11 illustrates this property for a force at point j and an angular deflection at point i. The structural influence coefficient, $[C_{ij}]$, is defined as the angular rotation about the Y–axis of the panel represented by control point i as a result of a unit force acting at a panel represented by control point j. Therefore, the column matrix of elastic deflection angles about the Y–axis is written as:

$$\{\Delta\alpha_{E_i}\} = [C_{ij}]\{F_j\} \qquad (7.45)$$

A discussion of methods for calculating the numerical magnitudes of the elements of the structural influence coefficient matrix, C_{ij}, is beyond the scope of this text. Such methods are considered part of the theory and application of the theory of structural panelling and finite element methods. It will be assumed here that a computer program for evaluating the elements of C_{ij} for any reasonable panelling scheme is available. References 7.2 through 7.6 contain methods for analyzing aeroelastic effects with structural matrix methods.

The method of aerodynamic and structural influence coefficients can be combined to determine the stability and control properties of an elastic airplane in steady state and in perturbed flight. This is discussed in Sections 7.3 and 7.4 respectively.

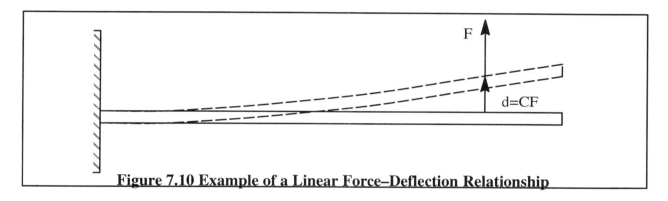

Figure 7.10 Example of a Linear Force–Deflection Relationship

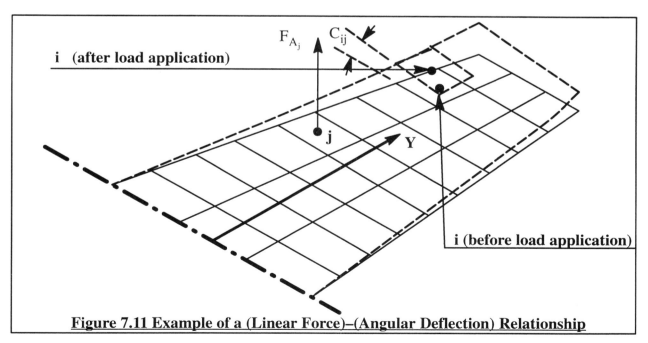

Figure 7.11 Example of a (Linear Force)–(Angular Deflection) Relationship

Table 7.1	Longitudinal Coefficients and Derivatives for a Rigid Airplane Using Aerodynamic Influence Coefficients

$$C_{D_0} = \frac{1}{S}\{1\}^T[A_{ij}]\left[\ \theta_{J_i}\ \right]\{\theta_{J_i}\} \approx 0 \ \text{for small}\ \theta_{J_i} \quad \text{Note: no friction drag is included!} \quad (7.33)$$

$$C_{D_\alpha} = \frac{2}{S}\{1\}^T[A_{ij}]\{\alpha_{J_{i_1}}\} \tag{7.34}$$

$$C_{D_{\delta_e}} = \frac{2}{S}\{1\}^T[A_{ij}]\{a_i\alpha_{J_{i_1}}\} \tag{7.35}$$

$$C_{D_q} = \frac{4}{S\bar{c}}\{1\}^T[A_{ij}]\{x_i\} \approx 0 \ \text{for most airplanes} \tag{7.36}$$

$$C_{L_0} = \frac{1}{S}\{1\}^T[A_{ij}]\{\theta_{J_i}\} \tag{7.37}$$

$$C_{L_\alpha} = \frac{1}{S}\{1\}^T[A_{ij}]\{1\} \tag{7.38}$$

$$C_{L_{\delta_e}} = \frac{1}{S}\{1\}^T[A_{ij}]\{a_i\} \tag{7.39}$$

$$C_{L_q} = \frac{2}{S\bar{c}}\{1\}^T[A_{ij}]\{x_i\} \tag{7.40}$$

$$C_{m_0} = \frac{1}{S\bar{c}}\{x_i\}^T[A_{ij}]\{\theta_{J_i}\} \tag{7.41}$$

$$C_{m_\alpha} = \frac{1}{S\bar{c}}\{x_i\}^T[A_{ij}]\{1\} \tag{7.42}$$

$$C_{m_{\delta_e}} = \frac{1}{S\bar{c}}\{x_i\}^T[A_{ij}]\{a_i\} \tag{7.43}$$

$$C_{m_q} = \frac{1}{S\bar{c}^2}\{x_i\}^T[A_{ij}]\{x_i\} \tag{7.44}$$

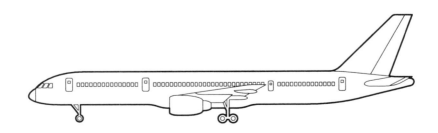

7.3   STABILITY AND CONTROL CHARACTERISTICS OF ELASTIC AIRPLANES IN STEADY STATE FLIGHT

To determine the relationship between elastic angular deflection of a panel on an elastic airplane, consider Figure 7.12.

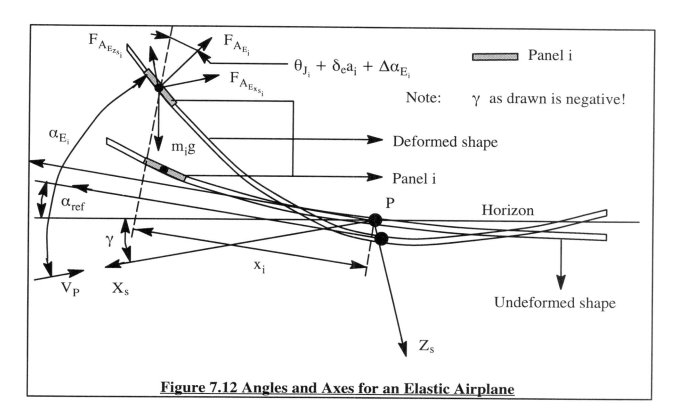

Figure 7.12 Angles and Axes for an Elastic Airplane

The elastic airplane aerodynamic force distribution as represented by the column matrix $\left\{ F_{A_{E_i}} \right\}$ can be determined by analogy to Eqn (7.23) as follows:

$$\left\{ F_{A_{E_i}} \right\} = \overline{q} \left[A_{ij} \right] \left\{ \alpha_{E_i} \right\} \tag{7.46}$$

where: α_{E_i} is the elastic airplane panel angle of attack at panel i. According to Figure 7.12 this angle can be written as:

$$\left\{ \alpha_{E_i} \right\} = \left\{ \alpha_{ref} + \theta_{J_i} + \delta_e a_i + \Delta \alpha_{E_i} \right\} \tag{7.47}$$

where: $\Delta \alpha_{E_i}$ is the actual elastic deformation of panel i. This deformation can be computed with the help of Eqn (7.45):

$$\{\Delta\alpha_{E_i}\} = [C_{ij}]\{m_i g\cos(\theta_{ref}) + F_{A_{E_i}}\cos(\theta_{J_i} + \delta_e a_i + \Delta\alpha_{E_i})\} \qquad (7.48)$$

In the latter equation it has been assumed that there are no significant vertical components due to thrust which assist in deforming the airplane. By substituting Eqn (7.48) into Eqn (7.47) and then substituting the result into Eqn (7.46) while also assuming that the cosine in Eqn (7.48) is approximately equal to 1.0, it is found that:

$$\{F_{A_{E_i}}\} = \bar{q}[A_{ij}]\{\{\alpha_{ref} + \theta_{J_i} + \delta_e a_i\} + [C_{ij}]\{m_i g\cos(\theta_{ref}) + F_{A_{E_i}}\}\} \qquad (7.49)$$

Note that at this point there was no reason to restrict the angle θ_{ref} to smallness. By inspection of Eqn (7.49), it is seen that the elastic airplane aerodynamic force distribution, $\{F_{A_{E_i}}\}$, is a function of itself. **The reader will do well to bear this typical characteristic of elastic airplane problems in mind!** With some matrix manipulation it is possible to rewrite Eqn (7.49) as follows:

$$\begin{bmatrix} \ddots & & \\ & 1 & \\ & & \ddots \end{bmatrix}\{F_{A_{E_i}}\} - \bar{q}[A_{ij}][C_{ij}]\{F_{A_{E_i}}\} = \bar{q}[A_{ij}]\{\{\alpha_{ref} + \theta_{J_i} + \delta_e a_i\} + [C_{ij}]\{m_i g\cos(\theta_{ref})\}\} \qquad (7.50)$$

In turn, this can be written as follows:

$$\left[\begin{bmatrix} \ddots & & \\ & 1 & \\ & & \ddots \end{bmatrix} - \bar{q}[A_{ij}][C_{ij}]\right]\{F_{A_{E_i}}\} = \bar{q}[A_{ij}]\{\{\alpha_{ref} + \theta_{J_i} + \delta_e a_i\} + [C_{ij}]\{m_i g\cos(\theta_{ref})\}\} \qquad (7.51)$$

Next, the so–called B–matrix is introduced:

$$[B] = \left[\begin{bmatrix} \ddots & & \\ & 1 & \\ & & \ddots \end{bmatrix} - \bar{q}[A_{ij}][C_{ij}]\right]^{-1} \qquad (7.52)$$

Note, that the B matrix is simply the inverse of the large square matrix which pre–multiplies the matrix $\{F_{A_{E_i}}\}$ in Eqn (7.51). By multiplying Eqn (7.51) by this B–matrix, an explicit solution for the elastic airplane aerodynamic force distribution matrix is obtained:

$$\{F_{A_{E_i}}\} = \bar{q}[B][A_{ij}]\{\{\alpha_{ref} + \theta_{J_i} + \delta_e a_i\} + [C_{ij}]\{m_i g\cos(\theta_{ref})\}\} \qquad (7.53)$$

The reader is asked to observe that for a rigid airplane the $[C_{ij}]$ is densely filled with zero's because a rigid airplane does not deform. Also, in that case, the B–matrix is equal to the unit–matrix! It is seen that in such a case Eqn (7.24a) is recovered for the case of zero pitch rate!

By analogy to Eqns (7.28) through (7.30), the following expressions can now be used to obtain the elastic airplane drag, lift and pitching moments:

$$D = -F_{A_{E_{x_s}}} \approx \left\{ \sin \, \alpha_{E_i} \right\}^T \left\{ F_{A_{E_i}} \right\} \tag{7.54}$$

$$L = -F_{A_{E_{z_s}}} \approx \left\{ \cos \alpha_{E_i} \right\}^T \left\{ F_{A_{E_i}} \right\} \tag{7.55}$$

$$M_A \approx \left\{ x_i \right\}^T \left\{ F_{A_{E_i}} \right\} \tag{7.56}$$

where the quantity $\left\{ F_{A_{E_i}} \right\}$ is determined by Eqn (7.53).

To find the steady state, elastic airplane coefficients and stability and control derivatives, it is first necessary to write Eqns (7.54) through (7.56) in coefficient form. At the same time it will be assumed that the matrix α_{E_i} contains only small angles. As a consequence:

$$C_D = \frac{D}{\bar{q}S} = \frac{1}{\bar{q}S} \left\{ \alpha_{E_i} \right\}^T \left\{ F_{A_{E_i}} \right\} \tag{7.57}$$

$$C_L = \frac{L}{\bar{q}S} = \frac{1}{\bar{q}S} \left\{ 1 \right\}^T \left\{ F_{A_{E_i}} \right\} \tag{7.58}$$

$$C_m = \frac{M_A}{\bar{q}S\bar{c}} = \frac{1}{\bar{q}S\bar{c}} \left\{ x_i \right\}^T \left\{ F_{A_{E_i}} \right\} \tag{7.59}$$

To find the elastic airplane coefficients for zero angle of attack, the values for α_{ref} and δ_e in Eqns (7.57) through (7.59), after substitution of Eqn (7.53), are set equal to zero. To find the derivatives with respect to angle of attack and elevator angle, Eqns (7.57) through (7.59) are simply differentiated (partially) with respect to these quantities. The results of these operations are presented in Table 7.2: Eqns (7.60) through (7.68). The reader should observe the fact that the B–matrix of Eqn (7.52) depends on the dynamic pressure. This implies that all elastic airplane derivatives, at any given Mach number, are still a function of altitude.

The problem of determining stability and control derivatives of elastic airplanes in perturbed flight is discussed in Section 7.4.

Another important problem in the design and manufacturing of highly elastic airplanes is the so–called jig–shape problem. An elastic airplane must be assembled to a shape (the jig–shape) which is different than the intended design cruise shape. How the jig shape can be determined is discussed in Section 7.5.

Note that if the B–matrix in Eqn (7.53) does not exist (this can happen if its inverse is singular!) the airplane can be considered as having diverged. The dynamic pressure at which this occurs is referred to as the dynamic pressure for airplane divergence.

Table 7.2	**Longitudinal Coefficients and Derivatives for an Elastic Airplane in a Straight Line, Steady State Flight Condition**

$$C_{D_0} = \frac{1}{S}\left\{\alpha_{E_{i_1}}\right\}^T [B][A]\left\{\theta_{J_i} + [C]\{m_i g\cos(\theta_{ref})\}\right\} \quad \text{Note: no friction drag included!} \quad (7.60)$$

$$C_{D_\alpha} = \frac{1}{S}\left\{\alpha_{E_{i_1}}\right\}^T [B][A]\{1\} \quad (7.61)$$

$$C_{D_{\delta_e}} = \frac{1}{S}\left\{\alpha_{E_{i_1}}\right\}^T [B][A]\{a_i\} \quad (7.62)$$

$$C_{L_0} = \frac{1}{S}\{1\}^T [B][A]\left\{\theta_{J_i} + [C]\{m_i g\cos(\theta_{ref})\}\right\} \quad (7.63)$$

$$C_{L_\alpha} = \frac{1}{S}\{1\}^T [B][A]\{1\} \quad (7.64)$$

$$C_{L_{\delta_e}} = \frac{1}{S}\{1\}^T [B][A]\{a_i\} \quad (7.65)$$

$$C_{m_0} = \frac{1}{S\bar{c}}\{x_i\}^T [B][A]\left\{\theta_{J_i} + [C]\{m_i g\cos(\theta_{ref})\}\right\} \quad (7.66)$$

$$C_{m_\alpha} = \frac{1}{S\bar{c}}\{x_i\}^T [B][A]\{1\} \quad (7.67)$$

$$C_{m_{\delta_e}} = \frac{1}{S\bar{c}}\{x_i\}^T [B][A]\{a_i\} \quad (7.68)$$

Note : $[B] = [\lceil 1 \rfloor - \bar{q}[A][C]]^{-1}$
Note: indices ij omitted from A, B and C matrices

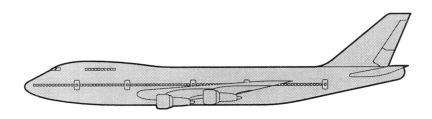

7.4 STABILITY AND CONTROL CHARACTERISTICS OF ELASTIC AIRPLANES IN PERTURBED STATE FLIGHT

7.4.1 DERIVATION OF ELASTIC AIRPLANE STABILITY DERIVATIVES FOR PERTURBED STATE FLIGHT

For rigid airplanes, in Chapter 1, the so–called perturbation substitution was used in deriving the equations of motion for airplanes in perturbed state flight. A similar technique will be used here to find the stability and control derivatives for a perturbed elastic airplane. Consider Eqn (7.46) and perform the perturbation substitution The result is:

$$\left\{ F_{A_{E_{i_1}}} + f_{A_{E_i}} \right\} = (\overline{q}_1 + \overline{q}_{perturbed}) \left[A_{ij} + \frac{\partial A_{ij}}{\partial M} \frac{M_1}{U_1} u \right] \left\{ \alpha_{E_{i_1}} + \alpha_{E_i} \right\} \qquad (7.69)$$

ss   ps   ss   ps   ss   ps   ss   ps

where: the subscripts ss and ps indicate steady state and perturbed state respectively

$\left\{ F_{A_{E_i}} \right\}$ is the steady state aerodynamic force distribution over the elastic airplane

$\left\{ f_{A_{E_i}} \right\}$ is the perturbed state aerodynamic force distribution over the elastic airplane

$\overline{q}_1$ is the steady state dynamic pressure

$\overline{q}_{perturbed}$ is the perturbed state increment in dynamic pressure

$\left[A_{ij} \right]$ is the (steady state) aerodynamic influence coefficient matrix

$\dfrac{\partial A_{ij}}{\partial M} \dfrac{M_1}{U_1} u$ is the perturbed state increment of the aerodynamic influence coefficient matrix

$\left\{ \alpha_{E_{i_1}} \right\}$ is the steady state elastic airplane angle of attack distribution. This distribution is assumed to be known. It can be computed with a method shown in Section 7.5.

$\left\{ \alpha_{E_i} \right\}$ is the perturbed state increment in elastic airplane angle of attack distribution

It can be shown with Eqn (3.102) in Chapter 3 that the perturbed dynamic pressure can be written as:

$$\overline{q}_{perturbed} = 2\overline{q}_1 \frac{u}{U_1} \qquad (7.70)$$

The perturbed state increment in the aerodynamic influence coefficient matrix is most readily determined by evaluating the A–matrix at two close but different Mach numbers and then using a difference equation to determine the perturbed increment.

By expanding Eqn (7.69), eliminating the steady state terms and eliminating higher order perturbed state terms, the following linearized version of Eqn (7.69) is obtained:

$$\left\{f_{A_{E_i}}\right\} = \overline{q}_1\left[\frac{2}{U_1}\left[A_{ij}\right] + \frac{M_1}{U_1}\left[\frac{\partial A_{ij}}{\partial M}\right]\right]\left\{\alpha_{E_{i_1}}\right\}u + \overline{q}_1\left[A_{ij}\right]\left\{\alpha_{E_i}\right\}$$ (7.71)

Observe that the perturbed aerodynamic force distribution depends on the steady state angle of attack distribution matrix. How this matrix may be determined is discussed in Section 7.5. In the analysis to follow the assumption is made that this matrix is known.

The matrix of the perturbed state increment in elastic airplane angle of attack distribution, $\left\{\alpha_{E_i}\right\}$ follows from:

$$\left\{\alpha_{E_i}\right\} = \alpha\{1\} - \frac{q}{U_1}\{x_i\} + \left\{\theta_{E_i}\right\}$$ (7.72)

where: α is the perturbed reference angle of attack of the airplane

q is the perturbed pitch rate of the airplane

x_i is the moment arm from the reference point P to the control point of panel i

θ_{E_i} is the perturbed elastic deformation of the airplane. By definition of the influence coefficient matrix, $\left[C_{ij}\right]$, this elastic deformation is interpreted as a rotation of a panel about an axis parallel to the Y–axis.

The elastic deformation of the airplane is caused by three types of perturbed force distributions acting on the airplane: aerodynamic, gravitational and inertial. These perturbed force distributions are given the following designations: $\left\{f_{A_{E_i}}\right\}$, $\left\{f_{g_i}\right\}$ and $\left\{f_{I_i}\right\}$ respectively.

The perturbed elastic deformation of the airplane, θ_{E_i}, may be determined from:

$$\left\{\theta_{E_i}\right\} = \left[C_{ij}\right]\left\{f_{A_{E_i}} - f_{g_i} - f_{I_i}\right\}$$ (7.73)

This relationship applies only as long as the cosines of the angles between panel normal vectors and the airplane stability X–axis system are approximately equal to 1.0. Also, the equation assumes that the loads acting on the panels and the panel deformations are perfectly in phase with each other. This is referred to as the quasi–steady–state assumption.

By analogy to Eqn (1.81c) it follows that the distribution matrix of perturbed gravitational forces can be written as:

$$\left\{f_{g_i}\right\} = \{m_i\}g\theta\sin(\theta_{ref})$$ (7.74)

By analogy to Eqn (1.81c) the perturbed inertial force distribution can be expressed as:

$$\left\{f_{I_i}\right\} = \left[\begin{smallmatrix} \diagdown \\ & m_i \\ & & \diagdown \end{smallmatrix}\right]\left\{\{1\}(\dot{w} - qU_1) - \{x_i\}\dot{q}\right\} \tag{7.75}$$

The next operation is to substitute Eqn (7.73) into Eqn (7.72). Next, substitute Eqn (7.72) into Eqn (7.71). The result of these substitutions is:

$$\left\{f_{A_{E_i}}\right\} = \overline{q}_1\left[\frac{2}{U_1}\left[A_{ij}\right] + \frac{M_1}{U_1}\left[\frac{\partial A_{ij}}{\partial M}\right]\right]\left\{\alpha_{E_{i_1}}\right\}u +$$
$$+ \overline{q}_1\left[A_{ij}\right]\left\{\alpha\{1\} - \frac{q}{U_1}\{x_i\} + \left[C_{ij}\right]\left\{f_{A_{E_i}} - f_{g_i} - f_{I_i}\right\}\right\} \tag{7.76}$$

This equation can be solve for the perturbed aerodynamic force distribution matrix, $\left\{f_{A_{E_i}}\right\}$ by using the B–matrix introduced in Eqn (7.52). The reader is asked to show that the result is:

$$\left\{f_{A_{E_i}}\right\} = \overline{q}_1\left[B_{ij}\right]\left[\frac{2}{U_1}\left[A_{ij}\right] + \frac{M_1}{U_1}\left[\frac{\partial A_{ij}}{\partial M}\right]\right]\left\{\alpha_{E_{i_1}}\right\}u +$$
$$+ \overline{q}_1\left[B_{ij}\right]\left[A_{ij}\right]\left\{\alpha\{1\} - \frac{q}{U_1}\{x_i\} + \left[C_{ij}\right]\left\{- f_{g_i} - f_{I_i}\right\}\right\} \tag{7.77}$$

After substituting Eqns (7.74) and (7.75) into Eqn (7.77) it is found that:

$$\left\{f_{A_{E_i}}\right\} = \overline{q}_1\left[B_{ij}\right]\left[\frac{2}{U_1}\left[A_{ij}\right] + \frac{M_1}{U_1}\left[\frac{\partial A_{ij}}{\partial M}\right]\right]\left\{\alpha_{E_{i_1}}\right\}u +$$
$$+ \overline{q}_1\left[B_{ij}\right]\left[A_{ij}\right]\left\{\alpha\{1\} - \frac{q}{U_1}\{x_i\} - \left[C_{ij}\right]\{m_i\}g\theta\sin(\theta_{ref})\right\} +$$
$$- \overline{q}_1\left[B_{ij}\right]\left[A_{ij}\right]\left[C_{ij}\right]\left[\begin{smallmatrix} \diagdown \\ & m_i \\ & & \diagdown \end{smallmatrix}\right]\left\{\{1\}(\dot{w} - qU_1) - \{x_i\}\dot{q}\right\} \tag{7.78}$$

Observe that the perturbed panel force matrix, $\left\{f_{A_{E_i}}\right\}$ depends on the following motion variables: u, α, q, θ, $\dot{w}$ and $\dot{q}$. Observe also that for a rigid airplane the matrix $\left[C_{ij}\right]$ is densely filled with zero's and that the B–matrix equals the unit matrix. Therefore, in the case of a rigid airplane the only motion variables involved in its aerodynamic force distribution matrix are: u, α and q.

Also notice that perturbation forces due to the variables θ, $\dot{w}$ and $\dot{q}$ are all associated with the mass distribution matrix, $\{m_i\}$. For that reason, those force components are referred to as inertial forces.

At this point the drag, lift and pitching moment coefficients for the perturbed elastic airplane are found by analogy to Eqns (7.57) through (7.59):

$$C_D = -\frac{1}{\overline{q}_1 S}\left\{\alpha_{E_{i_1}}\right\}^T\left\{f_{A_{E_i}}\right\} \tag{7.79}$$

$$C_L = -\frac{1}{\overline{q}_1 S}\{1\}^T\left\{f_{A_{E_i}}\right\} \tag{7.80}$$

$$C_m = \frac{1}{\overline{q}_1 S\overline{c}}\left\{x_i\right\}^T\left\{f_{A_{E_i}}\right\} \tag{7.81}$$

The next step is to carry out the partial differentiation process which leads to the stability derivatives of the perturbed elastic airplane. This partial differentiation is done with respect to the following variables:

dimensionless: α, $\dfrac{u}{U_1}$, $\dfrac{q\overline{c}}{2U_1}$ and θ

dimensional: $\ddot{\theta}$ and $\dot{w}$

The results are summarized in Table 7.3. In this table, the subscripts ij have been omitted from the A, B and C matrices. In this table the perturbed airplane derivatives are given for the elastic airplane in two components:

1)   those not associated with the mass matrix, $\{m_i\}$, are called the zero–mass derivatives or derivative components

2)   those associated with the mass matrix, $\{m_i\}$, are called the inertial derivatives or derivative components.

Note that the rigid airplane derivatives can be obtained from the elastic airplane derivatives by setting the C–matrix equal to zero and by setting the B–matrix equal to the unit matrix.

Clearly, in the case of an elastic airplane several "new" derivatives or derivative components occur, all associated with the mass distribution. This obviously adds additional complexity to the analysis of stability and control of elastic airplanes.

It would be desirable to have a mathematical model which does account for the effects of Table 7.3 but which does not require a change in the formulation of the mathematical model used to analyze rigid airplane stability and control. It is shown in Sub–section 7.4.2 how this can be achieved by using the so–called "equivalent elastic airplane derivative model".

Table 7.3 Longitudinal Stability Derivatives for Elastic and for Rigid Airplanes

Elastic Airplane				Rigid Airplane	
	Zero Mass		Inertial		
$C_{D_{\alpha_{\overline{E}}}}$	$\dfrac{1}{S}\left\{\alpha_{E_{i_1}}\right\}^T [B][A]\{1\}$			C_{D_α}	$\dfrac{1}{S}\left\{\alpha_{J_i}\right\}^T [A]\{1\}$
$C_{D_{q_{\overline{E}}}}$	$\dfrac{-2}{S\overline{c}}\left\{\alpha_{E_{i_1}}\right\}^T [B][A]\{x_i\}$	$C_{D_{q_I}}$	$\dfrac{U_1}{S}\left\{\alpha_{E_{i_1}}\right\}^T [B][A][C]\{m_i\}$	C_{D_q}	$\dfrac{-2}{S\overline{c}}\left\{\alpha_{J_i}\right\}^T [A]\{x_i\}$
$C_{D_{u_{\overline{E}}}}$	$\dfrac{1}{S}\left\{\alpha_{E_{i_1}}\right\}^T [B]\left[2[A] + M_1\left[\dfrac{\partial A}{\partial M}\right]\right]\left\{\alpha_{E_{i_1}}\right\}$			C_{D_u}	$\dfrac{1}{S}\left\{\alpha_{J_i}\right\}^T \left[2[A] + M_1\left[\dfrac{\partial A}{\partial M}\right]\right]\left\{\alpha_{J_i}\right\}$
$C_{L_{\alpha_{\overline{E}}}}$	$\dfrac{1}{S}\{1\}^T[B][A]\{1\}$			C_{L_α}	$\dfrac{1}{S}\{1\}^T[A]\{1\}$
$C_{L_{q_{\overline{E}}}}$	$\dfrac{-2}{S\overline{c}}\{1\}^T[B][A]\{x_i\}$	$C_{L_{q_I}}$	$\dfrac{U_1}{S}\{1\}^T[B][A][C]\{m_i\}$	C_{L_q}	$\dfrac{-2}{S\overline{c}}\{1\}^T[A]\{x_i\}$
$C_{L_{u_{\overline{E}}}}$	$\dfrac{1}{S}\{1\}^T[B]\left[2[A] + M_1\left[\dfrac{\partial A}{\partial M}\right]\right]\left\{\alpha_{E_{i_1}}\right\}$			C_{L_u}	$\dfrac{1}{S}\{1\}^T\left[2[A] + M_1\left[\dfrac{\partial A}{\partial M}\right]\right]\left\{\alpha_{J_i}\right\}$
$C_{m_{\alpha_{\overline{E}}}}$	$\dfrac{1}{S\overline{c}}\{x_i\}^T[B][A]\{1\}$			C_{m_α}	$\dfrac{1}{S\overline{c}}\{x_i\}^T[A]\{1\}$
$C_{m_{q_{\overline{E}}}}$	$\dfrac{-2}{S\overline{c}^2}\{x_i\}^T[B][A]\{x_i\}$	$C_{m_{q_I}}$	$\dfrac{U_1}{S\overline{c}}\{x_i\}^T[B][A][C]\{m_i\}$	C_{m_q}	$\dfrac{-2}{S\overline{c}^2}\{x_i\}^T[A]\{x_i\}$
$C_{m_{u_{\overline{E}}}}$	$\dfrac{1}{S\overline{c}}\{x_i\}^T[B]\left[2[A] + M_1\left[\dfrac{\partial A}{\partial M}\right]\right]\left\{\alpha_{E_{i_1}}\right\}$			C_{m_u}	$\dfrac{1}{S\overline{c}}\{x_i\}^T\left[2[A] + M_1\left[\dfrac{\partial A}{\partial M}\right]\right]\left\{\alpha_{J_i}\right\}$

Note: 1) The subscript $\overline{E}$ indicates zero mass, i.e. independence of the mass distribution

Note: 2) The subscript I indicates inertial (including mass), i.e. independence of the mass distribution

$$[B] = \left[[1] - \overline{q}_1[A][C]\right]^{-1}$$

$$\alpha_{E_{i_1}} = \alpha_1 + \theta_{J_i} + \Delta\alpha_{E_{i_1}}$$

$$\alpha_{J_i} = \alpha_1 + \theta_{J_i}$$

$C_{D_{\theta_I}}$	$\dfrac{-1}{S}\left\{\alpha_{E_{i_1}}\right\}^T [B][A][C]\{m_i\}g\sin\theta_1$
$C_{L_{\theta_I}}$	$\dfrac{-1}{S}\{1\}^T[B][A][C]\{m_i\}g\sin\theta_1$
$C_{m_{\theta_I}}$	$\dfrac{-1}{S\overline{c}}\{x_i\}^T[B][A][C]\{m_i\}g\sin\theta_1$
$C_{D_{\dot\theta_I}}$	$\dfrac{1}{S}\left\{\alpha_{E_{i_1}}\right\}^T [B][A][C]\{m_i x_i\}$
$C_{L_{\dot\theta_I}}$	$\dfrac{1}{S}\{1\}^T[B][A][C]\{m_i x_i\}$
$C_{m_{\dot\theta_I}}$	$\dfrac{1}{S\overline{c}}\{x_i\}^T[B][A][C]\{m_i x_i\}$
$C_{D_{\dot w_I}}$	$\dfrac{-1}{S}\left\{\alpha_{E_{i_1}}\right\}^T [B][A][C]\{m_i\}$
$C_{L_{\dot w_I}}$	$\dfrac{-1}{S}\{1\}^T[B][A][C]\{m_i\}$
$C_{m_{\dot w_I}}$	$\dfrac{-1}{S\overline{c}}\{x_i\}^T[B][A][C]\{m_i\}$

7.4.2 INTERPRETATION AND USE OF ELASTIC AIRPLANE STABILITY DERIVATIVES

It was shown in Sub–section 7.4.1 that elastic airplanes have fundamentally different stability derivatives than do rigid airplanes. The reasons for this are:

1) there are two types of loads which act on an airplane: aerodynamic and inertial (including gravitational). The inertial loads cause the structure to deform. That in turn causes changes in the aerodynamic loading, etc.

2) at any given Mach number, elastic airplane derivatives also depend on the steady state dynamic pressure. The B–matrix contains steady state dynamic pressure as a variable. In a rigid airplane there is no such dependence. As a result, at any given Mach number, elastic airplane stability derivatives will vary with altitude!

In general, airplane stability derivatives are caused by the change in aerodynamic loading due to a change in the motion variables. For that reason there will be stability derivatives due to aerodynamic effects associated with: α, u, q, and $\dot{\alpha}$.

In the formulation of Table 7.3 the stability derivatives were split into two categories:

1) those due to aeroelastic effects in the absence of inertial forces. These were called zero–mass derivatives or derivative components

2) those due to aeroelastic effects which are solely caused by inertial forces. These were called inertial derivatives or derivative components.

As a general rule the following inertial effects should be accounted for:

● linear accelerations
● angular accelerations
● changes in pitch attitude which alter the airplane orientation relative to the field of gravity

Therefore, stability derivatives due to: $\dot{u}$, $\dot{w}$, q (centrifugal), $\dot{q}$ (angular acceleration) and due to θ (orientation w.r.t. gravity) can also be expected to occur. Except for forward acceleration, $\dot{u}$, all other effects are accounted for in Table 7.3. The effect of forward accelerations on elastic airplane distortions are assumed to be negligible. Therefore, no derivatives due to $\dot{u}$ will appear.

Based on Table 7.3 it is now possible to formulate the longitudinal aerodynamic force and moment model of an elastic airplane shown in Table 7.4. Note that six derivatives in the "drag" equation Eqn (7.82) are considered negligible. Note also the "boxed" derivatives associated with pitch angular acceleration. These derivatives do not have a "mathematical home" in the rigid airplane force and moment formulation of Table 3.7 in Part I. Practical experience shows that the drag and lift effects due to pitch angular accelerations are quite negligible. However, the

Table 7.4   Perturbed Elastic Airplane, Longitudinal Aerodynamic Forces and Moments Using Zero Mass and Inertial Derivatives

will be neglected

$$f_{A_{x_{s_E}}} = -\left\{ C_{D_{\alpha_E}}\alpha + C_{D_{\dot{\alpha}_E}}\frac{\dot{\alpha}\bar{c}}{2U_1} + (C_{D_{u_E}}\frac{u}{U_1} + 2C_{D_1}) + C_{D_{q_E}}\frac{q\bar{c}}{2U_1} \right\}\bar{q}_1 S +$$

⟵——— Zero Mass Derivatives ———⟶

$$-\left\{ C_{D_{\dot{w}_I}}\dot{w} + C_{D_{q_I}}q + C_{D_{\theta_I}}\theta + \boxed{C_{D_{\ddot{\theta}_I}}\ddot{\theta}} \right\}\bar{q}_1 S \qquad (7.82)$$

⟵ Negligible Inertial Derivatives ⟶

$$f_{A_{z_{s_E}}} = -\left\{ C_{L_{\alpha_E}}\alpha + C_{L_{\dot{\alpha}_E}}\frac{\dot{\alpha}\bar{c}}{2U_1} + (C_{L_{u_E}}\frac{u}{U_1} + 2C_{L_1}) + C_{L_{q_E}}\frac{q\bar{c}}{2U_1} \right\}\bar{q}_1 S +$$

⟵——— Zero Mass Derivatives ———⟶

$$-\left\{ C_{L_{\dot{w}_I}}\dot{w} + C_{L_{q_I}}q + C_{L_{\theta_I}}\theta + \boxed{C_{L_{\ddot{\theta}_I}}\ddot{\theta}} \right\}\bar{q}_1 S \qquad (7.83)$$

⟵——— Inertial Derivatives ———⟶

$$m_{A_E} = \left\{ C_{m_{\alpha_E}}\alpha + C_{m_{\dot{\alpha}_E}}\frac{\dot{\alpha}\bar{c}}{2U_1} + (C_{m_{u_E}}\frac{u}{U_1} + 2C_{m_1}) + C_{m_{q_E}}\frac{q\bar{c}}{2U_1} \right\}\bar{q}_1 S\bar{c} +$$

⟵——— Zero Mass Derivatives ———⟶

$$+\left\{ C_{m_{\dot{w}_I}}\dot{w} + C_{m_{q_I}}q + C_{m_{\theta_I}}\theta + \boxed{C_{m_{\ddot{\theta}_I}}\ddot{\theta}} \right\}\bar{q}_1 S\bar{c} \qquad (7.84)$$

⟵——— Inertial Derivatives ———⟶

pitching moment due to pitch angular acceleration may not always be negligible. It is observed, that in the perturbed pitching moment equation (Eqn 1.82b) the pitch angular acceleration occurs as a multiplier of the pitching moment of inertia. It is therefore possible to consider the derivative $C_{m_{\ddot{\theta}_I}}$ as one which appears to "alter" the pitching moment of inertia of the airplane. How this can be done is shown in Section 7.6.

The aerodynamic lift force and pitching moment formulation of Table 7.4 has the disadvantage of being mathematically dissimilar to that of Table 3.7 (Part I) for the rigid airplane. It is possible to cast the aerodynamic lift force and pitching moment in a form very similar to that of Table 3.7. That is done by introducing the so-called "load factor" derivatives, $\frac{\partial C_L}{\partial n}$ and $\frac{\partial C_m}{\partial n}$.

Equations (7.85) and (7.86) define the perturbed elastic airplane lift coefficient and pitching moment coefficient in terms of these load factor derivatives:

$$C_{L_{\text{perturbed}}} = C_{L_{\alpha_E}}\alpha + C_{L_{\dot{\alpha}_E}}\frac{\dot{\alpha}\overline{c}}{2U_1} + C_{L_{u_E}}\frac{u}{U_1} + C_{L_{q_E}}\frac{q\overline{c}}{2U_1} + \frac{\partial C_L}{\partial n}n_{\text{perturbed}} + C_{L_{\ddot{\theta}}}\ddot{\theta} \qquad (7.85)$$

$$\underset{\longleftarrow}{\text{Zero Mass}}\longrightarrow \quad \underset{\longleftarrow}{\text{Inertial}}\longrightarrow$$

$$C_{m_{\text{perturbed}}} = C_{m_{\alpha_E}}\alpha + C_{m_{\dot{\alpha}_E}}\frac{\dot{\alpha}\overline{c}}{2U_1} + C_{m_{u_E}}\frac{u}{U_1} + C_{m_{q_E}}\frac{q\overline{c}}{2U_1} + \frac{\partial C_m}{\partial n}n_{\text{perturbed}} + C_{m_{\ddot{\theta}}}\ddot{\theta} \qquad (7.86)$$

$$\underset{\longleftarrow}{\text{Zero Mass}}\longrightarrow \quad \underset{\longleftarrow}{\text{Inertial}}\longrightarrow$$

Comparing this formulation with the corresponding equations in Table 7.4 it is seen that evidently the inertial effects due to $\dot{w}$, q and θ have been lumped together in the perturbed load factor, $n_{\text{perturbed}}$, which itself is defined by:

$$n \equiv 1 + n_{\text{perturbed}} = \frac{\left(C_{L_1} + C_{L_{\text{perturbed}}}\right)\left(\overline{q}_1 + \overline{q}_{\text{perturbed}}\right)S}{C_{L_1}\overline{q}_1 S} \qquad (7.87)$$

Expanding the right hand side and neglecting higher order terms yields:

$$n_{\text{perturbed}} = 2\frac{u}{U_1} + \frac{C_{L_{\text{perturbed}}}}{C_{L_1}} \qquad (7.88)$$

By comparison to Eqn (5.1b) in Part I it is seen that the perturbed load factor can also be written as:

$$n_{\text{perturbed}} = -\left(\frac{\dot{w}}{g} - \frac{U_1 q}{g} + \theta\sin\theta_1\right) \qquad (7.89)$$

Now compare Eqns (7.83) and (7.85) and observe that the following identity must always be satisfied:

$$C_{L_{\dot{w}_I}}\dot{w} + C_{L_{q_I}}q + C_{L_{\theta_I}}\theta \equiv \frac{\partial C_L}{\partial n}\left(-\frac{\dot{w}}{g} + \frac{U_1 q}{g} - \theta\sin\theta_1\right) \qquad (7.90)$$

From this identity it is found that the inertial lift coefficient derivatives are related to their corresponding load factor derivatives as follows:

$$C_{L_{\dot{w}_I}} = -\frac{1}{g}\frac{\partial C_L}{\partial n} \qquad (7.91a)$$

$$C_{L_{q_I}} = \frac{U_1}{g}\frac{\partial C_L}{\partial n} \qquad (7.91b)$$

$$C_{L_{\theta_I}} = -\frac{\partial C_L}{\partial n}\sin\theta_1 \qquad (7.91c)$$

Any one of Equations (7.91) can be used to evaluate $\dfrac{\partial C_L}{\partial n}$ in a practical case. By analogy to Eqn (7.90) it may be shown that:

$$C_{m_{\dot{w}_I}}\dot{w} + C_{m_{q_I}}q + C_{m_{0_I}}\theta \equiv \frac{\partial C_m}{\partial n}\left(-\frac{\dot{w}}{g} + \frac{U_1 q}{g} - \theta\sin\theta_1\right) \tag{7.92}$$

From this identity it is found that the inertial pitching moment coefficient derivatives are related to their corresponding load factor derivatives as follows:

$$C_{m_{\dot{w}_I}} = -\frac{1}{g}\frac{\partial C_m}{\partial n} \tag{7.93a}$$

$$C_{m_{q_I}} = \frac{U_1}{g}\frac{\partial C_m}{\partial n} \tag{7.93b}$$

$$C_{m_{0_I}} = -\frac{\partial C_m}{\partial n}\sin\theta_1 \tag{7.93c}$$

Any one of Equations (7.93) can be used to evaluate $\dfrac{\partial C_m}{\partial n}$ in a practical case. By substituting $n_{perturbed}$ from Eqn (7.88) into Eqn (7.85) and solving for $C_{L_{perturbed}}$ it is found that:

$$C_{L_{perturbed}} = \left[\frac{1}{1 - \frac{\partial C_L}{\partial n}\frac{1}{C_{L_{Trim}}}}\right]\left\{C_{L_\alpha}\alpha + C_{L_{\dot{\alpha}_E}}\frac{\dot{\alpha}\bar{c}}{2U_1} + \left(C_{L_{u_E}} + 2\frac{\partial C_L}{\partial n}\right)\frac{u}{U_1} + C_{L_{q_E}}\frac{q\bar{c}}{2U_1} + C_{L_{\ddot{\theta}_I}}\ddot{\theta}\right\} \tag{7.94}$$

At this point the following new notation is introduced:

$$C_{L_{\alpha_E}} = \left[\frac{C_{L_{\alpha_E}}}{1 - \frac{\partial C_L}{\partial n}\frac{1}{C_{L_{Trim}}}}\right] \tag{7.95}$$

$$C_{L_{\dot{\alpha}_E}} = \left[\frac{C_{L_{\dot{\alpha}_E}}}{1 - \frac{\partial C_L}{\partial n}\frac{1}{C_{L_{Trim}}}}\right] \tag{7.96}$$

$$C_{L_{u_E}} = \left[\frac{C_{L_{u_E}} + 2\frac{\partial C_L}{\partial n}}{1 - \frac{\partial C_L}{\partial n}\frac{1}{C_{L_{Trim}}}}\right] \tag{7.97}$$

$$C_{L_{q_E}} = \left[\frac{C_{L_{q_E}}}{1 - \frac{\partial C_L}{\partial n}\frac{1}{C_{L_{Trim}}}}\right] \tag{7.98}$$

$$C_{L_{\ddot{\theta}_E}} = \left[\frac{C_{L_{\ddot{\theta}_I}}}{1 - \frac{\partial C_L}{\partial n}\frac{1}{C_{L_{Trim}}}}\right] \tag{7.99}$$

These derivatives are called the equivalent elastic airplane lift coefficient derivatives.

It is now possible to cast the perturbed lift coefficient expression for an elastic airplane in the following format:

$$C_{L_{perturbed}} = C_{L_{\alpha_E}}\alpha + C_{L_{\dot{\alpha}_E}}\frac{\dot{\alpha}\bar{c}}{2U_1} + C_{L_{u_E}}\frac{u}{U_1} + C_{L_{q_E}}\frac{q\bar{c}}{2U_1} + \boxed{C_{L_{\ddot{\theta}_E}}\ddot{\theta}} \qquad (7.100)$$

The E–subscripted derivatives in Eqn (7.100) are those of Eqns (7.95) through (7.99). The boxed term in Eqn (7.100) can usually be neglected. The remaining terms, except for their physical meaning, are mathematically the same as the one for the rigid airplane in Eqn (3.162).

It is left to the reader to carry out a similar derivation for the aerodynamic pitching moment equation. By substituting $n_{perturbed}$ from Eqn (7.88) and Eqn (7.94) into Eqn (7.86) it is found that:

$$C_{m_{perturbed}} = \left\{ C_{m_{\alpha_E}} + \frac{\partial C_m}{\partial n}\left[\frac{C_{L_{\alpha_E}}}{C_{L_{trim}} - \frac{\partial C_L}{\partial n}}\right]\right\}\alpha + \left\{ C_{m_{\dot{\alpha}_E}} + \frac{\partial C_m}{\partial n}\left[\frac{C_{L_{\dot{\alpha}_E}}}{C_{L_{trim}} - \frac{\partial C_L}{\partial n}}\right]\right\}\frac{\dot{\alpha}\bar{c}}{2U_1} +$$

$$+ \left\{ C_{m_{u_E}} + 2\frac{\partial C_m}{\partial n} + \frac{\partial C_m}{\partial n}\left[\frac{C_{L_{u_E}} + 2\frac{\partial C_L}{\partial n}}{C_{L_{trim}} - \frac{\partial C_L}{\partial n}}\right]\right\}\frac{u}{U_1} + \qquad (7.101)$$

$$+ \left\{ C_{m_{q_E}} + \frac{\partial C_m}{\partial n}\left[\frac{C_{L_{q_E}}}{C_{L_{trim}} - \frac{\partial C_L}{\partial n}}\right]\right\}\frac{q\bar{c}}{2U_1} + \left\{ C_{m_{\ddot{\theta}_I}} + \frac{\partial C_m}{\partial n}\left[\frac{C_{L_{\ddot{\theta}_I}}}{C_{L_{trim}} - \frac{\partial C_L}{\partial n}}\right]\right\}\ddot{\theta}$$

At this point the following new notation is introduced:

$$C_{m_{\alpha_E}} = C_{m_{\alpha_E}} + \frac{\partial C_m}{\partial n}\left[\frac{C_{L_{\alpha_E}}}{C_{L_{trim}} - \frac{\partial C_L}{\partial n}}\right] \qquad (7.102)$$

$$C_{m_{\dot{\alpha}_E}} = C_{m_{\dot{\alpha}_E}} + \frac{\partial C_m}{\partial n}\left[\frac{C_{L_{\dot{\alpha}_E}}}{C_{L_{trim}} - \frac{\partial C_L}{\partial n}}\right] \qquad (7.103)$$

$$C_{m_{u_E}} = C_{m_{u_E}} + 2\frac{\partial C_m}{\partial n} + \frac{\partial C_m}{\partial n}\left[\frac{C_{L_{u_E}} + 2\frac{\partial C_L}{\partial n}}{C_{L_{trim}} - \frac{\partial C_L}{\partial n}}\right] \qquad (7.104)$$

$$C_{m_{q_E}} = C_{m_{q_E}} + \frac{\partial C_m}{\partial n}\left[\frac{C_{L_{q_E}}}{C_{L_{trim}} - \frac{\partial C_L}{\partial n}}\right] \qquad (7.105)$$

$$C_{m_{\dot{\theta}_E}} = C_{m_{\dot{\theta}_{\overline{E}}}} + \frac{\partial C_m}{\partial n}\left[\frac{C_{L_{\dot{\theta}_{\overline{E}}}}}{C_{L_{trim}} - \frac{\partial C_L}{\partial n}}\right] \tag{7.106}$$

These derivatives are called the equivalent elastic airplane pitching moment coefficient derivatives.

It is now possible to cast the perturbed pitching moment coefficient expression for an elastic airplane in the following format:

$$C_{m_{perturbed}} = C_{m_{\alpha_E}}\alpha + C_{m_{\dot{\alpha}_E}}\frac{\dot{\alpha}\overline{c}}{2U_1} + C_{m_{u_E}}\frac{u}{U_1} + C_{m_{q_E}}\frac{q\overline{c}}{2U_1} + \boxed{C_{m_{\dot{\theta}_E}}\ddot{\theta}} \tag{7.107}$$

The formulation for perturbed lift and pitching moment coefficients for rigid and for elastic airplanes are therefore seen to be quite similar. The boxed term in Eqn (7.107) can be viewed as an apparent modification of the airplane pitching moment of inertia. The numerical consequence of that to example airplanes will be discussed in Section 7.6.

The following physical interpretation is offered to allow the reader to distinguish between the elastic airplane derivatives with subscripts E and $\overline{E}$ respectively. For example:

- The derivative $C_{L_{\alpha_{\overline{E}}}}$ represents the lift–curve slope of the elastic airplane for zero mass distribution. This is equivalent to saying that this derivative is the lift–curve slope at constant load factor.

- The derivative $C_{L_{\alpha_E}}$ represents the lift–curve slope of the elastic airplane for varying load factor: in that case the mass distribution does matter!

The numerical examples of Section 7.6 show that significant numerical differences exist between these to derivatives.

For perturbed state flight conditions (varying load factor) the reader should use the derivatives with subscript E: these include the effect of the mass distribution.

For steady state flight conditions (constant load factor) the reader should use the derivatives with subscript $\overline{E}$.

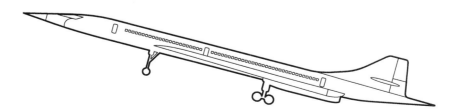

7.5   DETERMINING THE JIG–SHAPE OF ELASTIC AIRPLANES

Most airplanes with a significant cruise range requirement must have a high value for the trimmed lift–to–drag ratio in the design cruise condition. For a given amount of wetted area, the trimmed lift–to–drag ratio depends on the following factors:

- the center of gravity location
- the type and size of control surfaces used
- the camber and twist distribution (primarily of the lifting surfaces)

Designers of cruise vehicles pay much attention to assuring that, in the design cruise condition, the camber and twist distribution of the airplane is such that the trimmed lift–to–drag ratio is as high as possible. This is normally achieved with a mix of computational aerodynamics and checks in various windtunnel facilities. An important outcome of this work is a definition of the desired cruise shape (= cruise camber and twist distribution) of these airplanes.

Now recall the comments made in Section 7.2 about the equilibrium shape of an elastic airplane. That shape "springs back" to the unloaded or "jig shape", $\left\{\theta_{J_i}\right\}$, once the equilibrium load conditions in cruise are removed from the airplane. It is now assumed that when an airplane is assembled in its jigs, it is continually supported such that no strain energy is "pent up" in its structure. In that case, the jigs have to be set so that the airplane is assembled to its "jig shape' as previously defined. It will then deform into its desired cruise shape under the equilibrium load condition in cruising flight.

The first objective of this Section is to show how the jig shape of an elastic airplane can be derived from a known cruise shape. This is done in Sub–section 7.5.1.

In the derivation of the elastic airplane coefficients and derivatives for steady state flight, the equilibrium matrix of angles of attack, $\left\{\alpha_{E_{i_1}}\right\}$, was an important input. The second objective of this Section is to show how this matrix can be determined. This is done in Sub–section 7.5.2.

7.5.1 DETERMINING THE JIG SHAPE

In Section 7.3 it was shown (Eqn 7.48) that the elastic deformation matrix can be written in the following format:

$$\left\{\Delta\alpha_{E_i}\right\} = \left[C_{ij}\right]\left\{m_i g\cos(\theta_{ref}) + F_{A_{E_i}}\cos(\theta_{J_i} + \delta_e a_i + \Delta\alpha_{E_i})\right\} \tag{7.108}$$

Making the small angle assumption this is rewritten as:

$$\left\{\Delta\alpha_{E_i}\right\} = \left[C_{ij}\right]\left\{m_i g\cos(\theta_{ref}) + F_{A_{E_i}}\right\} \tag{7.109}$$

Next, substitute Eqns (7.46) and (7.47) into Eqn (7.109). The result is:

$$\left\{\Delta\alpha_{E_i}\right\} = \left[C_{ij}\right]\left\{m_i g\cos(\theta_{ref}) + \overline{q}[A]\left\{\alpha_{ref} + \theta_{J_i} + \delta_e a_i + \Delta\alpha_{E_i}\right\}\right\} \qquad (7.110)$$

It is assumed that the design cruise shape is known. Introducing the symbol $\left\{\theta_{i_{cruise}}\right\}$ for the design cruise shape it follows that:

$$\left\{\theta_{i_{cruise}}\right\} = \left\{\theta_{J_i} + \delta_e a_i + \Delta\alpha_{E_i}\right\} \qquad (7.111)$$

Presumably, in a trimmed cruise flight condition the elevator angle to trim will also be known. The jig shape can therefore be solved from Eqn (7.111) as:

$$\left\{\theta_{J_i}\right\} = \left\{\theta_{i_{cruise}} - \delta_e a_i - \Delta\alpha_{E_i}\right\} \qquad (7.112)$$

This equation still contains the unknown elastic twist distribution matrix $\left\{\Delta\alpha_{E_i}\right\}$. The most expedient way to find the jig shape is to proceed as follows. Solve Eqn (7.112) for $\left\{\Delta\alpha_{E_i}\right\}$:

$$\left\{\Delta\alpha_{E_i}\right\} = \left\{\theta_{i_{cruise}} - \delta_e a_i - \theta_{J_i}\right\} \qquad (7.113)$$

Substitute this result into Eqn (7.110):

$$\left\{\theta_{i_{cruise}} - \delta_e a_i - \theta_{J_i}\right\} = \left[C_{ij}\right]\left\{m_i g\cos(\theta_{ref}) + \overline{q}[A]\left\{\alpha_{ref} + \theta_{J_i} + \delta_e a_i + \theta_{i_{cruise}} - \delta_e a_i - \theta_{J_i}\right\}\right\} \qquad (7.114)$$

Note that the as yet unknown jig shape terms, $\left\{\theta_{J_i}\right\}$, on the right hand side of Eqn (7.114) cancel each other. It follows that the jig shape can be solve from Eqn (7.114) as:

$$\left\{\theta_{J_i}\right\} = \left\{\theta_{i_{cruise}} - \delta_e a_i\right\} - \left[C_{ij}\right]\left\{m_i g\cos(\theta_{ref}) + \overline{q}[A]\left\{\alpha_{ref} + \theta_{i_{cruise}}\right\}\right\} \qquad (7.115)$$

The column matrix $\left\{\theta_{J_i}\right\}$ is the desired jig shape of the elastic airplane. The elements of this matrix must then be translated into "jigging points" for the assembly jigs.

7.5.2 DETERMINING THE EQUILIBRIUM ANGLE OF ATTACK DISTRIBUTION

The equilibrium angle of attack distribution matrix, $\left\{\alpha_{E_i}\right\}$, appears as a required input in a number of stability derivatives in Table 7.3. This matrix may be obtained from Eqn (7.47) by defining each quantity as a steady state quantity:

$$\left\{\alpha_{E_{i_1}}\right\} = \left\{\alpha_1 + \theta_{J_i} + \delta_{e_1}a_i + \Delta\alpha_{E_{i_1}}\right\}$$ (7.116)

It will be assumed in the following analysis that the steady state angle of attack, α_1, and the steady state elevator angle, δ_{e_1}, are known. In that case the distribution of the elastic deformation angles, $\left\{\Delta\alpha_{E_{i_1}}\right\}$, may be determined from Eqn (7.48) as:

$$\left\{\Delta\alpha_{E_{i_1}}\right\} = \left[C_{ij}\right]\left\{m_i g + F_{A_{E_{i_1}}}\right\}$$ (7.117)

The matrix of steady state aerodynamic forces, $\left\{F_{A_{E_{i_1}}}\right\}$, may be found from Eqn (7.46) by again introducing steady state notation:

$$\left\{F_{A_{E_{i_1}}}\right\} = \overline{q}\left[A_{ij}\right]\left\{\alpha_{E_{i_1}}\right\}$$ (7.118)

By substituting Eqn (7.118) into Eqn (7.117) and then substituting the result into Eqn (7.116) it follows that:

$$\left\{\alpha_{E_{i_1}}\right\} = \left\{\alpha_1 + \theta_{J_i} + \delta_{e_1}a_i + \left[C_{ij}\right]\left\{m_i g + \overline{q}_1\left[A_{ij}\right]\left\{\alpha_{E_{i_1}}\right\}\right\}\right\}$$ (7.119)

The desired equilibrium angle of attack distribution matrix, $\left\{\alpha_{E_{i_1}}\right\}$, can be solved from this equation by introducing the following matrix:

$$\left[B_1\right] = \left[\left[\diagdown 1 \diagdown\right] - \overline{q}\left[C_{ij}\right]\left[A_{ij}\right]\right]^{-1}$$ (7.120)

Note that the matrix of Eqn (7.120) is not the same as the B–matrix of Eqn (7.52). The reason is that in matrix algebra, AC and CA do not have the same meaning!

With the introduction of the B_1–matrix of Eqn (7.120) the solution for $\left\{\alpha_{E_{i_1}}\right\}$ becomes:

$$\left\{\alpha_{E_{i_1}}\right\} = \left[B_1\right]\left\{\alpha_1 + \theta_{J_i} + \delta_{e_1}a_i + \left[C_{ij}\right]\{m_i g\}\right\}$$ (7.121)

7.6 DETERMINING LATERAL–DIRECTIONAL DERIVATIVES FOR ELASTIC AIRPLANES

At the time of publication of this text there still are no readily available, validated methods for estimating aerodynamic influence coefficient matrices for general lateral–directional applications. However, there are relatively easy ways around this problem. Some of these are discussed in this Section. Specifically, the following topics are addressed: in Sub–section 7.6.1 the determination of the elastic airplane roll damping derivative is discussed. In Sub–section 7.6.2 the effect of aeroelasticity on the directional stability derivative is presented. To simplify the matrix notation, the influence coefficient matrices A_{ij} and B_{ij} will be written as A and B respectively.

7.6.1 DETERMINATION OF THE ROLL DAMPING DERIVATIVE FOR AN ELASTIC AIRPLANE

By far the largest contribution to roll damping normally is that of the wing. Consider the panelled wing of Figure 7.13.

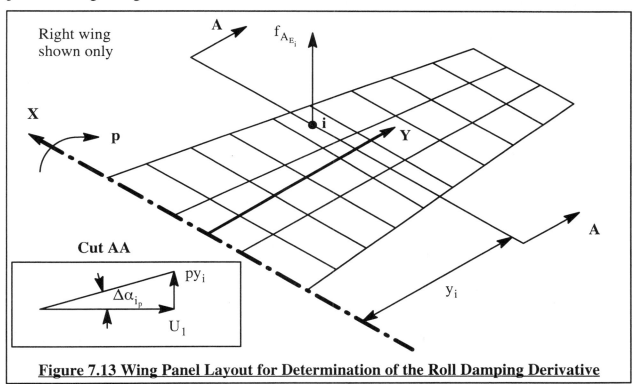

Figure 7.13 Wing Panel Layout for Determination of the Roll Damping Derivative

As a result of a positive roll rate, p an additional aerodynamic force distribution, $\left\{f_{A_{E_i}}\right\}$, develops which can be written as:

$$\left\{f_{A_{E_i}}\right\} = \overline{q}_1[A]\left\{\Delta\alpha_{i_p} + \Delta\alpha_{E_i}\right\} \tag{7.122}$$

where: $\Delta\alpha_{i_p}$ is the additional angle of attack induced onto panel i due to the roll rate p

$\Delta\alpha_{E_i}$ is the elastic deformation caused by the additional aerodynamic force distribution, $\left\{f_{A_{E_i}}\right\}$. The vector diagram insert in Figure 7.13 shows this angle.

The additional angle of attack matrix induced by roll rate may be expressed as:

$$\left\{\Delta\alpha_{i_p}\right\} = \frac{p}{U_1}\{y_i\}$$

(7.123)

The elastic deformation angles due to the roll rate induced forces $\left\{f_{A_{E_i}}\right\}$ can be determined from:

$$\left\{\Delta\alpha_{E_i}\right\} = [C]\left\{f_{A_{E_i}}\right\}$$

(7.124)

By substituting Eqns (7.124) and (7.123) into Eqn (7.122) it is found that:

$$\left\{f_{A_{E_i}}\right\} = \overline{q}_1[A]\left\{\frac{p}{U_1}\{y_i\} + [C]\left\{f_{A_{E_i}}\right\}\right\}$$

(7.125)

By using the B–matrix of Eqn (7.52) it is possible to solve for the additional aerodynamic force distribution, $\left\{f_{A_{E_i}}\right\}$, as follows:

$$\left\{f_{A_{E_i}}\right\} = \overline{q}_1\frac{p}{U_1}[B][A]\{y_i\}$$

(7.126)

The aerodynamic force matrix, $\left\{f_{A_{E_i}}\right\}$, yields a total rolling moment which is expressed as:

$$l_{A_{\text{due roll rate}}} = -\{y_i\}^T\left\{f_{A_{E_i}}\right\} = -\overline{q}_1\frac{p}{U_1}\{y_i\}^T[B][A]\{y_i\}$$

(7.127)

This rolling moment due to roll rate can be expressed in terms of an equivalent elastic airplane roll damping derivative as:

$$l_{A_{\text{due roll rate}}} = C_{l_{P_E}}\frac{pb}{2U_1}\overline{q}_1Sb$$

(7.128)

By setting Eqns (7.127) and (7.128) equal to each other the equivalent elastic roll damping derivative is found as:

$$C_{l_{P_E}} = \frac{-2}{Sb^2}\{y_i\}^T[B][A]\{y_i\}$$

(7.129)

Note that if the B–matrix does not exist (this can happen if its inverse is singular!) the wing can be considered as having diverged. The dynamic pressure at which this occurs is referred to as the dynamic pressure for wing divergence.

7.6.2 DETERMINATION OF THE DIRECTIONAL STABILITY DERIVATIVE FOR AN ELASTIC AIRPLANE

The directional stability of airplanes is made up primarily of a wing–fuselage contribution (usually unstable) and a vertical tail contribution (usually stable). In this Sub–section only the vertical tail contribution is considered. Figure 7.14 shows the geometric layout of a vertical tail. As shown in Figure 7.14 the fuselage is assumed to be rigid.

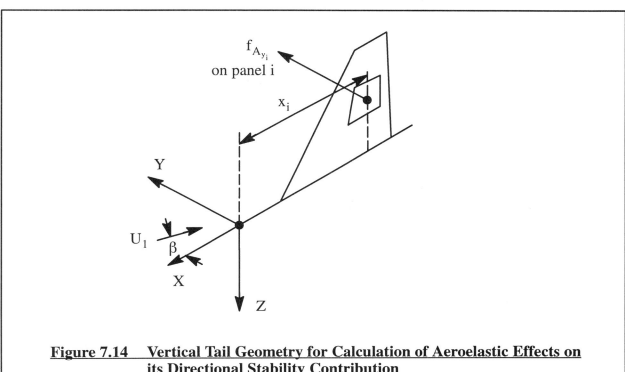

Figure 7.14   Vertical Tail Geometry for Calculation of Aeroelastic Effects on its Directional Stability Contribution

As a result of the airplane sideslip angle, β, an aerodynamic force distribution develops on the vertical tail which in turn causes an elastic deformation, $\Delta\beta_{E_i}$, of the panels. The equilibrium aerodynamic force distribution, $\left\{ f_{A_{y_{E_i}}} \right\}$, can be written as:

$$\left\{ f_{A_{y_{E_i}}} \right\} = -\overline{q}_1[A]\left\{ \beta\{1\} + \Delta\beta_{E_i} \right\} \qquad (7.130)$$

The elastic deformation matrix, $\Delta\beta_{E_i}$, follows from:

$$\left\{ \Delta\beta_{E_i} \right\} = [C]\left\{ f_{A_{y_{E_i}}} \right\} \qquad (7.131)$$

Substitution of Eqn (7.131) into Eqn (7.130) leads to:

$$\left\{ f_{A_{y_{E_i}}} \right\} = -\overline{q}_1[A]\left\{ \beta\{1\} + [C]\left\{ f_{A_{y_{E_i}}} \right\} \right\} \qquad (7.132)$$

The $\left\{ f_{A_{y_{E_i}}} \right\}$ matrix can be solved for by introducing a new type of B–matrix, the $\overline{B}$ matrix:

$$[\overline{B}] = [\ [\ \llcorner 1 \lrcorner] + \overline{q}[A][C]]^{-1} \tag{7.133}$$

$$\left\{ f_{A_{y_{E_i}}} \right\} = -\overline{q}_1[\overline{B}][A]\{1\}\beta \tag{7.134}$$

The column matrix of side forces, $\left\{ f_{A_{y_{E_i}}} \right\}$, gives rise to a column matrix of yawing moments which is written as:

$$\left\{ n_{A_{E_i}} \right\} = \llcorner x_i \lrcorner \left\{ f_{A_{y_{E_i}}} \right\} = -\overline{q}_1 \llcorner x_i \lrcorner [\overline{B}][A]\{1\}\beta \tag{7.135}$$

The total yawing moment which acts on the airplane is the sum of the elements of $\left\{ n_{A_{E_i}} \right\}$ which can be written as:

$$n_{A_E} = -\overline{q}_1\{1\}^T \llcorner x_i \lrcorner [\overline{B}][A]\{1\}\beta \llcorner x_i \lrcorner \tag{7.136}$$

or as:

$$n_{A_E} = -\overline{q}_1\beta\{x_i\}^T[\overline{B}][A]\{1\} \tag{7.137}$$

This yawing moment can also be written in terms of the equivalent elastic directional stability derivative, $C_{n_{\beta_E}}$:

$$n_{A_E} = C_{n_{\beta_E}}\beta\overline{q}Sb \tag{7.138}$$

From the latter it is possible to solve for $C_{n_{\beta_E}}$ and find:

$$C_{n_{\beta_E}} = \frac{-1}{Sb}\{x_i\}^T[\overline{B}][A]\{1\} \tag{7.139}$$

Because aft located vertical tails have negative moment arms, x_i , the vertical tail contribution to directional stability will usually come out as a positive number. Note that if the $\overline{B}$ matrix does not exist, the vertical tail will have diverged.

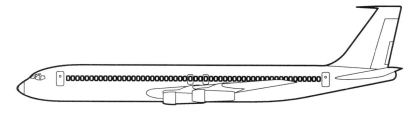

7.7 NUMERICAL EXAMPLES OF ELASTIC AIRPLANE STABILITY AND CONTROL DERIVATIVES

In this Section several numerical examples are given of elastic airplane stability and control derivatives. The examples were taken from Reference 7.7 and were determined for the Boeing 707–320B long range subsonic transport and the Boeing 2707 supersonic transport design.

7.7.1 NUMERICAL EXAMPLES: LONGITUDINAL STABILITY DERIVATIVES

Figures 7.15 through 7.18 show numerical examples for the following longitudinal derivatives: C_{L_α}, C_{m_α}, C_{m_q} and $C_{m_{\delta_e}}$ for the subsonic Boeing Model 707–320B. Note the significant effect of the mass distribution on the derivatives C_{L_α}, C_{m_α} and C_{m_q}. Also observe the large loss in elevator control power in Figure 7.18. This is caused mostly by aft fuselage bending!

Observe that for the M=0.82, 35,000 ft cruise case, the Prandtl–Glauert effect on lift–curve slope and on static longitudinal stability is apparently "washed out" by the effects of aeroelasticity.

It was seen in Eqn (7.107) and in Table 7.3 that an elastic airplane has a new type of inertial derivative called, $C_{m_{\ddot{\theta}_I}}$. This derivative can be thought of as an effective modification of the airplane pitching moment of inertia. Therefore, it makes sense to consider the ratio: $\dfrac{\left|C_{m_{\ddot{\theta}_I}}\right|\overline{q}_1 S\overline{c}}{I_{yy}}$.

Table 7.5 shows some numerical examples for this ratio as computed for the Boeing 707–320B and the Boeing 2707 (variable swept wing SST design of the 70's). It is seen that the effect of this derivative is not negligible for several important flight conditions.

Figures 7.19 through 7.22 show numerical examples for the following longitudinal derivatives: C_{L_α}, C_{m_α}, C_{m_q} and $C_{m_{\delta_e}}$ for the supersonic Boeing Model 2707. Note again the significant effect of the mass distribution on the derivatives C_{L_α}, C_{m_α} and C_{m_q} .

Figure 7.23 shows the effect of aeroelasticity on the computed location of the short period and phugoid roots for the Boeing Model 707–320B. For the flight case shown, the effect on these modes is not very dramatic.

7.7.2 NUMERICAL EXAMPLES: LATERAL–DIRECTIONAL STABILITY DERIVATIVES

Figures 7.24 and 7.25 show numerical examples for the roll–damping derivative, C_{l_p} , and the directional stability derivative, C_{n_β} , again for the Boeing Model 707–320B. The effects of aeroelasticity are seen to be very important. The effect on C_{l_p} is caused by lack of torsional stiffness. The effect on C_{n_β} is caused mostly by aft fuselage side bending.

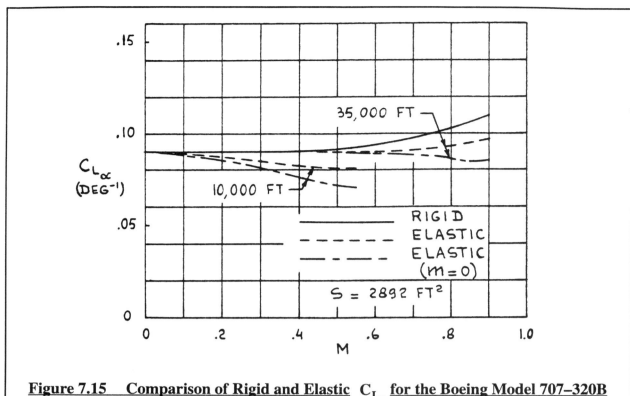

Figure 7.15   Comparison of Rigid and Elastic C_{L_α} for the Boeing Model 707–320B (Data from Reference 7.7)

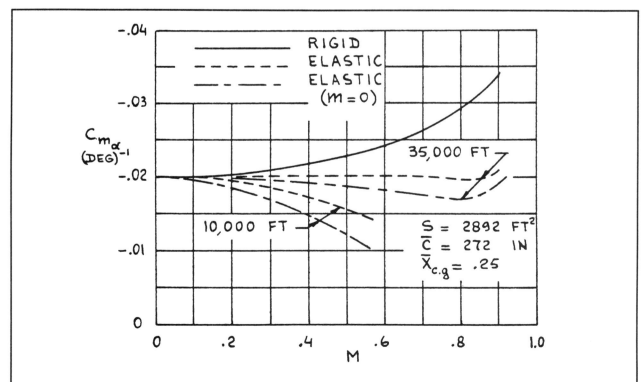

Figure 7.16   Comparison of Rigid and Elastic C_{m_α} for the Boeing Model 707–320B (Data from Reference 7.7)

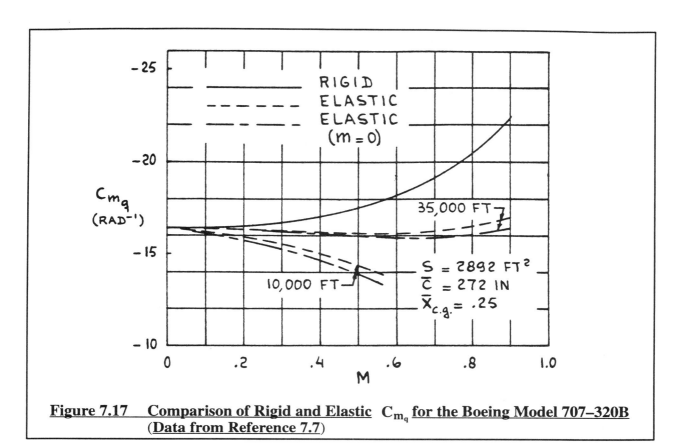

Figure 7.17   Comparison of Rigid and Elastic C_{m_q} **for the Boeing Model 707–320B (Data from Reference 7.7)**

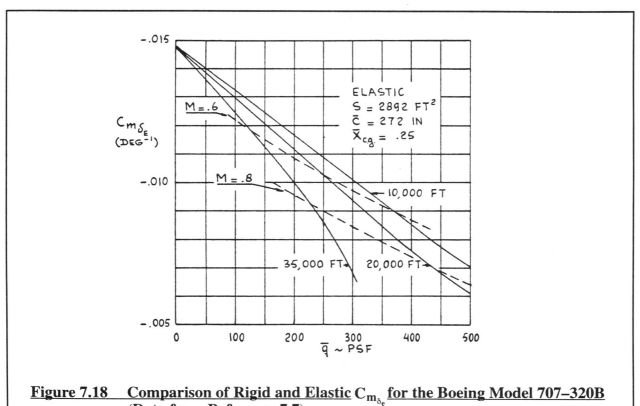

Figure 7.18   Comparison of Rigid and Elastic $C_{m_{\delta_e}}$ **for the Boeing Model 707–320B (Data from Reference 7.7)**

Table 7.5 Comparison of $C_{m_{\ddot{\theta}_I}}$ with Pitching Moment of Inertia

707-320B MACH NO.	ALTITUDE -FT.	I_{yy} 10^6 SLUG·FT^2 (Approximate)	$\dfrac{\left\|C_{m_{\ddot{\theta}_I}}\right\|}{I_{yy}/\bar{q}S_w\bar{c}}$
.255	10,000	5.025	.027
.365	↓		.052
.548		↓	.105
.800	35,000		.094
.850	↓		.106
.900		↓	.121

SST MACH NO.	ALTITUDE -FT.	GROSS WEIGHT -LBS.	WING SWEEP -DEG.	I_{yy} 10^6 SLUG·FT^2 (Approximate)	$\dfrac{\left\|C_{m_{\ddot{\theta}_I}}\right\|}{I_{yy}/\bar{q}S_w\bar{c}}$
.3	8,500	370,000	30	40.2	.0080
.5	9,600	↓	↓	↓	.0248
.7	11,000				.0217
.5	32,500	675,000	42	47.2	.0050
.7	26,000	↓			.0125
.9	23,500		↓	↓	.0198
.7	47,500	668,000	72	48.3	.0020
.9	37,000	↓			.0031
1.1	33,000			↓	.0097
1.3	30,000	520,000		47.6	.0425
1.5	24,000				.182
2.2	60,500				.0939
2.7	49,000	↓	↓	↓	.263

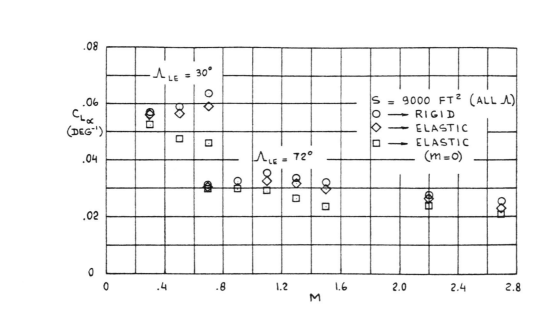

**Figure 7.19   Comparison of Rigid and Elastic C_{L_α} for the Boeing Model 2707
(Data from Reference 7.7)**

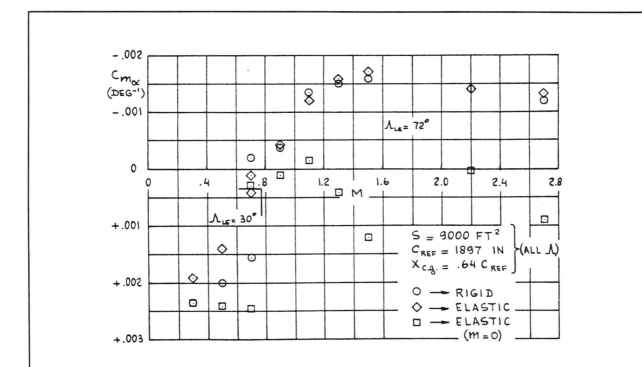

**Figure 7.20   Comparison of Rigid and Elastic C_{m_α} for the Boeing Model 2707
(Data from Reference 7.7)**

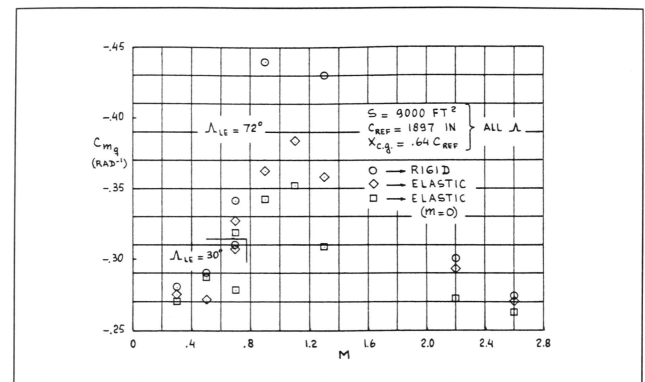

Figure 7.21 Comparison of Rigid and Elastic C_{m_q} for the Boeing Model 2707 (Data from Reference 7.7)

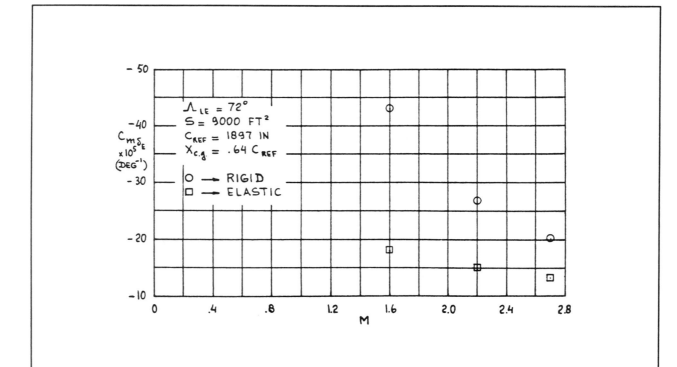

Figure 7.22 Comparison of Rigid and Elastic $C_{m_{\delta_e}}$ for the Boeing Model 2707 (Data from Reference 7.7)

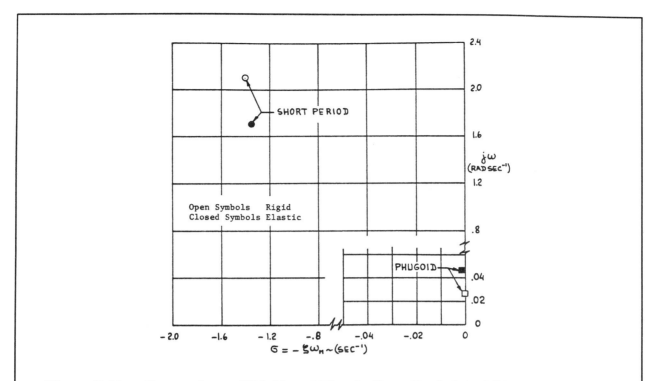

Figure 7.23   Comparison of Rigid and Elastic Short Period and Phugoid Dynamics for the Boeing Model 707–320B (Data from Reference 7.10)

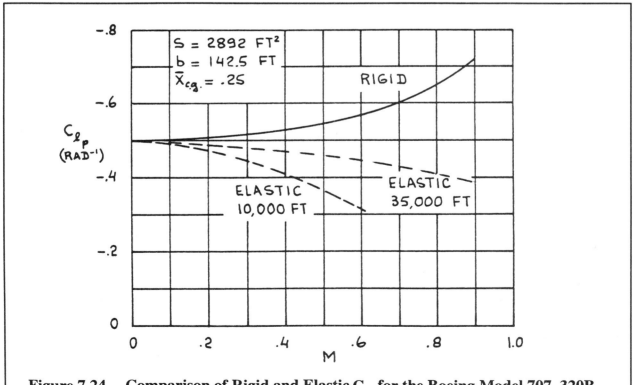

Figure 7.24   Comparison of Rigid and Elastic C_{l_p} for the Boeing Model 707–320B (Data from Reference 7.7)

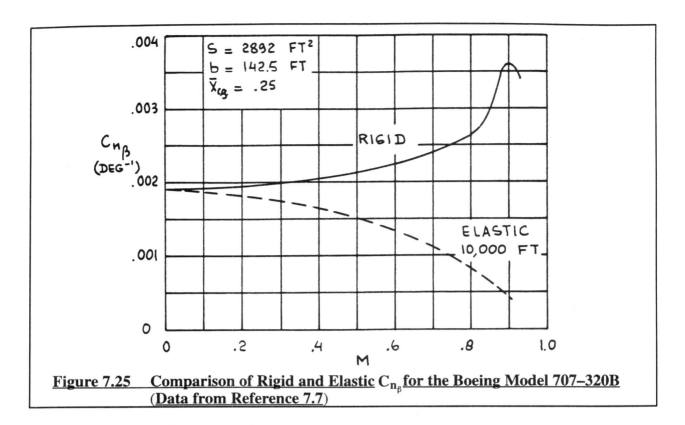

Figure 7.25   Comparison of Rigid and Elastic C_{n_β} for the Boeing Model 707–320B (Data from Reference 7.7)

7.8   SUMMARY FOR CHAPTER 7

In this chapter the reader was introduced to matrix methods for determining the stability and control derivatives of rigid and elastic airplanes. This was done through the use of aerodynamic and structural influence coefficient matrices which both use the same panelling scheme.

It was shown that in the case of elastic airplanes, the stability derivatives for steady state and for perturbed state flight conditions are fundamentally different. The main reason for the difference was shown to be the appearance of inertial effects (through the airplane mass distribution) which participate in the elastic deformation process and thereby alter the aerodynamic loading on the airplane.

Since elastic airplanes are kept in their cruise shape by a system of equilibrium load distributions, a question which occurs is how to manufacture an airplane in its assembly jigs so that it attains the correct shape in cruise. This led to the definition of the airplane jig shape.

The methodology used applies mostly to longitudinal stability and control cases. Examples were shown where the methods can also be used to determine certain lateral–directional stability and control derivatives. Finally, a series of numerical examples were presented to give the reader a feel for the magnitude of aeroelastic effects on stability and control.

For further study of aeroelastic effects on airplane stability and control, References 7.7 – 7.10 are recommended. Methods for using elastic windtunnel models in evaluating aeroelastic effects on stability and control are presented in References 7.11 and 7.12.

7.9   PROBLEMS FOR CHAPTER 7

7.1   Derive a matrix expression for the lift–to–pressure–drag ratio of a rigid airplane which has a known aerodynamic influence coefficient matrix [A], a known jig shape, $\left\{\theta_{J_i}\right\}$, and a known reference angle of attack, α_{ref}.

7.2   Derive a matrix expression for the aerodynamic center location of a rigid airplane which has the same characteristics as the airplane of problem 1 while the panel moment arms relative to the center of gravity are given by the matrix $\{x_i\}$. The center of gravity location is given as x_{cg} and the mean geometric chord as $\bar{c}$.

7.3   An airplane has a vertical tail with a known aerodynamic influence coefficient matrix [A] and a known structural influence coefficient matrix [C]. The vertical tail geometry relative to the c.g. is given in Figure 7.26. The airplane has a wing area of S and a wing span of b.

a) Derive a matrix expression for the vertical tail contribution to the

derivative $C_{l_{r_E}} = \partial C_l / \partial \dfrac{rb}{2U_1}$

b) Assume that the vertical tail itself is rigid but that the fuselage is elastically deformed such that a side load of $\left\{f_{A_{y_i}}\right\}$ leads to an effective change in sideslip angle, β_i, such that: $\beta_i = Kf_{A_{y_i}}$. The flexibility constant, k, should be assumed to be valid for all vertical tail panels i. See Figure 7.27. Derive a matrix expression for the vertical tail contribution to the same derivative $C_{l_{r_E}} = \partial C_l / \partial \dfrac{rb}{2U_1}$.

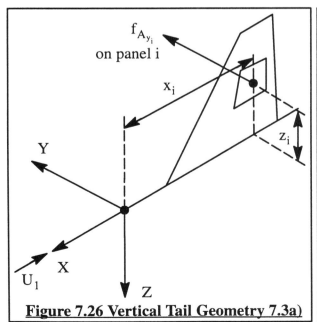

Figure 7.26 Vertical Tail Geometry 7.3a)

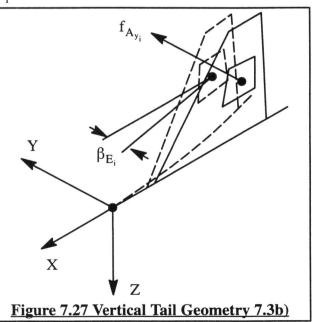

Figure 7.27 Vertical Tail Geometry 7.3b)

7.4   An airplane wing has a known aerodynamic influence coefficient matrix [A] and a known structural influence coefficient matrix [C]. The full span ailerons are mounted at the trailing edge as shown in Figure 7.28. The airplane has a wing area of S and a wing span of b. Derive a matrix expression for the aileron control power derivative, $C_{l_{\delta_{a_E}}}$. Hint: the reader should introduce a control surface distribution matrix, $\{a_i\}$, for these ailerons.

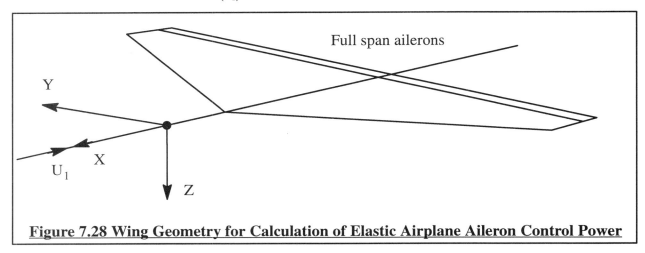

Figure 7.28 Wing Geometry for Calculation of Elastic Airplane Aileron Control Power

7.5   The vertical tail of an airplane wing has a known aerodynamic influence coefficient matrix [A] and a known structural influence coefficient matrix [C]. The full span rudder is mounted at the trailing edge as shown in Figure 7.29. The airplane has a wing area of S and a wing span of b. Derive a matrix expression for the rudder control power derivative, $C_{n_{\delta_{r_E}}}$. Hints:

    1) the reader should introduce a control surface distribution matrix, $\{a_i\}$, for this rudder.

    2) the reader should introduce appropriate panel moment arms

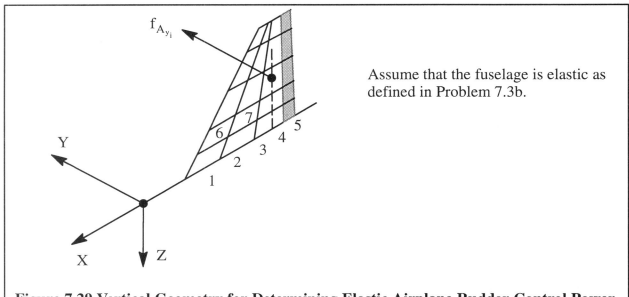

Figure 7.29 Vertical Geometry for Determining Elastic Airplane Rudder Control Power

7.6   A flying wing has a known aerodynamic influence coefficient matrix [A], and a known structural influence coefficient matrix [C]. The mass distribution matrix is $\{m_i\}$. Derive expressions for: $C_{l_{p_I}}$ and $C_{m_{q_I}}$. Note: neither of these derivatives exist in the case of rigid airplanes!

7.7   Repeat problem 7.7 for the vertical tail contribution of $C_{n_{r_I}}$ and $C_{l_{r_I}}$.

7.10   REFERENCES FOR CHAPTER 7

7.1   Woodward, F.A.; Analysis and Design of Wing–Body Combinations at Subsonic and Supersonic Speeds; Journal of Aircraft, Vol. 5, No. 6, Nov.–Dec., 1968.

7.2   Fung, Y.C.; An Introduction to the Theory of Aeroelasticity; John Wiley & Sons, Inc., 1955.

7.3   Bisplinghoff, R.L., Ashley, H. and Halfman, R.; Aeroelasticity; Addison–Wesley, 1955.

7.4   Bisplinghoff, R.L. and Ashley, H.; Principles of Aeroelasticity; John Wiley & Sons, Inc., 1963.

7.5   Martin, H.C.; Introduction to Matrix Methods of Structural Analysis; McGraw–Hill, New York, 1966.

7.6   Przemieniecki, J.S.; Theory of Matrix Structural Analysis; McGraw–Hill, New York, 1968.

7.7   Anon.; An Analysis of Methods for Predicting the Stability Characteristics of an Elastic Airplane; Appendix B – Methods for Determining Stability Derivatives; Boeing Document D6–20659–3; NASA Contractor Report CR–73275, November 1968.

7.8   Roskam, J. and Dusto, R.; A Method for Predicting Longitudinal Stability Derivatives for Rigid and Elastic Airplanes; Journal of Aircraft, Nov.–Dec., 1969.

7.9   Anon.; An Analysis of Methods for Predicting the Stability Characteristics of an Elastic Airplane; Appendix A – Equations of Motion and Stability Criteria; Boeing Document D6–20659–2; NASA Contractor Report CR–73274, November 1968.

7.10   Anon.; An Analysis of Methods for Predicting the Stability Characteristics of an Elastic Airplane; Appendix C – Methods for Predicting Stability and Response Characteristics; Boeing Document D6–20659–44; NASA Contractor Report CR–73276, November 1968.

7.11   Roskam, J,, Holgate, T. and Shimizu, G.; Elastic Wind Tunnel Models for Predicting Longi–tudinal Stability Derivatives of Elastic Airplanes; Journal of Aircraft, Nov.–Dec., 1968.

7.12   Abel, I.; A Critical Wind Tunnel Evaluation of a Technique for Predicting Static Aerodynamic Characteristics for a Highly Flexible Supersonic Transport Configuration; Paper presented at the AIAA/ASME 12th Structures, Structural Dynamics and Materials Conference, Anaheim, CA, April 1971.

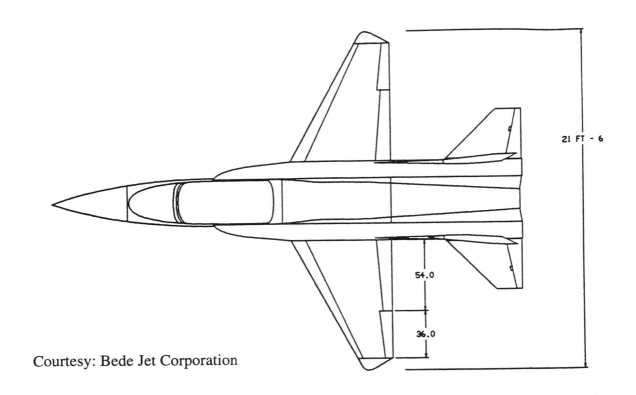

Courtesy: Bede Jet Corporation

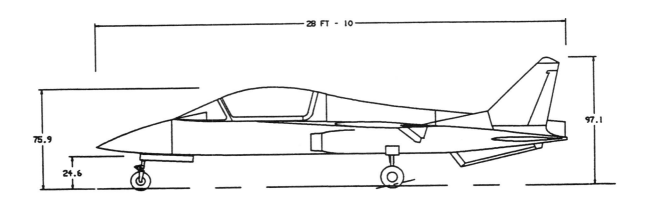

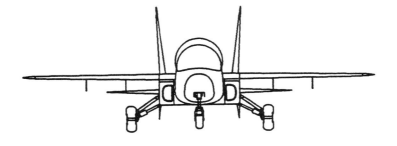

CHAPTER 8: THEORY AND APPLICATIONS OF BODE PLOTS

In this chapter, the theory and applications of Bode Plots are discussed. Bode plots are a logarithmic representation of the frequency response characteristics of airplanes or airplane components, such as control system loops and control system actuators.

Consider an airplane in a steady state flight condition. Assume that the airplane has a longitudinal control system as sketched in Figure 8.1.

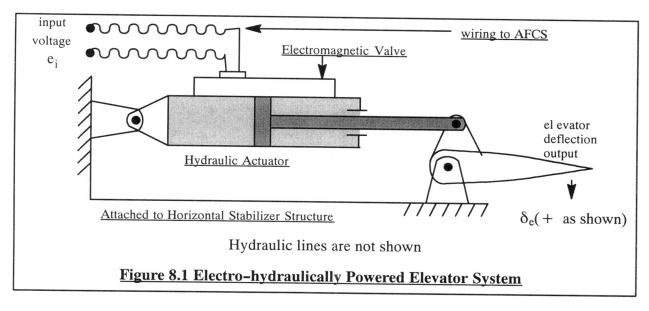

Figure 8.1 Electro-hydraulically Powered Elevator System

The elevator deflection angle, δ_e, responds to an electrical command signal, e_i, which may originate in a flight control computer and which is sent to an electro-magnetically controlled valve which in turn sends high pressure hydraulic fluid to one side of the piston. The piston, in turn, is linked to the elevator. Clearly, there will be some time delay (lag) between the creation of signal, e_i, and the elevator deflection, δ_e. This delay (or lag) should be as small as possible.

In the real world, the signal, e_i, changes continually because turbulence in the air will perturb the airplane, while the automatic flight control system (or the pilot) attempts to maintain constant pitch attitude. Therefore, it is of great interest to be able to predict how the elevator deflection, δ_e (output), will respond to the electrical input signal, e_i.

It was shown in Chapter 5 that airplane responses to control deflections can be predicted with the help of airplane transfer functions. Examples of such transfer function were: $u(s)/\delta_e(s)$, $\alpha(s)/\delta_e(s)$ and $\theta(s)/\delta_e(s)$. These transfer functions can be used to predict how perturbed speed, u, angle of attack, α, and pitch attitude, θ, vary with time, following some elevator input. The general idea of this was illustrated in Figure 5.10. Here again, a definite output, in this case the quantities (u, α and θ), are related to an input quantity, δ_e. The delay (lag) between output and input must not be too large.

It is well known that any signal, which varies with time, can be expanded in a Fourier series. As an example, the input signal, e_i, of Figure 8.1 can be written as follows:

$$e_i = \sum_{i=0}^{\infty} A_i \sin(\omega_i t) + \sum_{i=o}^{\infty} B_i \cos(\omega_i t) \tag{8.1}$$

The number of terms to be carried in this Fourier series depends on the desired accuracy. Theoretically, if the input signal, e_i, is a step input, an infinite number of terms are required. It is said on that basis, that the signal, e_i, contains an infinite amount of frequencies which range from zero to infinity.

In linear systems (i.e. systems which can be described by linear differential equations) the total output signal resulting from the input signal, e_i, can always be considered as the sum of output signals resulting from the individual input signals on the l.h.s. of Eqn (8.1). For this reason it is of interest to study the response behavior of the output signal in response to an input signal of constant amplitude, but of varying frequency. Such a response is called a frequency response. For airplanes this is of great importance because they fly in a turbulent environment. The response of the airplane to turbulence must be such that the crew and passengers are not endangered. They must also be reasonably comfortable.

The purpose of this chapter then is to discuss a method for predicting the frequency response of the airplane and its flight control system. A general method for computing frequency responses is developed in Sections 8.1 through 8.3. Applications of this method to the frequency response behavior of airplanes is discussed in Section 8.4. A powerful inverse application of the frequency response method is given in Section 8.5.

Frequency response methods are commonly used in determining airplane response to turbulence. A mathematical model for atmospheric turbulence as well as a method for assessing airplane response to turbulence is discussed in Reference 8.1.

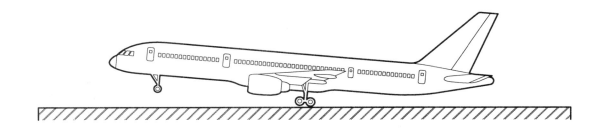

8.1 INTRODUCTION TO THE FREQUENCY RESPONSE OF LINEAR SYSTEMS

Assume, that a linear system, which is not unstable, is driven by a sinusoidal input signal:

$$e_1 = A_1 \sin(\omega_1 \, t) \tag{8.2}$$

Further assume that this signal is switched on to the system at time t=0. The output of the system will be similar to that shown in Figure 8.2. Note that both input and output in Figure 8.2 are to be measured in the same units, volts in this case.

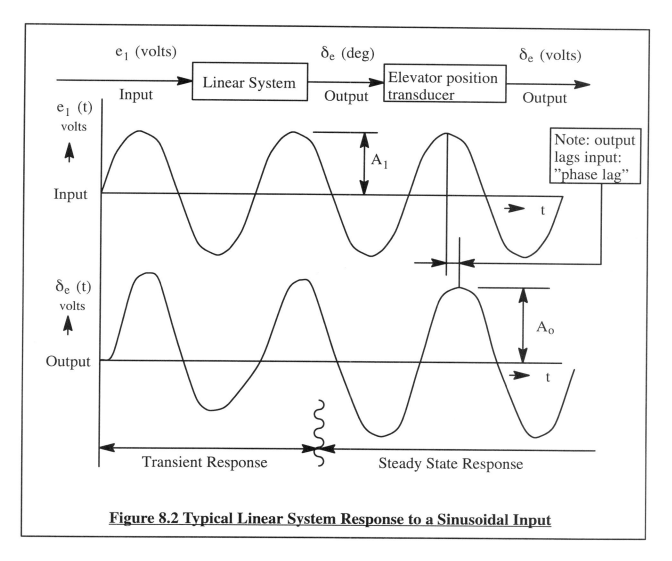

Figure 8.2 Typical Linear System Response to a Sinusoidal Input

During the time period immediately after t=0 the system output will not be purely sinusoidal. Instead, there will be a transient component to the response which dies out (vanishes) as time goes by, provided the system is not unstable. After some time, the output will 'settle' to a pure sinusoidal oscillation with the same frequency as the input but not necessarily in phase with the input. In general, the amplitude of the output will be different from that of the input. The steady state output of such a linear system may be written as:

$$\delta_e = A_0 \sin(\omega t + \phi) \qquad\qquad (8.3)$$

where: A_0 is the output amplitude

ω is the input=output frequency

ϕ is the so–called phase angle

Assuming that the transient response component of the system output dies out rapidly, the steady state component of the output as modelled by Eqn (8.3) is of great interest to system designers. The so–called real frequency response of a system is concerned only with the steady state components of the system output. In a practical situation, the real frequency response of a system can be measured by switching an input of given amplitude and frequency to the system. The output, once settled to its steady state, can be measured in terms of its amplitude and phase angle. In this manner it is possible to measure $\delta_e(\omega)/e_1(\omega)$ and $\phi(\omega)$ for a range of input frequencies. The ratio of output amplitude to input amplitude, $A_0(\omega)/A_i(\omega)$, is called the system **amplitude ratio**, while $\phi(\omega)$ is called the **phase shift**.

The real frequency response of a linear system is defined as the amplitude ratio, $A_0(\omega)/A_i(\omega)$ and the phase shift, $\phi(\omega)$, for the following range of input frequencies: $0 < \omega < \infty$. Plots of $A_0(\omega)/A_i(\omega)$ and $\phi(\omega)$ over a range of frequencies can be made in a variety of ways. One way is illustrated in Figure 8.3.

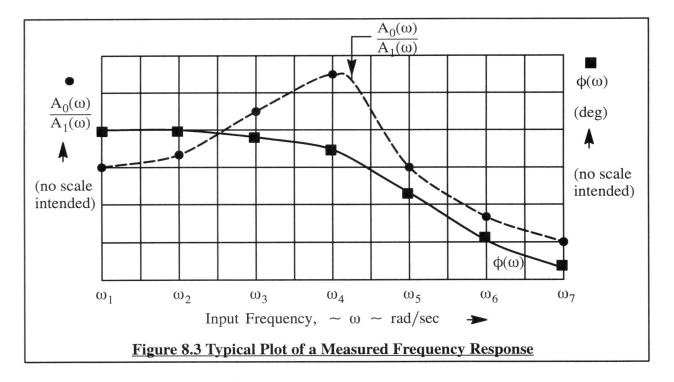

Figure 8.3 Typical Plot of a Measured Frequency Response

A frequently used method of plotting real frequency response in the design and analysis of airplane systems is the so–called Bode chart or Bode plot. In a Bode plot the frequency is plotted as the 10–based logarithm of frequency. The amplitude ratio is plotted as twenty times the 10–based logarithm of the amplitude ratio, also called decibels. In control system analysis and design it is customary to use the following definition:

$$\frac{A_0(\omega)}{A_1(\omega)} \Bigg|_{db} = 20 \log_{10} \frac{A_0(\omega)}{A_1(\omega)} \tag{8.4}$$

The symbol $|_{db}$ indicates that the amplitude ratio is measured in decibels. A typical example of a Bode plot is shown in Figure 8.4.

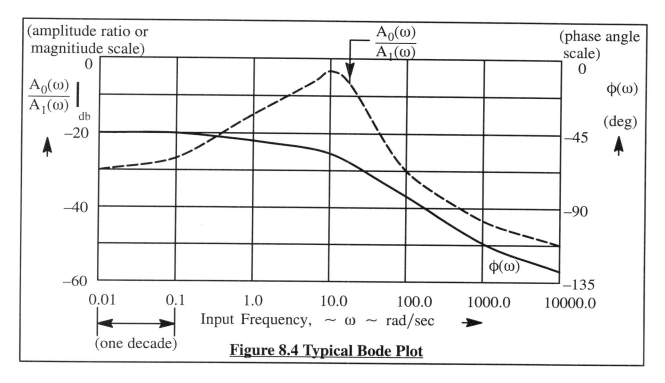

Figure 8.4 Typical Bode Plot

Observe, that the frequency in a Bode plot does not start at zero. For practical purposes, frequencies below 0.0001 rad/sec are considered to be close enough to zero. Typical airplane system frequencies range from 0.01 to 100 rad/sec., which is a frequency span of four decades. From here on, only the Bode plot method of representing frequency response behavior of linear systems will be used. There are two important reasons why frequency responses are plotted in a Bode format:

1) The amplitude ratios and the phase angles on a Bode plot can be conveniently approximated by a series of straight lines. A method for doing this very rapidly, the so–called method of asymptotic approximations, is discussed in Section 8.3.

2) The frequency response of a system which consists of a series of cascaded elements (which is the case in most airplane systems) can be found by graphical addition of the frequency response of the individual elements of that system.

To illustrate the second property, consider the system in Figure 8.5, which consists of two cascaded elements with transfer functions $G_1(s)$ and $G_2(s)$ respectively.

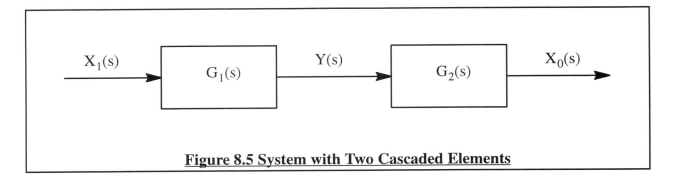

Figure 8.5 System with Two Cascaded Elements

If the input to the first system is given by: $X_1(t) = A_1 \sin(\omega t)$, the steady state output of the first system may be written as:

$$Y(t) = Y \sin(\omega t + \phi_1) \qquad (8.5)$$

where: ϕ_1 is the phase shift associated with the first element.

Note, that Y/A_1 is the amplitude ratio associated with the first system. For the second system, the steady state output can be written as:

$$X_0(t) = A_0 \sin(\omega t + \phi_1 + \phi_2) \qquad (8.6)$$

where: ϕ_2 is the phase shift associated with the second element.

Note, that A_0/Y is the amplitude ratio associated with the second system. Clearly, the overall system phase shift is $(\phi_1 + \phi_2)$. Also, the overall system amplitude ratio is:

$$\frac{A_0}{A_1} = \left(\frac{Y}{A_1}\right)\left(\frac{A_0}{Y}\right) \qquad (8.7)$$

It is now clear that for a system which consists of n cascaded elements, the total phase shift can be written as:

$$\text{System phase shift} = \sum_{i=1}^{i=n} \phi_i = \phi_1 + \phi_2 + \phi_3 + \dots\dots \qquad (8.8)$$

where: ϕ_i is the phase shift associated with element i.

Similarly, for the overall system amplitude ratio:

$$M = \text{System amplitude ratio} = \prod_{i=1}^{i=n} M_i = M_1 M_2 M_3 \dots\dots M_n \qquad (8.9)$$

where: M_i is the amplitude ratio associated with element i.

In the Bode plot, the phase contributions, ϕ_i, are plotted linearly and therefore, the ϕ_i values can simply be added together. However, the amplitude ratios are plotted on a logarithmic scale so that:

$$20 \log_{10} M = 20 \log_{10} M_1 + 20 \log_{10} M_2 + \dots + 20 \log_{10} M_n \qquad (8.10)$$

Therefore, on the Bode plot the amplitude ratios can also be simply added together.

An important application will now be discussed. For this application the so–called lag network of Figure 8.6 will be used. Such networks find many applications in airplane flight control systems as will be seen in Chapters 10 and 11. Before showing how a lag network responds to a sinusoidal input it is desirable to show how such a network responds to a step input. The discussion is therefore presented in two steps:

1) the response of a lag network to a step input

2) the response of the same lag network to a sinusoidal input

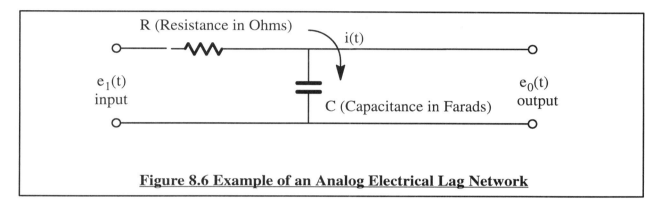

Figure 8.6 Example of an Analog Electrical Lag Network

1) the response of a lag network to a step input

The lag network of Figure 8.6 will be given a step input of magnitude E volts. The time domain representation of this step input is given in Figure 8.7.

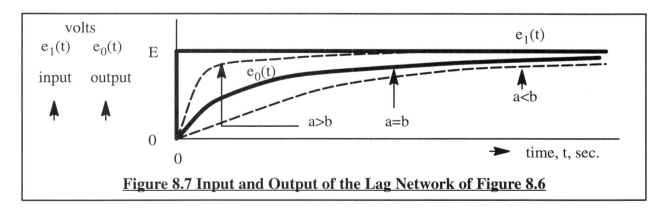

Figure 8.7 Input and Output of the Lag Network of Figure 8.6

According to Kirchhoff's Law, the following equations describe the time domain behavior of input voltage, output voltage and current:

$$\text{input}: \quad e_1(t) = Ri(t) + \frac{1}{C} \int_{-\infty}^{t} idt \qquad (8.11)$$

$$\text{output}: \quad e_0(t) = \frac{1}{C} \int_{-\infty}^{t} i\,dt \tag{8.12}$$

By applying the Laplace transformation these equations become:

$$\text{input}: \quad E_1(s) = Ri(s) + \frac{1}{Cs}i(s) \tag{8.13}$$

$$\text{output}: \quad E_0(s) = \frac{1}{Cs}i(s) \tag{8.14}$$

By eliminating $i(s)$ from these equations it is found that:

$$\frac{E_0(s)}{E_1(s)} = \frac{1/RC}{s + 1/RC} = \frac{a}{s + a} = G(s) \tag{8.15}$$

where: $G(s)$ is called the open loop transfer function of the lag network. Since the input to the system was a step input with a magnitude of $e_1(t) = E$ volts, the output can be written as:

$$E_0(s) = \frac{Ea}{s(s + a)} = \frac{A_1}{s} + \frac{A_2}{s + a} \tag{8.16}$$

where the coefficients A_1 and A_2 are the coefficients of the so–called partial fraction expansion of the output Laplace transform of the system. By application of the Theorem of Residues (consult Reference 8.2, pages 522–529) these coefficients are found as:

$$A_1 = E \quad \text{and}: \quad A_2 = -E \tag{8.17}$$

Therefore, the output Laplace transform becomes:

$$E_0(s) = \frac{E}{s} - \frac{E}{s + a} \tag{8.18}$$

The time domain inverse of the system output (see Appendix C, Part I) can be expressed as:

$$e_0(t) = E - Ee^{-at} = E(1 - e^{-at}) = \{e_1(t)\}(1 - e^{-at}) \tag{8.19}$$

It is seen from Eqn (8.19) that the output, $e_0(t)$, lags behind the input, $e_1(t)$, but eventually catches up and becomes identical with the input. Figure 8.7 also illustrates this behavior. It is said that the output follows the input. Electro–hydraulic actuators have transfer functions very much like Eqn (8.15). Those actuators therefore produce a control surface deflection which lags the input signal. Such a lag must be as small as possible. It is seen from Eqn (8.19) that the lag will be small, as long as the constant 'a' is large. In Section 8.2, the constant 'a' is referred to as the open loop system 'break frequency'. It is shown in Figure 8.7, that the higher the break frequency, a, the faster the response of a system. However, actuators with a high break frequency tend to be more expensive than actuators with a low break frequency.

It is seen from Eqns (8.15) and (8.19) that the ratio of output–to–input can be written as:

$$\frac{E_0(s)}{E_1(s)} = \frac{a}{(s + a)} \quad \text{and} \quad e_0(t)/e_1(t) = (1 - e^{-at}) \tag{8.20}$$

The reader is encouraged to compare these results with the single–degree–of–freedom roll rate response to a step input aileron deflection of Eqn (5.133) in Part I of this text.

2)   the response of a lag network to a sinusoidal input

Next, consider the case of a sinusoidal input which is written as:

$$e_1(t) = E_1 \sin (\omega_1 t) \tag{8.21}$$

The Laplace transform of this input signal is:

$$E_1(s) = \frac{E_1 \omega_1}{s^2 + \omega_1^2} \tag{8.22}$$

The Laplace transform of the output signal is:

$$E_0(s) = \left(\frac{a}{s + a}\right)\left(\frac{E_1 \omega_1}{s^2 + \omega_1^2}\right) \tag{8.23}$$

Employing the partial fraction expansion method, this output becomes:

$$E_0(s) = \frac{K_1}{s + a} + \frac{K_2}{s + j\omega_1} + \frac{K_3}{s - j\omega_1} \tag{8.24}$$

The coefficients, K_1, K_2 and K_3 can be found by applying the Theorem of Residues (see Ref. 8.2, pages 522–529). This yields:

$$K_1 = \left\{(a)\left(\frac{E_1 \omega_1}{s^2 + \omega_1^2}\right)\right\}_{s = -a} \tag{8.25}$$

$$K_2 = \left\{\left(\frac{a}{s + a}\right)\left(\frac{E_1 \omega_1}{s - j\omega_1}\right)\right\}_{s = -j\omega_1} \tag{8.26}$$

$$K_3 = \left\{\left(\frac{a}{s + a}\right)\left(\frac{E_1 \omega_1}{s + j\omega_1}\right)\right\}_{s = +j\omega_1} \tag{8.27}$$

By substituting Eqns (8.25) through (8.27) into Eqn (8.24) and rearranging it follows that:

$$E_0(s) = \left\{\left(\frac{aE_1 \omega_1}{a^2 + \omega_1^2}\right)\left(\frac{1}{s + a}\right)\right\} - \left\{\left(\frac{s + a}{s^2 + \omega_1^2}\right)\left(\frac{aE_1 \omega_1}{a^2 + \omega_1^2}\right)\right\} \tag{8.28}$$

By using the appropriate Laplace transform pairs of Appendix C, Part I is can be shown that the time domain inverse of Eqn (8.28) is:

$$E_0(t) = \left(\frac{aE_1\omega_1}{a^2 + \omega_1^2}\right) e^{-at} - \left[\frac{aE_1}{\sqrt{a^2 + \omega_1^2}}\right] \sin(\omega_1 t + \phi) \tag{8.29}$$

where:

$$\phi = -\arctan\left(\frac{\omega_1}{a}\right) \tag{8.30}$$

The first term in Eqn (8.29) is the transient response component of the output of the system. As long as the system is stable (a>0), this term will gradually vanish. The second term in Eqn (8.29) is the steady state response term. **Note that it has the same frequency as the input!** This steady state response term has an amplitude and phase angle given by:

$$\text{Steady state amplitude} = \left|\frac{aE_1}{\sqrt{a^2 + \omega_1^2}}\right| \qquad \text{phase} \measuredangle = -\arctan\left(\frac{\omega_1}{a}\right) \tag{8.31}$$

Observe that the output amplitude, for a low input frequency, approaches the input amplitude. Also observe, that for a very high input frequency, the output amplitude will vanish.

Observe further that for a low input frequency, the phase angle approaches zero. Also observe that for a very high input frequency, the phase angle will tend toward –90 degrees.

The amplitude ratio of the steady state response of the lag network is found from Eqn (8.29):

$$\text{Amplitude ratio} = \left(\frac{E_0}{E_1}\right) = \left[\frac{a}{\sqrt{a^2 + \omega_1^2}}\right] \tag{8.32}$$

At this point the following observation is made: by substituting $(s = j\omega_1)$ into the open loop transfer function of the system {see Eqn (8.15)} and finding the absolute magnitude and phase angle of the result of that substitution, it is found that:

$$|\ G(s)\ |_{s=j\omega_1} = \left|\ \frac{a}{j\omega_1 + a}\ \right| = \left[\frac{a}{\sqrt{a^2 + \omega_1^2}}\right] \tag{8.33}$$

and:

$$\measuredangle\{G(s)\}_{s=j\omega_1} = \measuredangle\left(\frac{a}{j\omega_1 + a}\right) = -\arctan\left(\frac{\omega_1}{a}\right) \tag{8.34}$$

It therefore appears that the amplitude ratio and the phase angle of a stable, linear system can be found directly by substituting $(s = j\omega_1)$ into the open loop transfer function of the system instead of deriving these quantities from the time domain response. A general proof of this extremely useful property is given in Section 8.2.

8.2 DETERMINATION OF THE FREQUENCY RESPONSE OF LINEAR SYSTEMS DIRECTLY FROM THE SYSTEM OPEN LOOP TRANSFER FUNCTION

Consider the arbitrary linear system with open loop transfer function G(s) of Figure 8.8.

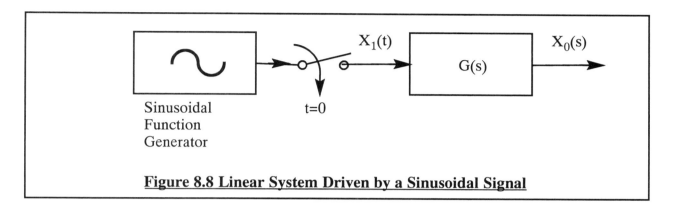

Figure 8.8 Linear System Driven by a Sinusoidal Signal

This system is driven by a sinusoidal signal. It will be assumed, that the transfer function G(s) consists of the ratio of a numerator polynomial in s to a denominator polynomial in s. Such a ratio can be thought of as consisting of a series of first order numerator factors $(s + Z_j)$ with j running from 1 to m and a series of denominator factors $(s + P_i)$ with i running from 1 to n. In addition, there will generally exist some remaining constant, K. Therefore:

$$G(s) = \frac{K(s + Z_1)(s + Z_2)\ldots\ldots\ldots(s + Z_m)}{(s + P_1)(s + P_2)\ldots\ldots\ldots(s + P_n)} \tag{8.35}$$

The numerator characteristic equation roots, $-Z_1$, $-Z_2$ through $-Z_m$, are called the **open loop system zeros**. The denominator characteristic equation roots, $-P_1$, $-P_1$ through $-P_n$, are called the **open loop system poles**. If all poles are positive (so that the corresponding characteristic equation roots are all negative) the system is called stable. The poles in that case are in the left side of the s–plane.

Assume, that the input signal of Figure 8.8 is modelled as:

$$X_1(t) = A\sin(\omega t) \tag{8.36}$$

with the Laplace transform:

$$X_1(s) = \frac{A\omega}{s^2 + \omega^2} \tag{8.37}$$

The output Laplace transform of the system can now be expressed as:

$$X_0(s) = \frac{A\omega K(s + Z_1)(s + Z_2)\ldots\ldots\ldots(s + Z_m)}{(s^2 + \omega^2)(s + P_1)(s + P_2)\ldots\ldots\ldots\ldots(s + P_n)} \qquad (8.38)$$

By expanding Eqn (8.38) in partial fractions:

$$X_0(s) = \underbrace{\frac{\overline{K}_0}{s + j\omega} + \frac{K_0}{s - j\omega}}_{\text{Steady state}} + \underbrace{\frac{K_1}{s + P_1} + \frac{K_2}{s + P_2} + \ldots\ldots + \frac{K_n}{s + P_n}}_{\text{Transient state}} \qquad (8.39)$$

If the system has only stable poles, the time domain inverses of the transient terms will vanish, whether the poles are real or complex! Therefore, when considering the steady state (ss) frequency response of the system, only the two steady state terms need to be considered:

$$X_0(s)|_{ss} = \frac{\overline{K}_0}{s + j\omega} + \frac{K_0}{s - j\omega} \qquad (8.40)$$

where: K_0 is the residue of $X_0(s)$ at the point $s = j\omega$, while $\overline{K}_0$ is the residue of $X_0(s)$ at the point $s = -j\omega$. Also, according to the theory of complex variables, K_0 is the complex conjugate of $\overline{K}_0$. The residue, K_0, may be determined from Eqn (8.38). It is found that:

$$K_0 = \left(\frac{A\omega K}{2j\omega}\right)\frac{(j\omega + Z_1)(j\omega + Z_2)\ldots\ldots\ldots(j\omega + Z_m)}{(j\omega + P_1)(j\omega + P_2)\ldots\ldots\ldots\ldots(j\omega + P_n)} = -j\left(\frac{A}{2}\right)G(j\omega) \qquad (8.41)$$

where:

$$G(j\omega) = G(s)|_{s = j\omega} \qquad (8.42)$$

Since K_0 will in general be a complex number, it can be expressed with a real and imaginary part as:

$$K_0 = a + jb \qquad (8.43)$$

Because $\overline{K}_0$ is the complex conjugate of K_0 it can be written as:

$$\overline{K}_0 = a - jb \qquad (8.44)$$

With the help of Eqns (8.43) and (8.44) it is now possible to rewrite Eqn (8.40) as:

$$X_0(s)|_{ss} = \frac{\overline{K}_0}{s + j\omega} + \frac{K_0}{s - j\omega} = \frac{(\overline{K}_0 + K_0)s}{s^2 + \omega^2} + \frac{j\omega(K_0 - \overline{K}_0)}{s^2 + \omega^2} =$$

$$= \frac{2as}{s^2 + \omega^2} - \frac{2b\omega}{s^2 + \omega^2} \qquad (8.45)$$

From the latter and from the appropriate transform pairs of Appendix C, Part I it is found that:

$$X_0(t)|_{ss} = 2a\cos(\omega t) - 2b\sin(\omega t) = \sqrt{4a^2 + 4b^2}\sin(\omega t + \phi) \qquad (8.46)$$

with:

$$\phi = \arctan\left(\frac{a}{-b}\right) \qquad (8.47)$$

The output–to–input amplitude ratio and phase angle can therefore be written as:

$$M = \frac{\sqrt{4a^2 + 4b^2}}{A} \qquad (8.48)$$

and:

$$\phi = \arctan\left(\frac{a}{-b}\right) \qquad (8.49)$$

Note from Eqn (8.43) that a and b are related to K_0 by:

$$\sqrt{4a^2 + 4b^2} = 2\sqrt{a^2 + b^2} = 2|K_0| \qquad (8.50)$$

Also note from Eqn (8.41) that:

$$|K_0| = \frac{A}{2}|G(j\omega)| \qquad (8.51)$$

When substituting Eqns (8.50) and (8.51) into Eqn (8.48) it follows that:

$$\boxed{M(\omega) = |G(j\omega)|} \qquad (8.52)$$

For the system phase shift, consider Figure 8.9 and Eqn (8.49).

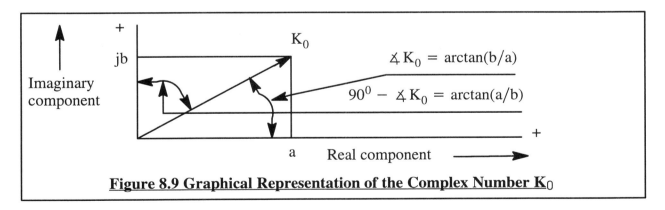

Figure 8.9 Graphical Representation of the Complex Number K_0

With Figure 8.9, Eqn (8.49) and Eqn (8.41) it follows that:

$$\phi = \arctan\{a/(-b)\} = -\arctan(a/b) = -(\angle K_0 - 90^0) =$$
$$= -\angle(K_0/j) = -\angle\left\{-\frac{j}{j}\left(\frac{A}{2}\right)G(j\omega)\right\} = \angle G(j\omega) \qquad (8.53)$$

From Eqn (8.53) it follows that:

$$\boxed{\phi = \angle\, G(j\omega)}$$
(8.54)

Equations (8.52) and (8.54) demonstrate the very useful fact that the steady state amplitude ratio and phase shift of a linear system can be obtained directly from the system transfer function $G(s)$. The procedure is simply to substitute $s = j\omega$ into the transfer function and evaluate the absolute magnitude and phase angle of the result.

At this point, three examples will be discussed:

Example 1)   Frequency response of a first order lag

Example 2)   Frequency response of a first order lead–lag

Example 3)   Frequency response of a second order lag

As the reader progresses through the material of Chapters 8, 9 and 10 it will become clear that all these systems have direct applications to the study of airplane open and closed loop dynamics.

Example 1)   Frequency response of a first order lag

The open loop transfer function of a first order lag can be written as:

$$G(s) = \frac{K}{s + a}$$
(8.55)

This system has one pole and no zeros. A so–called pole–zero plot of this system is shown in Figure 8.10.

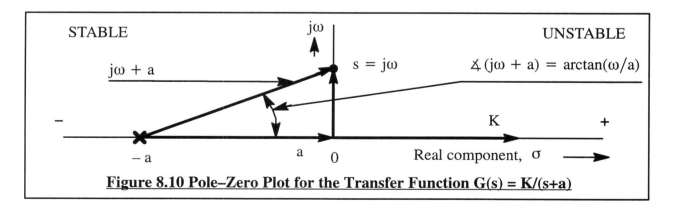

Figure 8.10 Pole–Zero Plot for the Transfer Function G(s) = K/(s+a)

The amplitude ratio of this system is found by applying Eqn (8.52) to Eqn (8.55):

$$M = |G(j\omega)| = \left| \frac{K}{j\omega + a} \right| = \frac{K}{|j\omega + a|} = \frac{K}{\sqrt{\omega^2 + a^2}}$$
(8.56)

The phase shift of this system is found by applying Eqn (8.54) to Eqn (8.55):

$$\phi \ = \ \measuredangle \, G(j\omega) \ = \ \measuredangle \, K \ - \ \measuredangle \, (j\omega + a) \ = \ - \ \measuredangle \, (j\omega + a) \ = \ - \arctan\frac{\omega}{a} \qquad (8.57)$$

From Eqn (8.57) and from Figure 8.10 it is clear that when the input frequency, ω, is very small, the phase angle, ϕ, is close to zero degrees. When the frequency, ω, approaches infinity, the phase angle, ϕ, will approach –90 degrees.

From Eqn (8.56) it is also clear that when the input frequency, ω, is very small, the amplitude ratio, M, will be M=K/a. On the other hand, for very high input frequency, ω, the amplitude ratio will approach zero: the system no longer reacts to input signals of very high frequency.

These behaviors are graphically illustrated in the Bode plot of Figure 8.11.

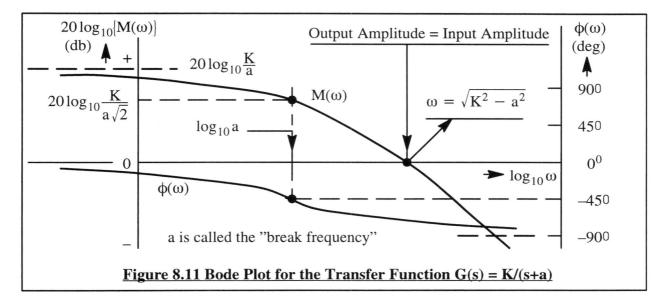

Figure 8.11 Bode Plot for the Transfer Function G(s) = K/(s+a)

Note that $(-\infty)$db on the Bode magnitude scale implies that the system output amplitude vanishes in relation to the system input amplitude.

Several observations are in order:

a)   At a frequency ω=a, the so–called **break–frequency** of the system, the amplitude ratio is exactly 0.707 of what the amplitude ratio would be at zero frequency.

b)   Also, at the system break frequency, the phase angle is exactly –45⁰.

c)   When the output amplitude equals the input amplitude, M = 1.0 and therefore, $M(\omega) = 0$ db. The frequency for which this occurs is called the magnitude cross–over frequency: $\omega_{magn.cross-over} = \sqrt{K^2 - a^2}$

The reader should memorize these facts.

Example 2)   Frequency response of a first order lead–lag

The open loop transfer function of a lead–lag system can be expressed by:

$$G(s) = \frac{K(s + b)}{(s + a)} \tag{8.58}$$

This system has one pole and one zero. A so–called pole–zero plot of this system is shown in Figure 8.12.

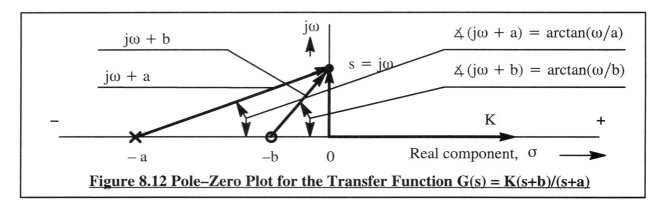

Figure 8.12 Pole–Zero Plot for the Transfer Function G(s) = K(s+b)/(s+a)

The amplitude ratio of this system is found by applying Eqn (8.52) to Eqn (8.58):

$$M = |G(j\omega)| = \left|\frac{K(j\omega + b)}{(j\omega + a)}\right| = \frac{K|(j\omega + b)|}{|(j\omega + a)|} = K\frac{\sqrt{\omega^2 + b^2}}{\sqrt{\omega^2 + a^2}} \tag{8.59}$$

The phase shift of this system is found by applying Eqn (8.54) to Eqn (8.58):

$$\phi = \angle G(j\omega) = \angle K + \angle (j\omega + b) - \angle (j\omega + a) =$$
$$= \arctan\frac{\omega}{b} - \arctan\frac{\omega}{a} \tag{8.60}$$

From Eqn (8.59) and from Figure 8.12 it is clear that when the input frequency, ω, is very small, the phase angle, ϕ, is close to zero degrees. As the frequency approaches the value b (which in this example is assumed to be smaller than the value a), the phase angle increases positively (this is called 'lead'). For frequencies between b and a the phase angle peaks out and gradually becomes less positive. When the frequency, ω, approaches infinity, the phase angle, ϕ, will again approach zero degrees.

From Eqn (8.60) it is also clear that when the input frequency, ω, is very small, the amplitude ratio, M, will be M=Kb/a. On the other hand, for very high frequency, the amplitude ratio will approach the value K: at very high frequencies (s+b) and (s+a) tend to become the same.

These behaviors are graphically illustrated in the Bode plot of Figure 8.13.

The reader is asked to determine at what frequency the phase angle 'peaks out' and what the phase angle is at that frequency. Both should be expressed as functions of a and b.

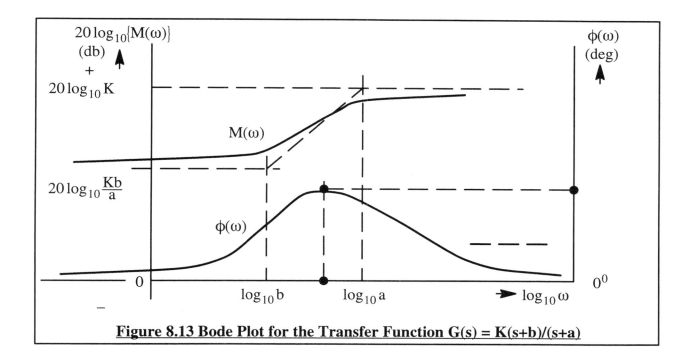

Figure 8.13 Bode Plot for the Transfer Function G(s) = K(s+b)/(s+a)

Example 3)   Frequency response of a second order lag

The open loop transfer function of a second order lag can be written as:

$$G(s) = \frac{K}{s^2 + 2\zeta\omega_n s + \omega_n^2} \tag{8.61}$$

This system has two poles (complex conjugates) and no zeros. A pole–zero plot of this system is shown in Figure 8.14.

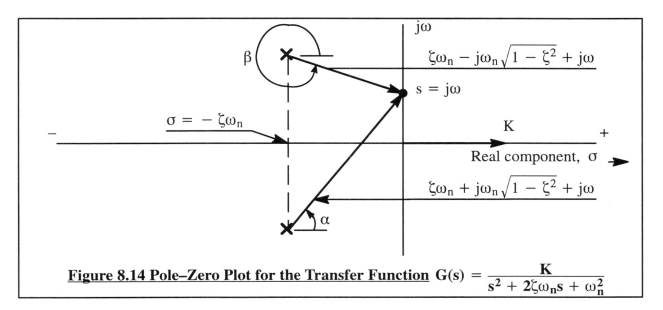

Figure 8.14 Pole–Zero Plot for the Transfer Function $G(s) = \dfrac{K}{s^2 + 2\zeta\omega_n s + \omega_n^2}$

The amplitude ratio of this system is found by applying Eqn (8.52) to Eqn (8.61):

$$M = |G(j\omega)| = \frac{K}{\left\{(\omega_n^2 - \omega^2)^2 + (2\zeta\omega_n\omega)^2\right\}^{1/2}} \tag{8.62}$$

The phase shift of this system is found by applying Eqn (8.54) to Eqn (8.61):

$$\phi = \measuredangle G(j\omega) = -\arctan\frac{2\zeta\omega_n\omega}{(\omega_n^2 - \omega^2)} \tag{8.63}$$

From Eqn (8.63) and from Figure 8.14 it is clear that when the input frequency, ω, is very small, the phase angle, ϕ, is close to zero degrees. As the frequency approaches the value ω_n (which is the undamped natural frequency of the system), the phase angle decreases toward -90 degrees. At a frequency exactly equal to ω_n, the phase angle is exactly equal to -90 degrees. As the frequency increases toward infinity, the phase angle continues to decrease toward a value of -180 degrees.

From Eqn (8.62) it is also clear that when the input frequency, ω, is very small, the amplitude ratio, M, will be $M = K/\omega_n^2$. As the frequency increases, the amplitude ratio approaches a maximum. This maximum occurs exactly at a frequency of:

$$\omega_{peak\ magnitude} = \omega_{r(esonance)} = \omega_n\sqrt{1 - 2\zeta^2} \tag{8.64}$$

The amplitude ratio at $\omega = \omega_r$ (= resonance frequency) is given by:

$$M_{peak\ magnitude} = M(\omega = \omega_r) = \frac{K}{2\zeta\omega_n^2\sqrt{1 - \zeta^2}} \qquad (\zeta < 0.707) \tag{8.65}$$

These behaviors are graphically illustrated in the Bode plot of Figure 8.15.

Because nearly all airplane and airplane system transfer functions can be thought of as combinations of first order lags (or leads) and/or second order lags (or leads) the behavior of these fundamental transfer functions is very important.

To plot the actual magnitude and phase lines on a Bode plot requires that a range of frequency values be substituted in the appropriate transfer functions and that the result of those substitutions be evaluated for absolute magnitude and for phase angle. To do this by hand is a lot of work. Computers can carry out this task, including the plotting, very rapidly. However, it is possible to approximate any transfer function in the Bode plot by a series of straight lines. Such an approximation is referred to as the 'asymptotic approximation'. Knowledge of the asymptotic approximation method is very useful, even when using computers/computer graphics to determine the Bode plots of system transfer functions. The asymptotic approximation method is discussed in Section 8.3.

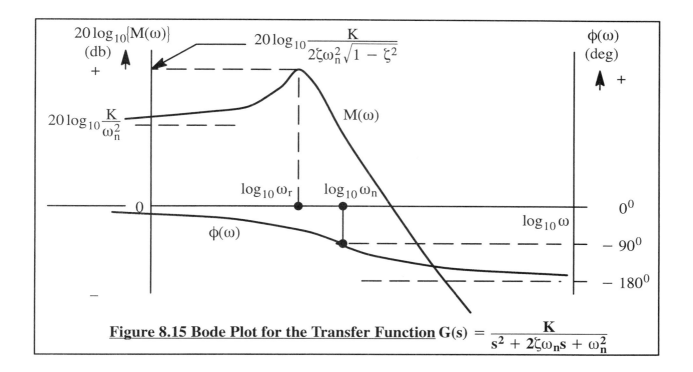

Figure 8.15 Bode Plot for the Transfer Function $G(s) = \dfrac{K}{s^2 + 2\zeta\omega_n s + \omega_n^2}$

8.3 ASYMPTOTIC APPROXIMATIONS TO REAL FREQUENCY RESPONSE OF TRANSFER FUNCTIONS

The purpose of this section is to discuss a method by which it is possible to rapidly determine the real frequency response of linear systems in a Bode plot format. The discussion starts with very simple cases and gradually builds up to actual airplane applications.

8.3.1 DIFFERENTIATORS AND INTEGRATORS

Consider the transfer function of a **differentiator**:

$$G(s) = s \qquad\qquad (8.66)$$

The frequency response of such a differentiator is found from:

$$M(\omega) = |G(j\omega)| = \omega \qquad\qquad (8.67)$$

$$\phi(\omega) = \angle G(j\omega) = +90^0 \qquad\qquad (8.68)$$

A change in frequency of a factor 10 is referred to as one decade. For a frequency of 1.0 rad/sec, the magnitude is 1.0, which amounts to 0 db on the Bode magnitude scale. For a frequency of 10.0 rad/sec, the magnitude is 10.0, which amounts to 20 db on the Bode magnitude scale. Therefore, it follows that the magnitude plot of the differentiator $G(s)=s$ passes through 0 db at $\omega=1$ rad/sec and through 20 db at $\omega=10$ rad/sec. It has a slope of +20 db/decade. The phase angle of the differentiator is independent of frequency and always equal to + 90 degrees. Figure 8.16 shows the Bode plot for the transfer function of Eqn (8.66).

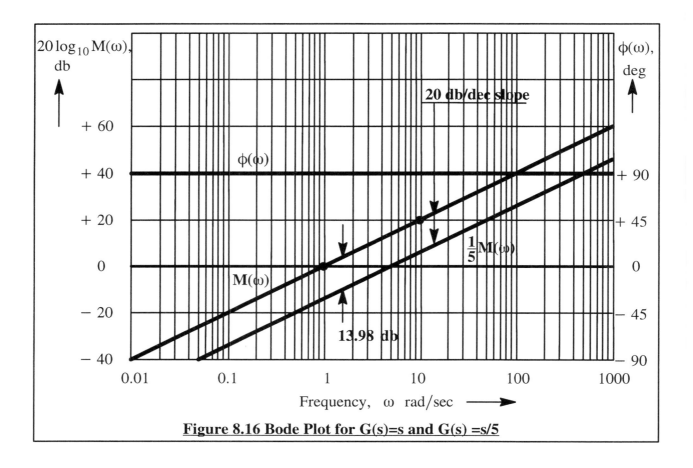

Figure 8.16 Bode Plot for G(s)=s and G(s) =s/5

Next, consider the following transfer function:

$$G(s) = Ks \tag{8.69}$$

where: K is an arbitrary, positive constant. Note that, for positive K:

$$20\log_{10}K\omega = 20\log_{10}K + 20\log_{10}\omega \quad \text{and :} \quad \phi(Kj\omega) = \phi(j\omega) \tag{8.70}$$

If K=1/5, the Bode plot for Eqn (8.69) is obtained from that of Eqn (8.66) by merely shifting the magnitude plot down over the amount of $\{20\log_{10}(1/5)\} = 13.98$ db: see Figure 8.16. The phase plot stays the same.

Next, consider the transfer function of an **integrator**:

$$G(s) = \frac{K}{s} \tag{8.71}$$

The frequency response of such an integrator is found from:

$$M(\omega) = |G(j\omega)| = \frac{K}{\omega} \tag{8.72}$$

$$\phi(\omega) = \measuredangle G(j\omega) = \measuredangle K - \measuredangle(j\omega) = -90^0 \tag{8.73}$$

Figure 8.17 shows the Bode plot for the transfer function of Eqn (8.71) for K=1 and for K=6.

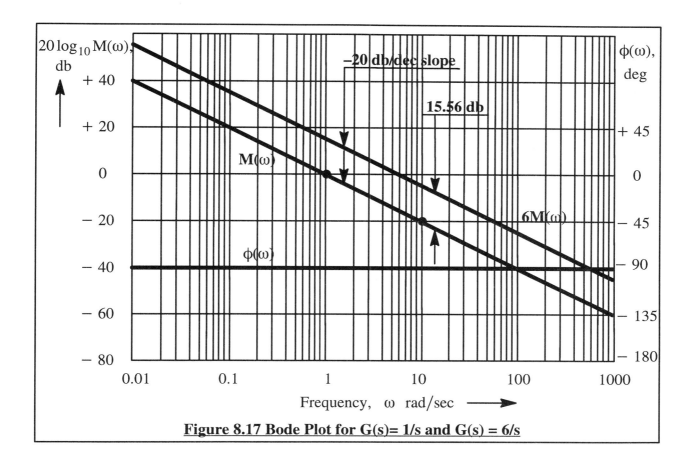

Figure 8.17 Bode Plot for G(s)= 1/s and G(s) = 6/s

Note that the magnitude of 1/s passes through 1 rad/sec at 0 db while it has a slope of -20 db/dec. The magnitude plot of 6/s is simply shifted upward over $\{20 \log_{10} (6)\} = 15.56$ db. The phase plot for K/s is a constant -90 deg line.

Next, consider the transfer function of a **double integrator**:

$$G(s) = \frac{K}{s^2} \tag{8.74}$$

The reader is asked to use the properties of Eqns (8.8) and (8.9) to show that the Bode plot for the cases K=1.0 and K=9.0 are as shown in Figure 8.18. Observe, that the phase angle, for positive K, is always -180 degrees. Also observe, that the magnitude plot now has a slope of -40 db/dec.

The reader is asked to generalize this to the case of:

$$G(s) = \frac{K}{s^n} \tag{8.75}$$

when n>0 and when n<0 as well as for K>0 and K<0.

In the next development, which deals with a first order lead and lag transfer function, the properties of the differentiator and integrator functions will be used.

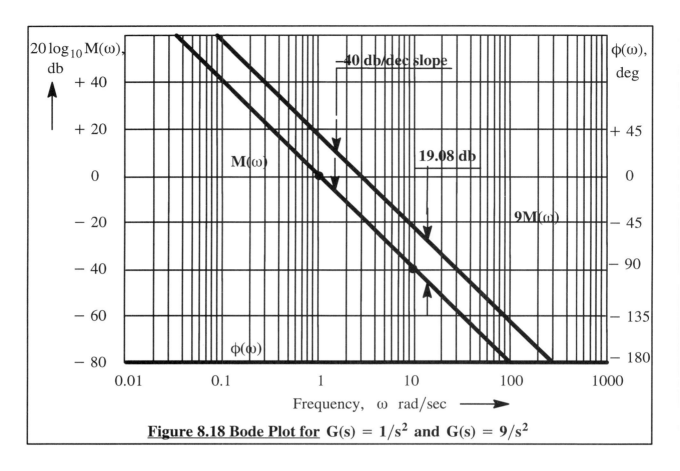

Figure 8.18 Bode Plot for $G(s) = 1/s^2$ **and** $G(s) = 9/s^2$

8.3.2 FIRST ORDER LEAD AND LAG TRANSFER FUNCTIONS

Consider the transfer function of a first order lead:

$$G(s) = \frac{(s + a)}{a} \tag{8.76}$$

The real frequency response for this transfer function follows from:

$$G(j\omega) = \frac{(j\omega + a)}{a} \tag{8.77}$$

Applying Eqns (8.52) and (8.54) it is seen that:

$$M(\omega) = \frac{1}{a}\sqrt{\omega^2 + a^2} \tag{8.78}$$

and:

$$\phi(\omega) = \arctan\left(\frac{\omega}{a}\right) \tag{8.79}$$

Observe from Eqn (8.77) that for very low frequencies, i.e. for $\omega \ll a$, the amplitude ratio of this lead transfer function is approximately 1.0. On the Bode plot that means 0 db. For high frequencies, i.e. for $\omega \gg a$, the amplitude ratio is approximately ω/a. According to Figure 8.16, the Bode plot of that approximation is a straight line passing through $\omega = a$ and having a slope of +20 db/dec. These characteristics are illustrated in Figure 8.19. The actual frequency response differs from the asymptotic approximation to a significant extent only in the vicinity of ω=a. Note, that exactly at ω=a the difference is exactly $\sqrt{2} = 0.707$. In decibels this amounts to 3.01 db. At ω=2a and at ω=a/2 the difference is exactly equal to $\sqrt{1.25} = 1.118$. In decibels this equals 0.97 db. A good mnemonic is to refer to this as the **1–3–1 Rule**.

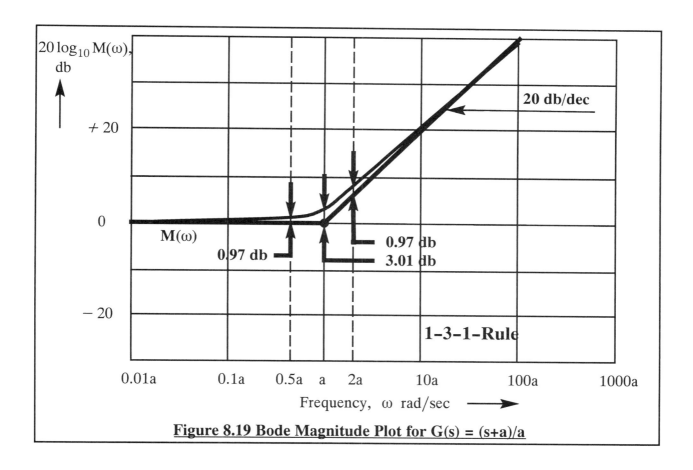

Figure 8.19 Bode Magnitude Plot for G(s) = (s+a)/a

The phase angle behavior, according to Eqn (8.79), is plotted in Figure 8.20. At the system break frequency, ω=a (point P in Figure 8.20), a tangent is drawn to the actual phase curve, φ(ω).

That tangent line has a slope of 65.96 deg/decade. This tangent intersects the zero degrees phase line at ω=0.208a. It intersects the +90 degrees phase line at 4.81a. Note, that the actual phase plot, φ(ω), can be reasonably approximated by three straight lines: line AB for frequencies below

0.208a, line BC for frequencies ranging from 0.208a to 4.81a and finally, line CD for frequencies above 4.81a. The reader is asked to check the numbers in Figure 8.20. The straight line segments approximation according to these observations is referred to as the **1/5–1–5 Rule**.

These ideas will now be extended to the following lead–lag transfer function:

$$G(s) = \frac{500(s + 10)}{(s + 100)} \qquad (8.80)$$

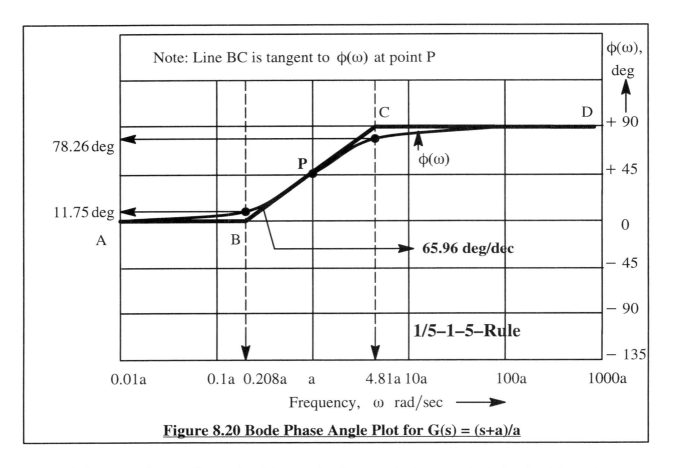

Figure 8.20 Bode Phase Angle Plot for G(s) = (s+a)/a

It is convenient to first write this transfer function in its so–called standard format:

$$G(s) = \frac{500 \times 10}{100}\left(\frac{s + 10}{10}\right)\left(\frac{100}{s + 100}\right) = 50\left(\frac{s + 10}{10}\right)\left(\frac{100}{s + 100}\right) \tag{8.81}$$

If s=0 is substituted in the standard format of a transfer function, all transfer function components take on the value of 1.0 (or 0 db), except for the pre–multiplying constant.

The construction of the asymptotic approximations to the Bode magnitude and phase plots are shown in Figures 8.21 and 8.22 respectively.

The asymptotic approximations to the first order lead and lag magnitudes are indicated in Figure 8.21 by the dashed straight lines. The overall transfer function magnitude starts out at 20 $\log_{10} 50 = 34$ db. With the 1–3–1 rule, the curved (and dashed) line was sketched in. It is seen that the asymptotic approximations are pretty good.

The asymptotic approximations to the first order lead and lag phase angles are indicated in Figure 8.22 by the dashed straight lines. The 1/5–1–5 rule was used in their construction. The line segments ABCDEF represent the sum of the asymptotic contributions and therefore the asymptotic approximation to the total phase angle behavior of the transfer function of Eqn (8.80).

Figure 8.23 shows an actual Bode plot of this system. Comparing the actual plot with the asymptotic approximation plots, it is seen that they are very close, except at the break frequencies.

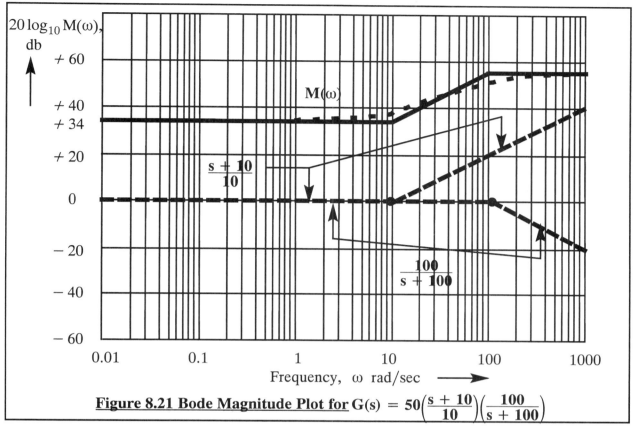

Figure 8.21 Bode Magnitude Plot for $G(s) = 50\left(\dfrac{s+10}{10}\right)\left(\dfrac{100}{s+100}\right)$

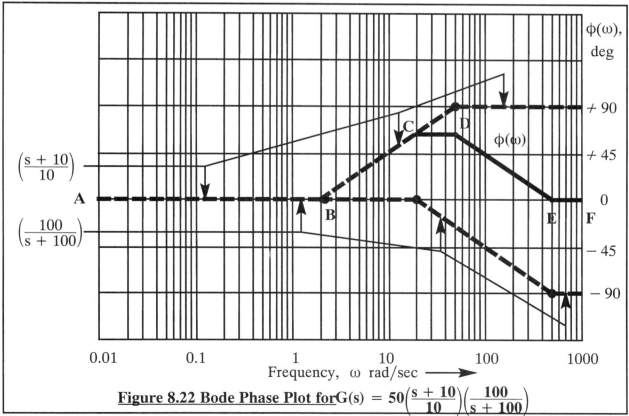

Figure 8.22 Bode Phase Plot for $G(s) = 50\left(\dfrac{s+10}{10}\right)\left(\dfrac{100}{s+100}\right)$

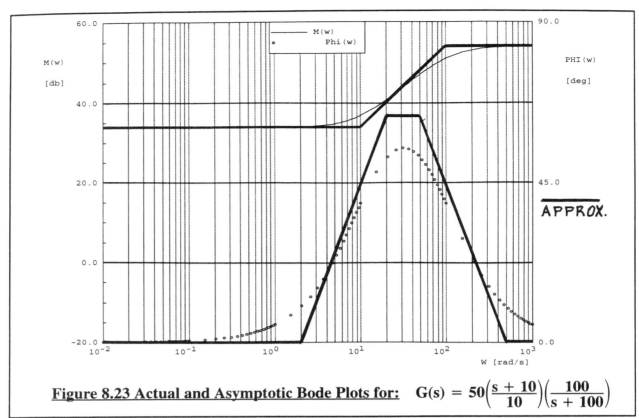

Figure 8.23 Actual and Asymptotic Bode Plots for: $\quad G(s) = 50\left(\dfrac{s + 10}{10}\right)\left(\dfrac{100}{s + 100}\right)$

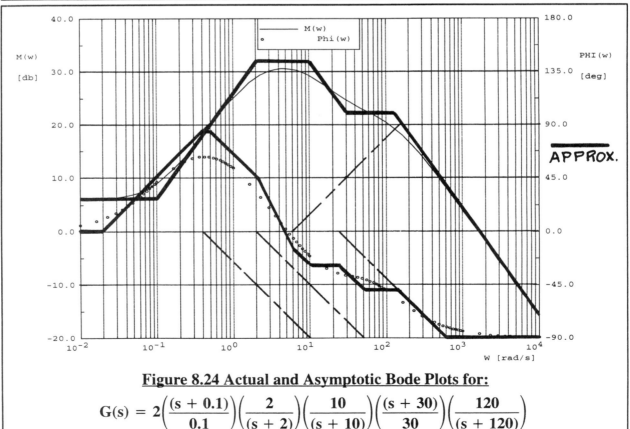

Figure 8.24 Actual and Asymptotic Bode Plots for:

$$G(s) = 2\left(\frac{(s + 0.1)}{0.1}\right)\left(\frac{2}{(s + 2)}\right)\left(\frac{10}{(s + 10)}\right)\left(\frac{(s + 30)}{30}\right)\left(\frac{120}{(s + 120)}\right)$$

As a final example in the discussion of first order lead–lag transfer functions, consider the following:

$$G(s) = \frac{1600(s + 0.1)(s + 30)}{(s + 2)(s + 10)(s + 120)} \tag{8.82}$$

This transfer function can be written in the following standard format:

$$G(s) = 2\left(\frac{(s + 0.1)}{0.1}\right)\left(\frac{2}{(s + 2)}\right)\left(\frac{10}{(s + 10)}\right)\left(\frac{(s + 30)}{30}\right)\left(\frac{120}{(s + 120)}\right) \tag{8.83}$$

A Bode phase and magnitude plot of this transfer function is shown in Figure 8.24. The associated asymptotic approximations are also shown. It is seen that the approximations are good.

8.3.3   SECOND ORDER LEAD AND LAG TRANSFER FUNCTIONS

It was seen in Chapter 5 that airplane open loop transfer functions contain not only first order leads and lags but also second order (quadratic) leads and lags. Consider the following second order transfer function:

$$G(s) = \frac{\omega_n^2}{s^2 + 2\zeta\omega_n s + \omega_n^2} \tag{8.84}$$

This equation also represents the so–called standard format for this transfer function. The reader will have observed that in the standard format, when the input frequency is set equal to zero, the transfer function has the value of 1.0.

The frequency response of this system is similar to that of Eqn (8.61) but with: $K = \omega_n^2$. Because the frequency response of a second order depends on two parameters (ω_n and ζ) it has been found convenient to 'normalize' the input frequency, ω , by dividing by the undamped natural frequency, ω_n . This is done by introducing the normalized frequency, u, defined as:

$$u = \frac{\omega}{\omega_n} \tag{8.85}$$

Substituting u into Eqn (8.84) and applying Eqns (8.52) and (8.54) yields:

$$M(u) = \frac{1}{\sqrt{(1 - u^2) + (2\zeta u)^2}} \tag{8.86}$$

$$\phi(u) = -\arctan\left(\frac{2\zeta u}{1 - u^2}\right) \tag{8.87}$$

The consequence of normalizing the input frequency in this manner is that the amplitude ratio and phase angle now depend on one variable only: u. Figures 8.25 and 8.26 present plots of M(u) and $\phi(u)$ respectively for a range of values of the damping ratio, ζ .

Now consider the asymptotic behavior of this second order transfer function.

First, consider the magnitude. At very low frequencies, the magnitude is seen to be 1.0. Therefore, the 0 db line in the Bode plot is the low frequency asymptote. At very high frequencies,

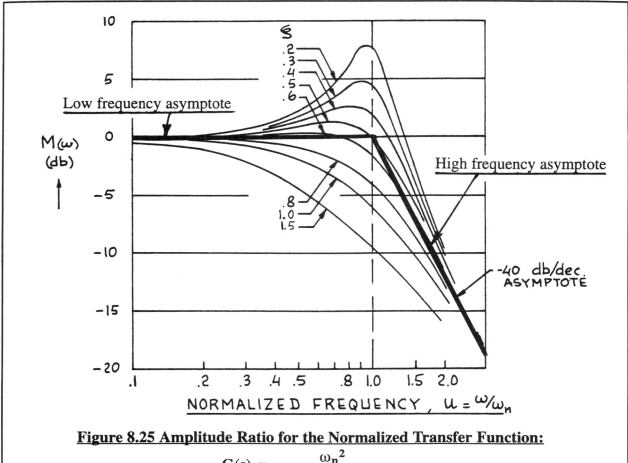

Figure 8.25 Amplitude Ratio for the Normalized Transfer Function:

$$G(s) = \frac{\omega_n^2}{s^2 + 2\zeta\omega_n s + \omega_n^2}$$

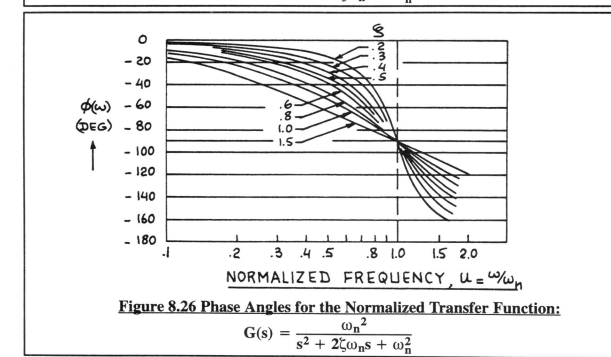

Figure 8.26 Phase Angles for the Normalized Transfer Function:

$$G(s) = \frac{\omega_n^2}{s^2 + 2\zeta\omega_n s + \omega_n^2}$$

the transfer function tends to behave like a double integrator. Comparing with Figure 8.18 the reader is asked to show that the high frequency asymptote to the magnitude plot is a straight line with a slope of –40 db/decade and passing through u=1.0 which means through $\omega = \omega_n$. The low and high frequency asymptotes are indicated in Figure 8.25.

Note that for frequencies close to the undamped natural frequency (u=1) the actual magnitude behavior differs significantly from that of the asymptotes. The difference between the asymptotes and the actual magnitude plot is seen to be strongly dependent on the damping ratio, ζ.

Second, consider the phase angles. Eqn (8.87) suggests that at very low frequencies the phase angle of the second order transfer function approaches zero degrees. For very high frequencies, the phase angles approach – 180 degrees. This is consistent with the behavior of the double integrator of Figure 8.18. Again, for frequencies close to the undamped natural frequency, the actual phase behavior depends strongly on the damping ratio, ζ.

By drawing a straight line tangent to any one of the second order phase plots, an intermediate phase asymptote can be constructed according to the rules illustrated in Figure 8.27.

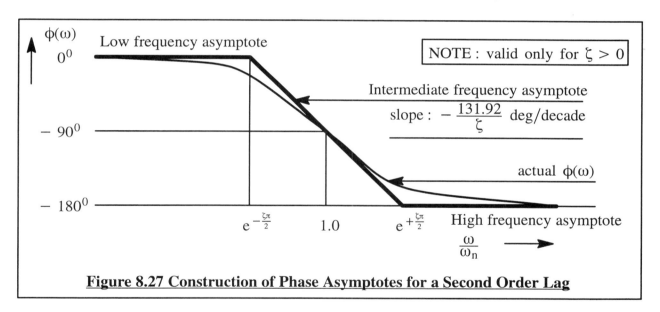

Figure 8.27 Construction of Phase Asymptotes for a Second Order Lag

With a calculator, it is easy to determine the break–points $e^{+\frac{\zeta\pi}{2}}$ and $e^{-\frac{\zeta\pi}{2}}$ on the frequency scale for any value of damping ratio, ζ. Nevertheless, Figure 8.28 which shows the numerical value of these break–points for damping ratios ranging from 0 to 1.0 may be useful to some readers.

Finally, consider an example application for a combined first and second order transfer function transfer function:

$$G(s) = \frac{100(s + 2)}{s(s^2 + 4s + 100)} \qquad (8.88)$$

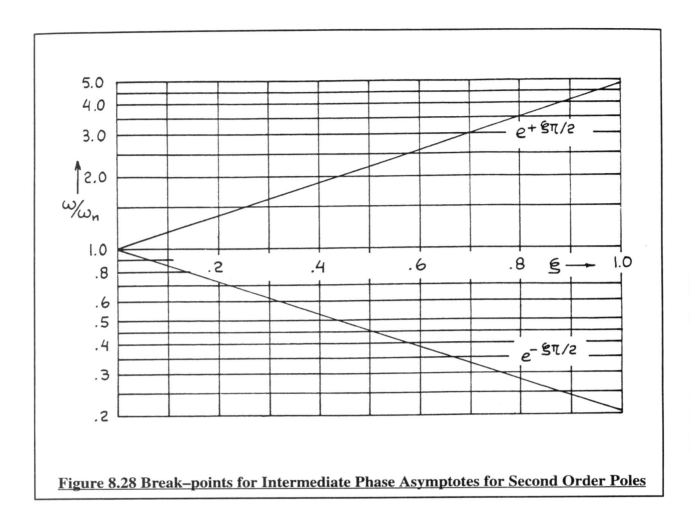

Figure 8.28 Break–points for Intermediate Phase Asymptotes for Second Order Poles

In the standard format this becomes:

$$G(s) = 2\left(\frac{1}{s}\right)\left(\frac{(s+2)}{2}\right)\left(\frac{100}{(s^2 + 4s + 100)}\right) \tag{8.88a}$$

The actual and asymptotic magnitude and phase plots for this transfer function are given in Figure 8.29. Observe the following facts:

1) The magnitude plot at very low frequencies is the integrator, 1/s shifted upward over $20\log_{10}2 = 6.02$ db

2) The phase plot at very low frequencies starts at –90 degrees. The phase plot, at very high frequencies approaches –180 degrees because the transfer function in Eqn (8.88) has three poles and one zero.

In the next Sub–section a summary is given of the amplitude and phase angle properties of first and second order transfer functions.

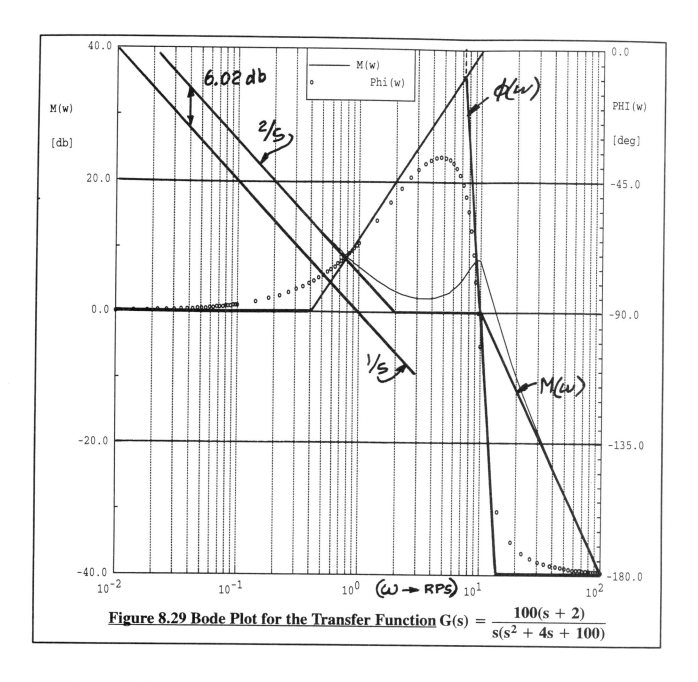

Figure 8.29 Bode Plot for the Transfer Function $G(s) = \dfrac{100(s+2)}{s(s^2+4s+100)}$

8.3.4 SUMMARY OF AMPLITUDE AND PHASE ANGLE PROPERTIES OF FIRST AND SECOND ORDER TRANSFER FUNCTIONS

It is useful to summarize the amplitude ratio and phase angle properties of first and second order transfer functions. Figure 8.30 portrays the low and high frequency amplitude (magnitude) characteristics of first and second order transfer functions in relation to their asymptotes. Note that the high frequency asymptotes have been rotated about the break frequency such that they are aligned with the low frequency asymptotes. This rotation was done in a manner such that the vertical distance between the actual magnitude and the asymptotic magnitude is retained at **each** frequency above the break frequency. Note that all magnitude plots when represented in this manner are symmetrical about a vertical line through the break frequency.

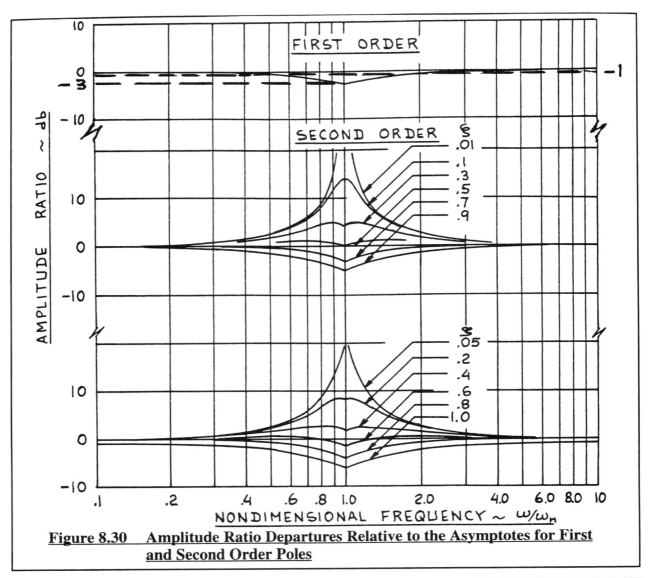

Figure 8.30   Amplitude Ratio Departures Relative to the Asymptotes for First and Second Order Poles

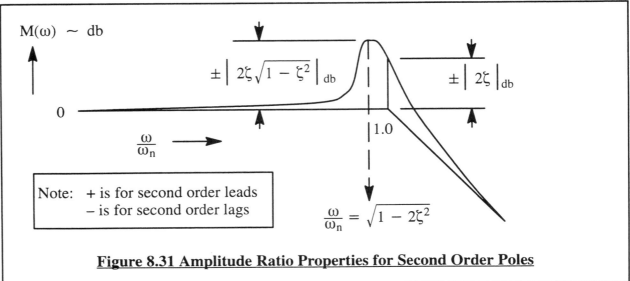

Figure 8.31 Amplitude Ratio Properties for Second Order Poles

In Figure 8.31 the magnitude behavior of an arbitrary second order lag is summarized in relation to its asymptotes. The reader is asked to prove that the expressions given in Figure 8.31 are correct.

In Figure 8.32 the phase angle characteristics of first and second order lags are presented. The intermediate phase angle asymptotes are also shown. For the second order lag only the intermediate phase angle asymptote for a damping ratio of 0.2 is shown.

8.4 APPLICATIONS OF BODE PLOTS TO AIRPLANES

In this section, several applications and interpretations of Bode plots for airplanes will be discussed. Before showing how the method applies to the complete airplane transfer functions of Chapter 5 (Part I) a simple application to the case of airplane bank angle response to an aileron input will be presented.

Assume that an airplane is in level cruising flight and that the airplane is continually perturbed by turbulence. The pilot (or auto–pilot) will try to keep the wings level by applying a countering aileron deflection whenever the bank angle deviates from level flight. The pilot input to the ailerons can be thought of as a signal with a large frequency content. Therefore, the frequency response of the bank angle to the aileron input is of interest.

Consider the business jet data of Table 5.10 and assume that the single degree of freedom approximation to the rolling mode of the airplane is an accurate one. From Table 5.10 the open loop bank–angle–to–aileron transfer function is:

$$G(s) = \frac{\phi(s)}{\delta_a(s)} = \frac{6.8}{s(s + 0.44)} = 15.45\left(\frac{1}{s}\right)\left(\frac{0.44}{s + 0.44}\right) \tag{8.89}$$

The actual and approximate Bode plot for this system is shown in Figure 8.33.

The frequency at which the magnitude (=amplitude ratio) plot crosses the 0 db line is called the magnitude crossover frequency. For the airplane of Figure 8.33 this magnitude crossover frequency is about 2.6 rad/sec. It will be shown that typical pilot bandwidths range up to about 4 rad/sec. Within his own bandwidth the pilot will therefore obtain good bank angle response by using the ailerons.

An autopilot has a wider bandwidth than do human pilots. Assume that the auto–pilot has a bandwidth of say 20 rad/sec. The amplitude ratio of bank angle to aileron at that frequency is a little better than –40 db. At –40 db, the bank angle to aileron amplitude ratio is only 0.01! In other words, the airplane no longer responds to aileron inputs at a frequency level of 20 rad/sec. That may not be bad as long as the frequency content of lateral atmospheric disturbances is not significant in that same frequency range. Happily it is not, so all is well.

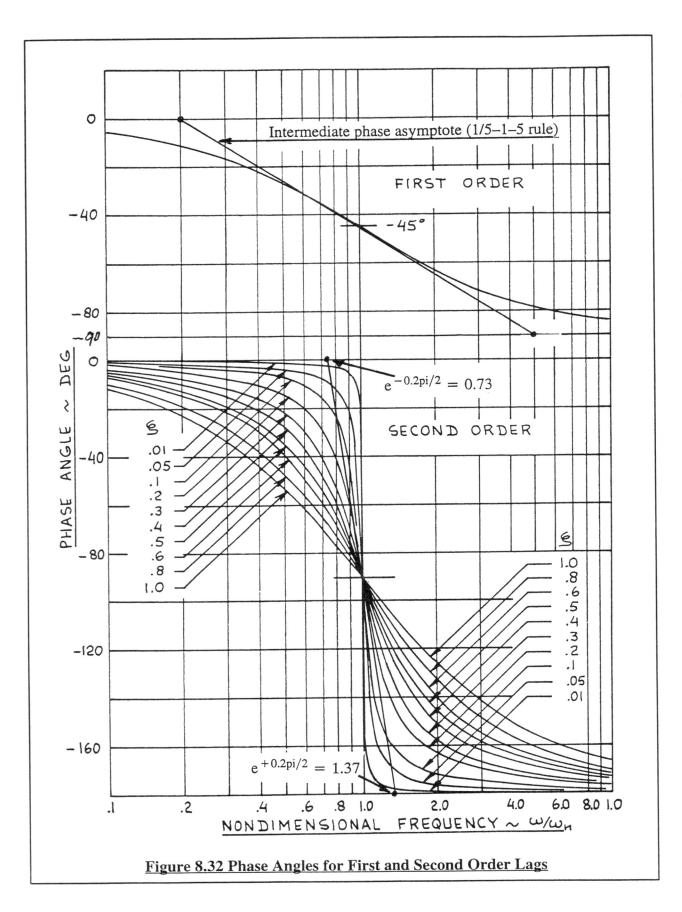

Figure 8.32 Phase Angles for First and Second Order Lags

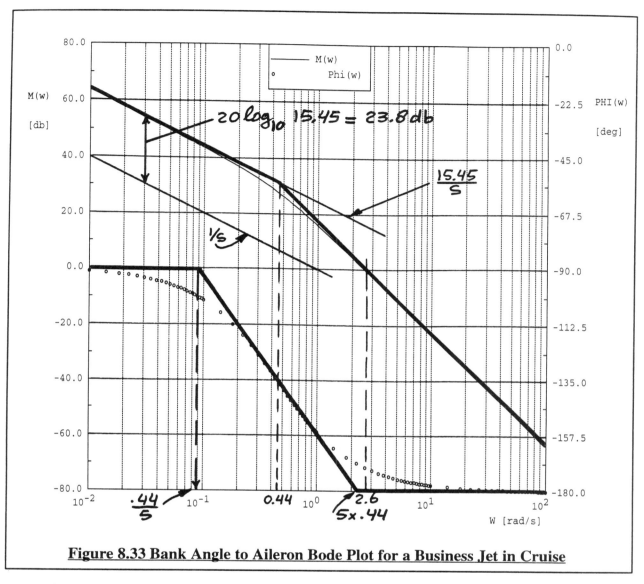

Figure 8.33 Bank Angle to Aileron Bode Plot for a Business Jet in Cruise

Now assume, that some newly designed airplane is predicted to have a crossover frequency of 1 rad/sec. That would not be acceptable in a manned airplane. What can the designer of the airplane do about this?

There are only two possibilities, according to Figure 8.33.

First, if it is possible to increase the break frequency from 0.44 to about 2.6 rad/sec, the bank angle response might be acceptable. The problem with this solution is that it requires a larger, negative value of the dimensional derivative, L_p. According to Table 5.7, increasing the derivative L_p in the negative sense requires either more roll damping or less rolling moment of inertia. Depending on the type of airplane and its mission, the option to change these quantities may no longer exist.

Second, it is possible to raise the zero–frequency gain of the transfer function. Comparing with Eqn (5.128) it is seen that this in turn requires more aileron control power. Whether or not the aileron size can be increased at this stage of the design depends on the amount of flap space required and on the location of the rear spar. The latter also has a major influence on torsional rigidity and on fuel volume.

This example illustrates the depth of flying qualities analysis that must enter into the design of an airplane, lest undesirable characteristics are found when it is too late to make design changes. In the remainder of this section a series of important airplane frequency responses will be presented and discussed. For these examples, the business jet of Chapter 5 will be used.

8.4.1 BODE PLOTS FOR SPEED, ANGLE OF ATTACK AND PITCH ATTITUDE ANGLE RESPONSE TO ELEVATOR INPUTS

All frequency response plots in this Sub–section were obtained with the AAA program described in Appendix A, Part I. The following frequency responses will be presented and discussed:

1. Bode Plot for Speed to Elevator Frequency Response
2. Bode Plot for Angle of Attack to Elevator Frequency Response
3. Bode Plot for Pitch Attitude Angle to Elevator Frequency Response

All these responses pertain to a business jet in a maximum weight, cruise flight condition. For aerodynamic and other input data as well as for the airplane transfer functions the reader is referred to Table 5.4 in Chapter 5.

1. Bode Plot for Speed to Elevator Frequency Response

Figure 8.34 shows the amplitude ratio and phase angle plots for the speed–to–elevator transfer function. Eqn (8.90) shows that transfer function in its standard format.

$$\frac{u(s)}{\delta_e(s)} = \frac{5,236.5\left\{\left(\frac{1}{-718.5}\right)s + 1\right\}\left\{\left(\frac{1}{0.8828}\right)s + 1\right\}}{\left(\frac{s^2}{(2.8324)^2} + \frac{2(0.3535)s}{(2.8324)} + 1\right)\left(\frac{s^2}{(0.0920)^2} + \frac{2(0.0461)s}{(0.0920)} + 1\right)} \tag{8.90}$$

The magnitude cross–over frequency is seen to be about 8 rad/sec. That would imply that the airplane responds well with a change in speed to oscillatory elevator inputs at such a frequency. Anyone who has piloted conventional airplanes knows that this is not the case. Airplanes respond with speed changes to elevator inputs only for slowly varying inputs. What went wrong?

What went wrong is that the speed–to–elevator response plotted in Figure 8.34 is not dimensionless. What should have been plotted is the $(u/U_1)/\delta_e$ instead of the u/δ_e transfer function. In a Bode plot this results in a magnitude (=gain) change of $20\log_{10}U_1$. The speed of the airplane in this flight condition (Table 5.4, Part I) is 400 kts = 675.2 fps. In Figure 8.34 this amounts to a

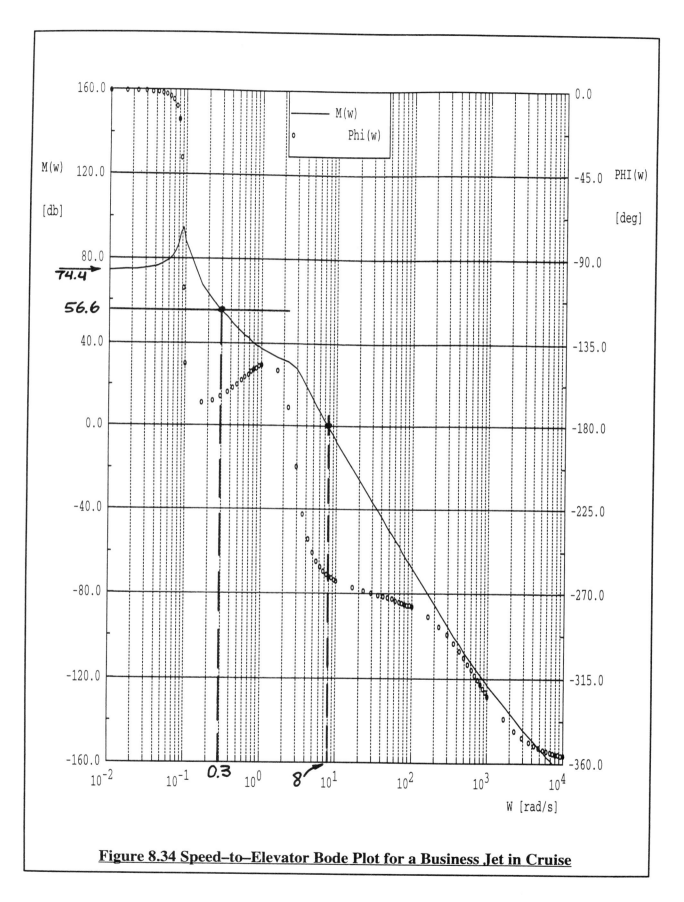

Figure 8.34 Speed–to–Elevator Bode Plot for a Business Jet in Cruise

gain change of 56.6 db. Therefore, the 56.6 db line (also indicated in Figure 8.34) represents the actual zero db line. Therefore, the magnitude cross–over frequency is only about 0.3 rad/sec. That is in agreement with pilot observations which indicate that the elevator is not a good way to control speed with high frequency inputs. With low frequency inputs it works fine.

These observations also agree with the fact that the short period mode (frequency of 2.8 rad/sec) can be thought of as a mode where changes in speed are negligible. The reader may remember from Chapter 5 that this was in fact the basis for the so–called short period approximation!

The reader is urged to verify the magnitude and phase plots by applying the asymptotic method of Section 8.3. Since phase plots are known to cause the greatest amount of confusion, the reader is encouraged to set up a phase angle budget of each transfer function component. An example of such a phase angle budget is given in Table 8.1 for the transfer function of Eqn (8.90). The inexperienced reader should verify the phase angle ranges given in Table 8.1 by drawing phasor diagrams similar to the one of Figure 8.12.

Table 8.1 Phase Angle Budget for the Transfer Function of Eqn (8.90)			
Component	Type	Phase angle at very low frequencies, deg	Phase angle at very high frequencies, deg
$-\,K_{u_{\delta_e}}$	zero–frequency gain	-180	-180
Phugoid	second order lag	0	-180
Short period	second order lag	0	-180
T_{u_1} term	first order lead (in this case a zero in the r.h.s. of the s–plane)	$+180$	$+90$
T_{u_1} term	first order lead	0	$+90$
	Transfer Function Sum:	0	-360

The implications of the phase angle behavior of the Bode plot in Figure 8.34 will be discussed in Chapter 9.

2. Bode Plot for Angle of Attack to Elevator Frequency Response

Figure 8.35 shows the amplitude ratio and phase angle plots for the angle–of–attack–to–elevator transfer function. Eqn (8.91) shows that transfer function in its standard format.

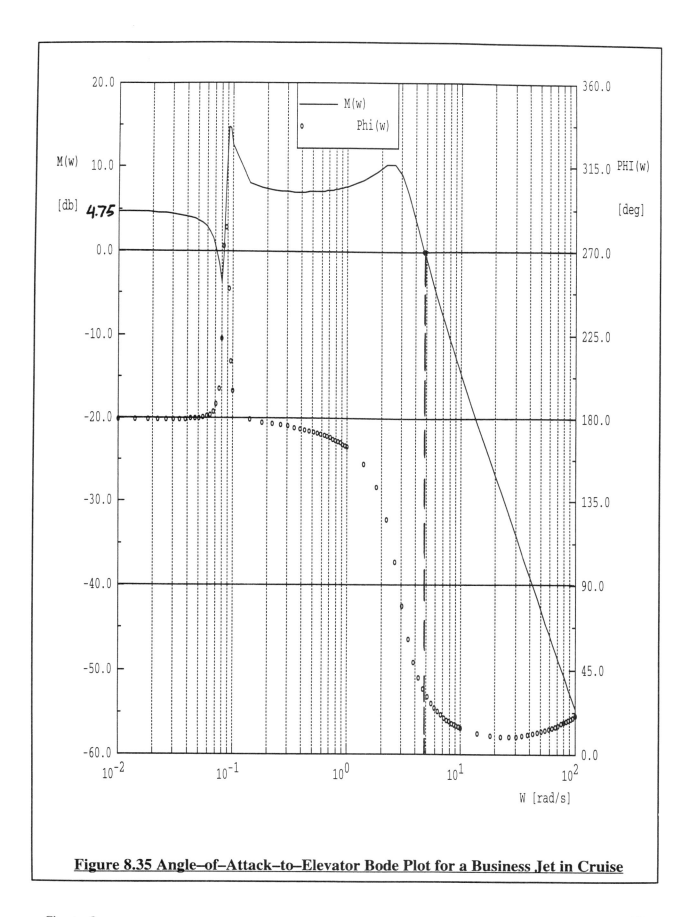

Figure 8.35 Angle–of–Attack–to–Elevator Bode Plot for a Business Jet in Cruise

$$\frac{\alpha(s)}{\delta_e(s)} = \frac{-1.7278\left\{\left(\frac{1}{282.9}\right)s + 1\right\}\left(\frac{s^2}{(0.0812)^2} + \frac{2(0.0456)s}{(0.0812)} + 1\right)}{\left(\frac{s^2}{(2.8324)^2} + \frac{2(0.3535)s}{(2.8324)} + 1\right)\left(\frac{s^2}{(0.0920)^2} + \frac{2(0.0461)s}{(0.0920)} + 1\right)} \tag{8.91}$$

The magnitude cross–over frequency is seen to be about 5 rad/sec. Since human pilot bandwidths range typically up to about 4 rad/sec, a pilot will have good control over angle of attack with the elevator. Note that the two magnitude cross overs at about 0.08 rad/sec are not counted here as cross–overs. The reason is that for all practical purposes the two quadratics in the numerator and denominator of Eqn (8.91) cancel each other. As a result, during the phugoid transient, the angle of attack will change very little. The transfer function which results from omitting the low frequency quadratics in the numerator and in the denominator is referred to as the short–period approximation.

The implications of the phase angle behavior of the Bode plot in Figure 8.35 will be discussed in Chapter 9.

As an exercise the reader should draw the asymptotic magnitude and phase Bode plots into Figure 8.35.

3. Bode Plot for Pitch Attitude Angle to Elevator Frequency Response

Figure 8.36 shows the amplitude ratio and phase angle plots for the angle–of–attack–to–elevator transfer function. Eqn (8.92) shows that transfer function in its standard format.

$$\frac{\theta(s)}{\delta_e(s)} = \frac{-1.7109\left\{\left(\frac{1}{0.6310}\right)s + 1\right\}\left\{\left(\frac{1}{0.0104}\right)s + 1\right\}}{\left(\frac{s^2}{(2.8324)^2} + \frac{2(0.3535)s}{(2.8324)} + 1\right)\left(\frac{s^2}{(0.0920)^2} + \frac{2(0.0461)s}{(0.0920)} + 1\right)} \tag{8.92}$$

The magnitude cross–over frequency is seen to be about 5 rad/sec. Therefore, a pilot will have excellent control over the pitch attitude angle with the elevator.

The implications of the phase angle behavior of the Bode plot in Figure 8.36 will be discussed in Chapter 9.

Now consider the data in Table 8.2. These data were obtained by reading the magnitudes of the speed, angle–of–attack and pitch–attitude Bode plots of Figures 8.34 through 8.36 in decibels at the phugoid and short period break frequencies.

It is seen that, at the phugoid frequency, the angle of attack response is negligible compared to that of speed and pitch attitude angle. At the short period frequency, the speed response is negligible compared to that of angle of attack and pitch attitude angle. These findings agree with those of the corresponding phasor diagrams of Figure 5.14.

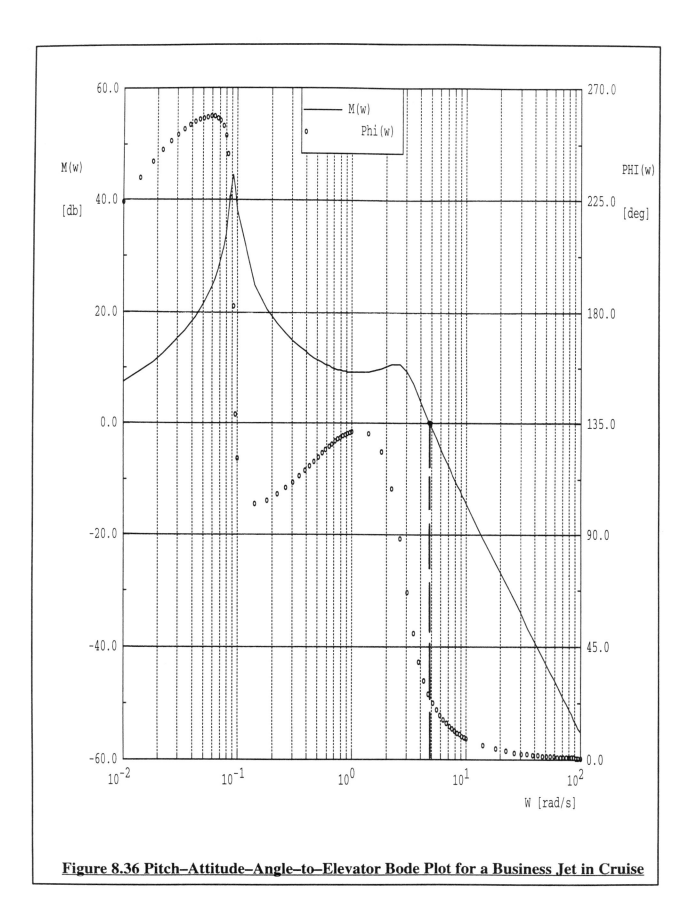

Figure 8.36 Pitch–Attitude–Angle–to–Elevator Bode Plot for a Business Jet in Cruise

Table 8.2 Magnitudes of Elevator Frequency Responses at Break Frequencies				
Mode	Break Frequency (rad/sec)	Magnitude in db of: (u/U_1)	α	θ
Elevator Response				
Phugoid	0.092	37	14	54
Short Period	2.83	−29	11	11
		Magnitude in $1/20$ invlog$_{10}$ of: (u/U_1)	α	θ
Elevator Response				
Phugoid	0.092	70.8	5.0	501
Short Period	2.83	0.04	3.5	3.5

8.4.2 BODE PLOTS FOR SIDESLIP ANGLE, BANK ANGLE AND HEADING ANGLE RESPONSE TO AILERON AND RUDDER INPUTS

All frequency response plots in this Sub–section were obtained with the AAA program described in Appendix A, Part I. The following frequency responses will be presented and discussed:

1. Bode Plot for Sideslip Angle to Aileron Frequency Response
2. Bode Plot for Bank Angle to Aileron Frequency Response
3. Bode Plot for Heading Angle to Aileron Frequency Response

4. Bode Plot for Sideslip Angle to Rudder Frequency Response
5. Bode Plot for Bank Angle to Rudder Frequency Response
6. Bode Plot for Heading Angle to Rudder Frequency Response

All these responses pertain to a business jet in a maximum weight, cruise flight condition. For aerodynamic and other input data as well as for the airplane transfer functions the reader is referred to Table 5.10 in Chapter 5.

1. Bode Plot for Sideslip Angle to Aileron Frequency Response

Figure 8.37 shows the amplitude ratio and phase angle plots for the sideslip angle to aileron transfer function. Eqn (8.93) shows that transfer function in its standard format:

$$\frac{\beta(s)}{\delta_a(s)} = \frac{23.4\left\{\left(\frac{1}{0.0782}\right)s + 1\right\}\left\{\left(\frac{1}{1.3362}\right)s + 1\right\}}{\left\{\left(\frac{1}{0.0010}\right)s + 1\right\}\left\{\left(\frac{1}{0.5003}\right)s + 1\right\}\left(\frac{s^2}{(1.6882)^2} + \frac{2(0.0387)s}{(1.6882)} + 1\right)} \quad (8.93)$$

The response of the airplane sideslip angle to aileron inputs must be put into context with

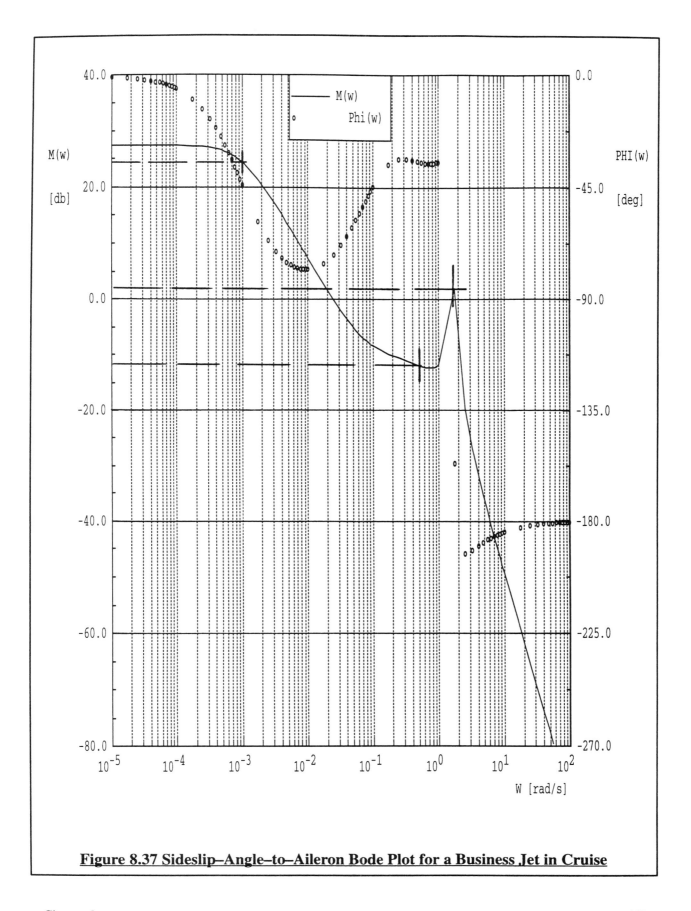

Figure 8.37 Sideslip–Angle–to–Aileron Bode Plot for a Business Jet in Cruise

the response in the other lateral directional motion variables, ϕ and ψ. A discussion of the response of these angles to aileron inputs is given next.

2. Bode Plot for Bank Angle to Aileron Frequency Response

Figure 8.38 shows the amplitude ratio and phase angle plots for the bank angle to aileron transfer function. Eqn (8.94) shows that transfer function in its standard format.

$$\frac{\phi(s)}{\delta_a(s)} = \frac{12,359\left(\dfrac{s^2}{(1.6226)^2} + \dfrac{2(0.0579)s}{(1.6226)} + 1\right)}{\left\{\left(\dfrac{1}{0.0010}\right)s + 1\right\}\left\{\left(\dfrac{1}{0.5003}\right)s + 1\right\}\left(\dfrac{s^2}{(1.6882)^2} + \dfrac{2(0.0387)s}{(1.6882)} + 1\right)} \tag{8.94}$$

The response of the airplane bank angle to aileron inputs must be put into context with the response in the other lateral directional motion variables, β and ψ. A discussion of the heading angle response to aileron inputs is given next. A discussion of the sideslip angle response to aileron input was given under item 1. One obvious feature of Eqn (8.94) is the approximate cancellation of the numerator and denominator quadratics. Since the spiral root is seen to be close to the origin, the bank angle response to aileron should therefore agree closely with that of the single degree of freedom bank–angle–to–aileron transfer function. This approximation is overlaid in Figure 8.38 from Figure 8.33. The agreement is very good.

3. Bode Plot for Heading Angle to Aileron Frequency Response

Figure 8.39 shows the amplitude ratio and phase angle plots for the heading angle to aileron transfer function. Eqn (8.95) shows that transfer function in its standard format.

$$\frac{\psi(s)}{\delta_a(s)} = \frac{580.4\left\{\left(\dfrac{1}{-1.2147}\right)s + 1\right\}\left(\dfrac{s^2}{(1.4596)^2} + \dfrac{2(0.5909)s}{(1.6226)} + 1\right)}{s\left\{\left(\dfrac{1}{0.0010}\right)s + 1\right\}\left\{\left(\dfrac{1}{0.5003}\right)s + 1\right\}\left(\dfrac{s^2}{(1.6882)^2} + \dfrac{2(0.0387)s}{(1.6882)} + 1\right)} \tag{8.95}$$

Note that the quadratics in the numerator and denominator again tend to cancel each other.

The response of the airplane heading angle to aileron inputs must be put into context with the response in the other lateral directional motion variables, ϕ and β. A discussion of the heading angle response to aileron inputs is given next.

At the spiral mode break frequency of 0.001 rad/sec the magnitudes of β, ϕ and ψ are seen to be about 24 db, 80 db and 110 db respectively. Clearly, the magnitudes of the heading angle and bank angle responses are much greater than that of the sideslip response. This supports the conclusion reached by the spiral mode phasor diagram in Figure 5.22 that sideslip is not an important variable in the spiral mode.

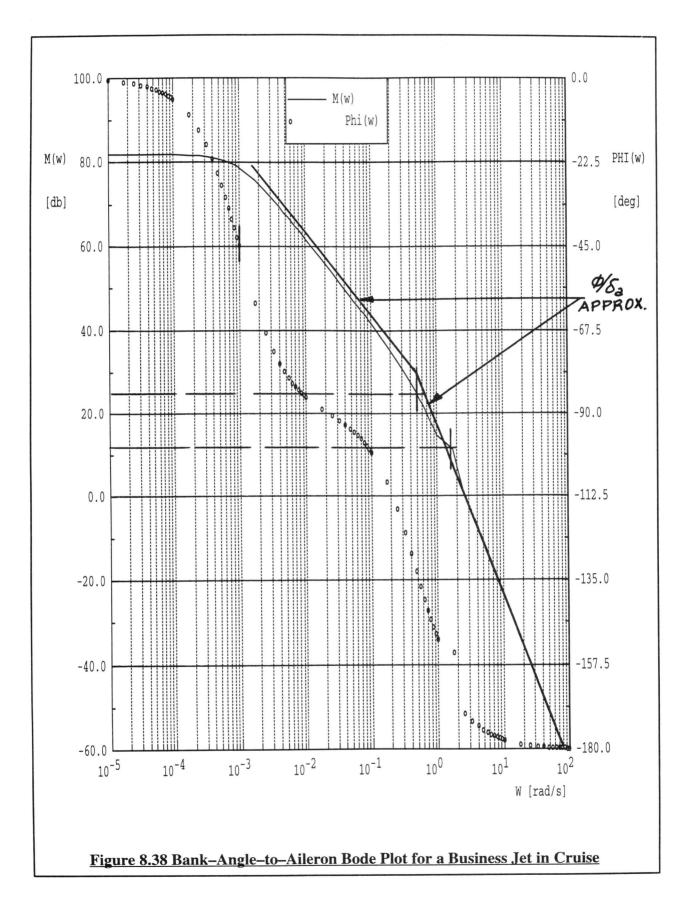

Figure 8.38 Bank–Angle–to–Aileron Bode Plot for a Business Jet in Cruise

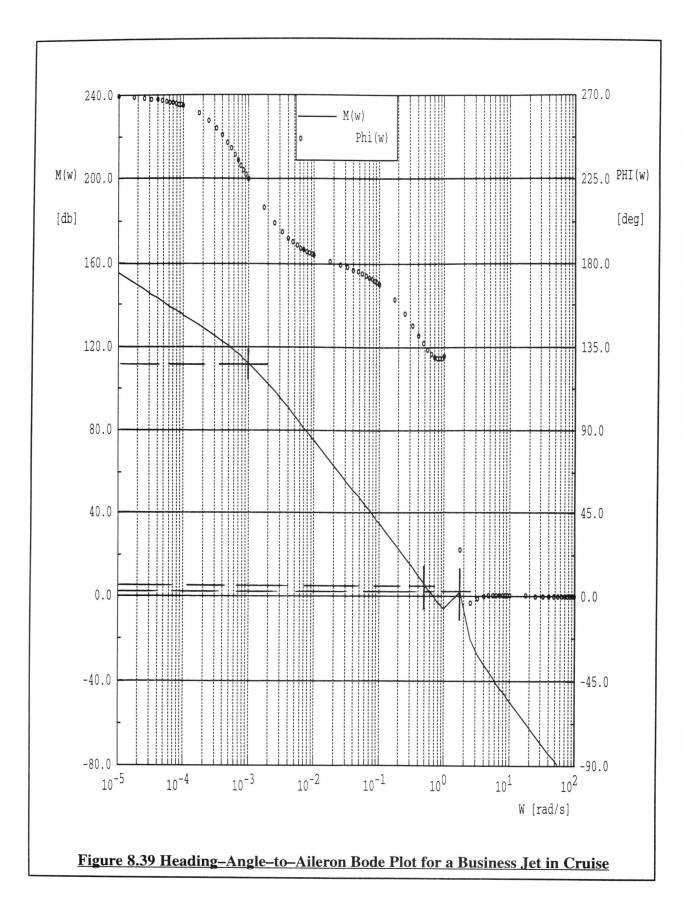

Figure 8.39 Heading–Angle–to–Aileron Bode Plot for a Business Jet in Cruise

At the roll mode break frequency of 0.5 rad/sec the magnitudes of β, ϕ and ψ are -12, $+25$ db and $+5$ db respectively. Therefore, in the vicinity of this frequency sideslip is not important, bank angle clearly is while the heading angle shows only a small degree of participation. This again is supported by the roll mode phasor diagram in Figure 5.22.

At the dutch roll mode break frequency of 1.7 rad/sec, the magnitudes of β, ϕ and ψ are 2 db, 12 db and 2 db respectively. This suggests that around the dutch roll frequency, the bank angle is most important, with the sideslip and heading angle also being relatively important contributors. Again this agrees with the conclusion drawn from the dutch roll phasor diagram in Figure 5.22.

The numerator and one of the denominator quadratics in the bank angle and heading angle to aileron transfer functions of Eqns (8.94) and (8.95) are seen to approximately cancel each other. Note that this does not happen in the sideslip to aileron transfer function of Eqn (8.93).

4. Bode Plot for Sideslip Angle to Rudder Frequency Response

Figure 8.40 shows the amplitude ratio and phase angle plots for the sideslip angle to rudder transfer function. Eqn (8.96) shows that transfer function in its standard format.

$$\frac{\beta(s)}{\delta_r(s)} = \frac{-6.188\left\{\left(\frac{1}{-0.0114}\right)s + 1\right\}\left\{\left(\frac{1}{108.2}\right)s + 1\right\}\left\{\left(\frac{1}{0.4655}\right)s + 1\right\}}{\left\{\left(\frac{1}{0.0010}\right)s + 1\right\}\left\{\left(\frac{1}{0.5003}\right)s + 1\right\}\left(\frac{s^2}{(1.6882)^2} + \frac{2(0.0387)s}{(1.6882)} + 1\right)} \tag{8.96}$$

The response of this airplane in sideslip to rudder inputs must be put into context with the response in the other lateral directional motion variables, ϕ and ψ. A discussion of the response to rudder inputs is given after item 6.

5. Bode Plot for Bank Angle to Rudder Frequency Response

Figure 8.41 shows the amplitude ratio and phase angle plots for the bank angle to rudder transfer function. Eqn (8.97) shows that transfer function in its standard format.

$$\frac{\phi(s)}{\delta_r(s)} = \frac{-3,599\left\{\left(\frac{1}{-3.0413}\right)s + 1\right\}\left\{\left(\frac{1}{2.7189}\right)s + 1\right\}}{\left\{\left(\frac{1}{0.0010}\right)s + 1\right\}\left\{\left(\frac{1}{0.5003}\right)s + 1\right\}\left(\frac{s^2}{(1.6882)^2} + \frac{2(0.0387)s}{(1.6882)} + 1\right)} \tag{8.97}$$

The response of this airplane in bank angle to rudder inputs must be put into context with the response in the other lateral directional motion variables, β and ψ. A discussion of the response to rudder inputs is given after item 6.

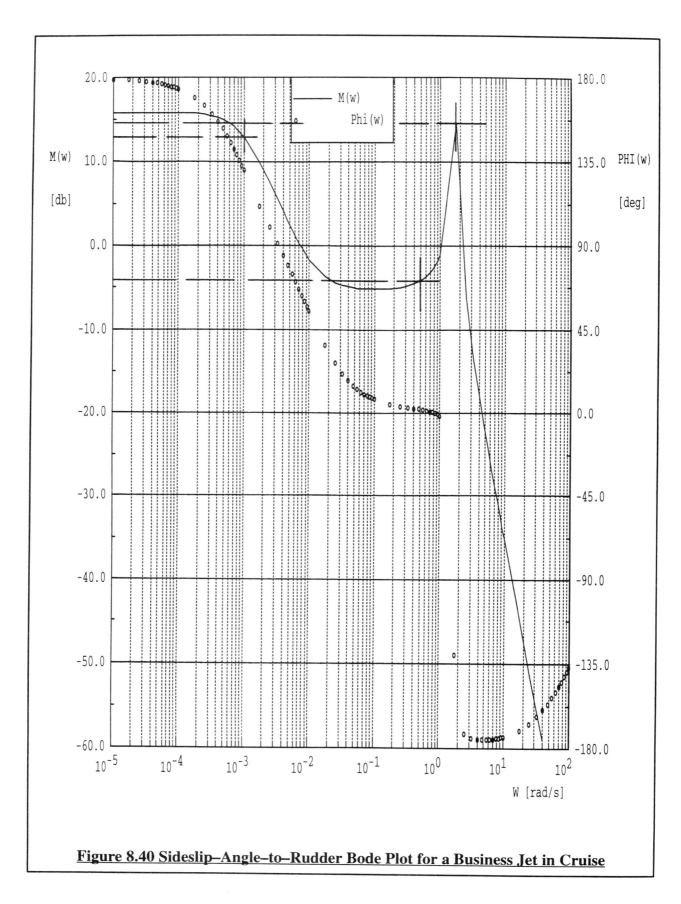

Figure 8.40 Sideslip–Angle–to–Rudder Bode Plot for a Business Jet in Cruise

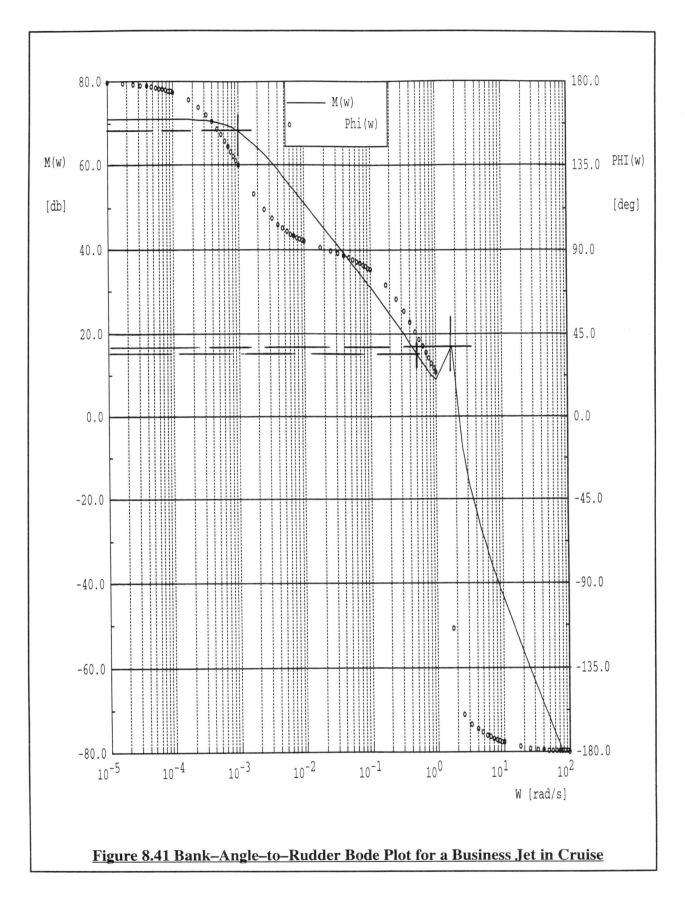

Figure 8.41 Bank–Angle–to–Rudder Bode Plot for a Business Jet in Cruise

6. Bode Plot for Heading Angle to Rudder Frequency Response

Figure 8.42 shows the amplitude ratio and phase angle plots for the heading angle to rudder transfer function. Eqn (8.98) shows that transfer function in its standard format.

$$\frac{\psi(s)}{\delta_r(s)} = \frac{-169.04\left\{\left(\frac{1}{0.7307}\right)s + 1\right\}\left(\frac{s^2}{(0.4456)^2} + \frac{2(-0.2675)s}{(0.4456)} + 1\right)}{s\left\{\left(\frac{1}{0.0010}\right)s + 1\right\}\left\{\left(\frac{1}{0.5003}\right)s + 1\right\}\left(\frac{s^2}{(1.6882)^2} + \frac{2(0.0387)s}{(1.6882)} + 1\right)} \tag{8.98}$$

The response of this airplane in heading angle to rudder inputs must be put into context with the response in the other lateral directional motion variables, ϕ and β. A discussion of the response of sideslip angle, bank angle and heading angle to rudder inputs is given next.

At the spiral mode break frequency of 0.001 rad/sec, the magnitudes of β, ϕ and ψ are 13 db, 69 db and 102 db respectively. This observation again supports the conclusion drawn from the spiral phasor diagram of Figure 5.22 that sideslip is not important in the spiral mode but bank angle and heading angle are.

At the roll mode break frequency of 0.5 rad/sec, the magnitudes of β, ϕ and ψ are –4db, 17 db and –7 db respectively. This again supports the conclusion drawn from the role mode phasor diagram in Figure 5.22 that in the roll mode the sideslip and heading angle are negligible while the bank angle is important.

At the dutch roll mode break frequency of 1.7 rad/sec, the magnitudes of β, ϕ and ψ are 14.5 db, 8 db and 17 db respectively. One more time, this supports the conclusion drawn from the dutch roll mode phasor diagram in Figure 5.22 that all variables are important in the dutch roll mode.

Now consider the data in Table 8.3. Observe, that in the vicinity of the dutch roll frequency, the rudder is much more powerful than the aileron in exciting the sideslip angle. This is as expected. Also note, that in the vicinity of the roll mode break frequency, the aileron is more powerful than the rudder in exciting bank angle. That also is as it should be.

In the region of the dutch roll frequency, the rudder is much more powerful in exciting all variables than the aileron. A yaw damper should therefore work really well in increasing the undesirably low dutch roll damping ratio of 0.04. However, a pilot could damp the dutch roll himself better by using the aileron: it stirs up the other variables in a minimal manner while still providing good control over the bank angle.

Finally, in the vicinity of the spiral mode break frequency, aileron control is more powerful than rudder control in controlling heading and bank angle.

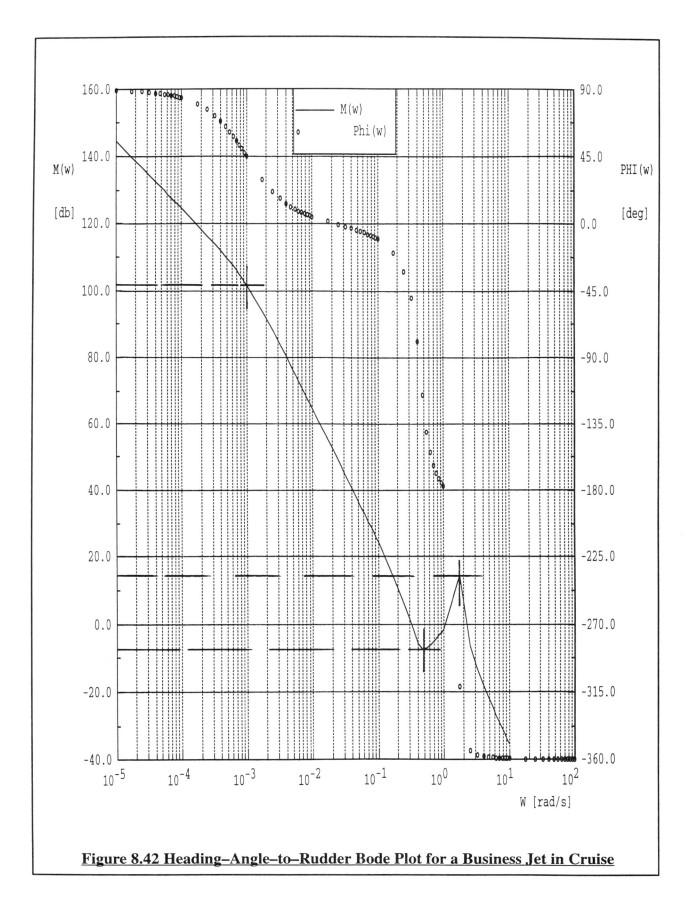

Figure 8.42 Heading–Angle–to–Rudder Bode Plot for a Business Jet in Cruise

Table 8.3 Magnitudes of Aileron and Rudder Frequency Responses at Break Frequencies

Mode	Break Frequency (rad/sec)	Magnitude in db of: β	ϕ	ψ
Aileron Response				
Spiral	0.001	24	80	110
Roll	0.5	−12	25	5
Dutch Roll	1.7	2	12	2
Rudder Response				
Spiral	0.001	13	69	102
Roll	0.5	−4	17	−7
Dutch Roll	1.7	14.5	8	17

8.5   AN INVERSE APPLICATION OF BODE PLOTS

It will be shown in Chapter 10 that in the analysis of closed loop flight control systems, situations arise where the transfer functions of mechanical, electro–mechanical, hydraulic and (or) electro–hydraulic systems are required. In many cases, such transfer functions can be difficult to obtain from the corresponding equations of motion. The reason for this may be the occurrence of non–linearities and friction. In many such cases it is convenient to run a frequency response test on the system, plot the response as a Bode plot and from that, using the method of asymptotic approximations, deduce the transfer functions. An example of such an application will now be presented.

Consider the aileron flight control system of a small business jet, including the autopilot servo system which drives it: see Figure 8.43. Next, consider the analytical block diagram for the servo system as shown in Figure 8.44.

Determining the equations of motion of the torquer (=electric motor) and the cables+capstan+aileron system together is very difficult indeed. From the block diagram of Figure 8.44 it is seen that the following responses can be measured experimentally:

a) δ_a (aileron) output to ε (motor amplifier) input

b) $\dot{\delta}_c$ (torquer rate) output to ε (motor amplifier) input

Examples of the time domain records of these measured responses for the case of an input frequency of 1 Herz (6.28 rad/sec) are shown in Figure 8.45. With records such as those shown in Figure 8.45 taken over a wide range of input frequencies it is possible to prepare the experimental

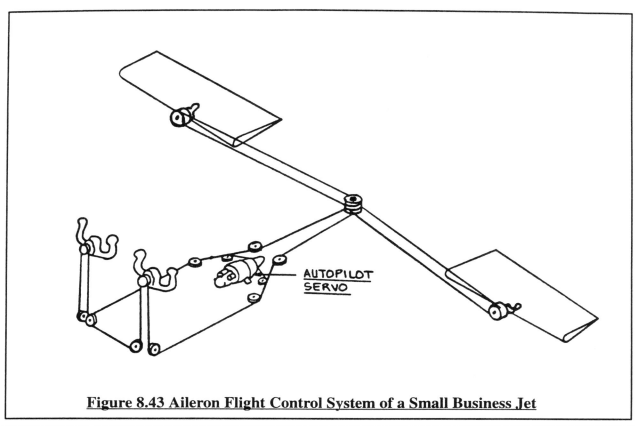

Figure 8.43 Aileron Flight Control System of a Small Business Jet

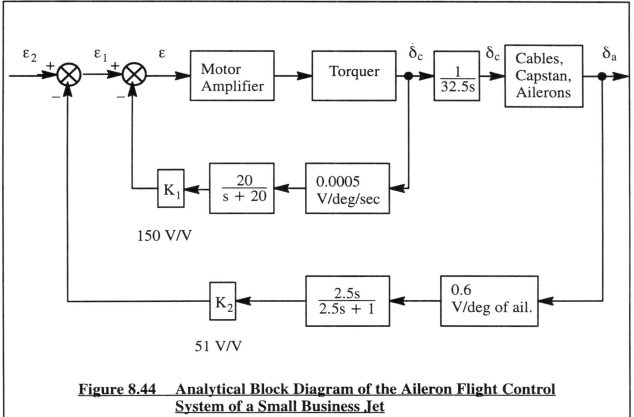

**Figure 8.44   Analytical Block Diagram of the Aileron Flight Control
System of a Small Business Jet**

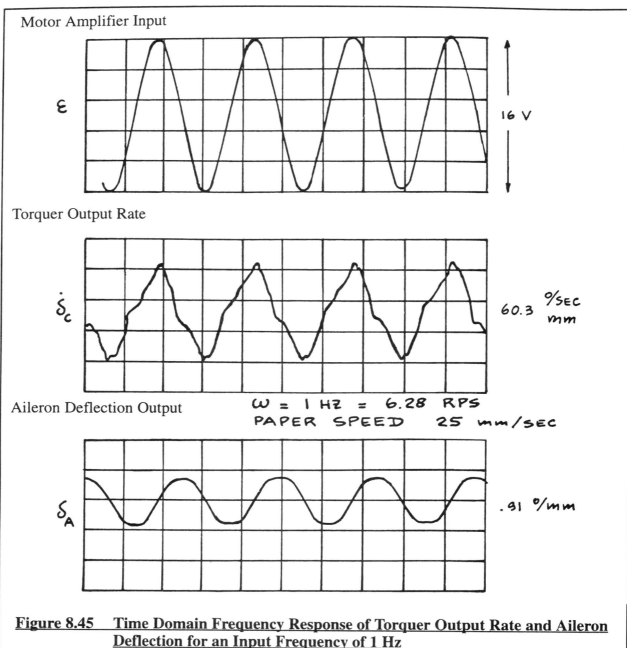

Figure 8.45   Time Domain Frequency Response of Torquer Output Rate and Aileron Deflection for an Input Frequency of 1 Hz

Bode magnitude plots of Figures 8.46 and 8.47. The next problem is to identify any potential first or second order break frequencies using the 1–3–1 rule of page 649. With some experience and some imagination this is not difficult to do. Figures 8.46 and 8.47 show the asymptotic approximations which 'fit' the experimental Bode magnitude data sketched in. From these asymptotic approximations it is immediately possible to determine the corresponding transfer functions:

$$\frac{\delta_a(s)}{\epsilon(s)} = 1.31\left(\frac{2.7}{s + 2.7}\right)\left(\frac{30}{s + 30}\right) \tag{8.99}$$

and

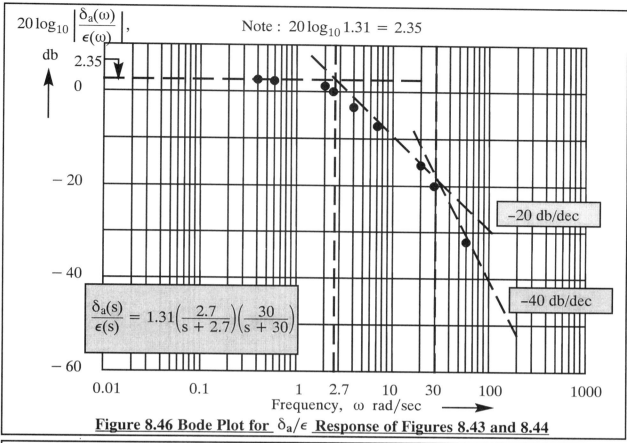

Figure 8.46 Bode Plot for δ_a/ϵ Response of Figures 8.43 and 8.44

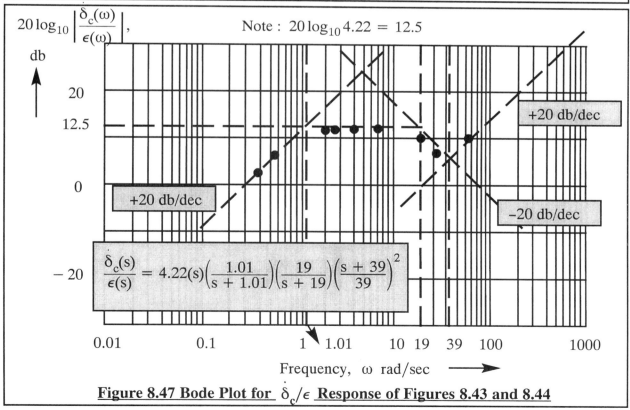

Figure 8.47 Bode Plot for $\dot{\delta}_c/\epsilon$ Response of Figures 8.43 and 8.44

$$\frac{\dot{\delta}_c(s)}{\varepsilon(s)} = 4.22 \text{ s} \left(\frac{1.01}{s+1.01}\right)\left(\frac{19}{s+19}\right)\left(\frac{s+39}{39}\right)^2 \tag{8.100}$$

From these latter two equations it is now possible to derive the transfer function of the cables+capstan+aileron system as:

$$\frac{\delta_a(s)}{\delta_c(s)} = 32.5(s)\underbrace{\frac{1.31\left(\frac{2.7}{s+2.7}\right)\left(\frac{30}{s+30}\right)}{4.22 \text{ s} \left(\frac{1.01}{s+1.01}\right)\left(\frac{19}{s+19}\right)\left(\frac{s+39}{39}\right)\left(\frac{s+39}{39}\right)}}_{\text{see Fig. 8.44}} \tag{8.101}$$

Equation (8.101) can be cleaned up to yield:

$$\frac{\delta_a(s)}{\delta_c(s)} = 10.09\left(\frac{s+1.01}{1.01}\right)\left(\frac{2.7}{s+2.7}\right)\left(\frac{s+19}{19}\right)\left(\frac{30}{s+30}\right)\left(\frac{39}{s+39}\right)^2 \tag{8.102}$$

If desired, the reader can invert Eqn (8.101) to obtain the time domain response of aileron versus torquer position.

The reader should wonder whether or not in–flight aerodynamic hingemoments have any bearing on the aileron response. After all, the frequency response experiments, an example of which is shown in Figure 8.45, were carried out with the airplane on the ground and inside a hangar. To analyze whether or not the aerodynamic hingemoments are important, consider the time domain inverse of Eqn (8.99). First, Eqn (8.99) is rewritten as follows:

$$\delta_a(s)\left(s^2 + 32.7s + 81\right) = 81K_{\delta_a}\varepsilon(s) \tag{8.103}$$

where: $K_{\delta_a} = 1.31$

Inversion to the time domain now yields:

$$\ddot{\delta}_a(t) + 32.7\dot{\delta}_a(t) + 81\delta_a(t) = 81K_{\delta_a}\varepsilon(t) \tag{8.104}$$

Because aerodynamic hingemoments are linearly proportional to aileron deflection, the effect of the aileron hingemoment on Eqn (8.104) is to modify the aileron term only:

$$\ddot{\delta}_a(t) + 32.7\dot{\delta}_a(t) + \left(81 - H_{\delta_a}\right)\delta_a(t) = 81K_{\delta_a}\varepsilon(t) \tag{8.105}$$

where:

$$H_{\delta_a} = C_{h_{\delta_a}}\bar{q}S_a\bar{c}_a \tag{8.106}$$

The following values can be computed from the aileron hingemoment derivative, $C_{h_{\delta_a}}$:

For cruising flight: $|C_{h_{\delta_a}}| = 0.00158$ /deg

For landing approach: $|C_{h_{\delta_a}}| = 0.00130$ /deg

For this business jet airplane, it is found that:

For cruising flight: $|H_{\delta_{a_{cruise}}}| = 0.00158 \times 248 \times 11.88 \times 1.25 = 5.82 \text{ftlbs/deg}$

For landing approach: $|H_{\delta_{a_{approach}}}| = 0.00130 \times 52 \times 11.88 \times 1.25 = 1.00 \text{ftlbs/deg}$

It is concluded that the hingemoment effect modifies the constant 81 in Eqn (8.104) in a negligible manner so that the transfer function of Eqn (8.102) for the aileron system can be used at all flight conditions.

The inverse Bode application illustrated here has been used by the author on a number of occasions to find the transfer functions of systems for which the equations of motion are difficult to obtain.

8.6   SUMMARY FOR CHAPTER 8

In this chapter the reader is introduced to the frequency response method also known as the Bode method. It is shown that the Bode magnitude and phase angles can be obtained from system transfer functions by the expedient of substituting $s = j\omega$.

The method of asymptotic approximations is used to rapidly evaluate Bode magnitudes and phase angles for first and second order systems. Applications to airplane response to control inputs are discussed. Bode plots are shown to be a powerful way to judge flying qualities.

A powerful inverse method is presented which allows the rapid determination of transfer functions of hardware systems for which the equations of motion may not be readily available.

8.7   PROBLEMS FOR CHAPTER 8

8.1   Substitute Eqns (8.25) through (8.27) into Eqn (8.24) and show that Eqns (8.28) and (8.29) are correct.

8.2   Show, that Eqn (8.41) is correct.

8.3   Show, that Eqn (8.45) is correct.

8.4   Show, that Eqns (8.46) and (8.47) are correct.

8.5   Find an expression for that value of input frequency for which the phase angle of the lead–lag system of Eqn (8.60) is a maximum. What is the frequency in that case?

8.6   For the system of Eqn (8.61), show that the peak magnitude and resonance frequency expressions of Eqns (8.64) and (8.65) are correct.

8.7   The reader is asked to generalize the Bode plot trends for the case of:

$$G(s) = \frac{K}{s^n} \qquad (8.75)$$

when n>0 and when n<0 as well as for K>0 and K<0 in any combination.

8.8   Sketch the approximate Bode magnitude and phase plots into Figures 8.35 through 8.42. Comment on the differences between the actual and approximate Bode plots.

8.9   Construct $M(\omega)$ and $\phi(\omega)$ for a system with the following transfer function:

$$G(s) = \frac{25}{s(s + 2)(s + 8)} \qquad (8.76)$$

8.10   Construct $M(\omega)$ and $\phi(\omega)$ for a system with the following transfer function:

$$G(s) = \frac{2(s + 4)}{(s^2 + 4)} \qquad (8.77)$$

8.11   Construct the complete and approximate $M(\omega)$ and $\phi(\omega)$ for a system with the following transfer function:

$$G(s) = \frac{900(s + 1)}{s(s^2 + 6s + 9)(s + 10)} \qquad (8.78)$$

8.9   REFERENCES FOR CHAPTER 8

8.1   Etkin, B.; Dynamics of Atmospheric Flight; John Wiley & Sons, N.Y., 1972.

8.2.   Pipes, L.A.; Applied Mathematics for Engineers and Physicists; McGraw Hill Book Company, N.Y.; 1958.

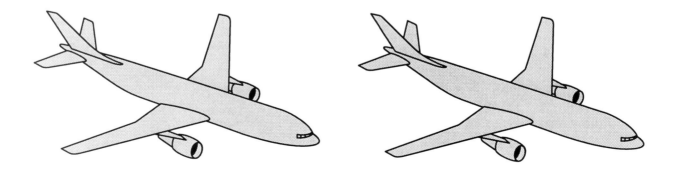

CHAPTER 9:   CLASSICAL CONTROL THEORY WITH APPLICATIONS TO AIRPLANES

It was shown in Chapter 5 that the dynamic stability behavior of airplanes can become unacceptable when the magnitudes of undamped natural frequency, damping ratio and/or time constants do not meet certain limits which are defined in the flying quality specifications. In addition, hand–flying airplanes for long periods of time in turbulent atmospheric conditions is a tedious task at best which can lead to crew fatigue. To alleviate these problems, stability augmentation systems and automatic flight control systems have been introduced. The design of such systems requires an insight into the theory of feedback control systems.

In this chapter, several aspects of classical control theory essential to understanding automatic flight control systems are discussed. To give the reader an early insight into the potential of feedback control systems an introductory example is presented in Section 9.1. This example will clearly illustrate the potential of feedback control in modifying the inherent dynamics of a system.

The study of feedback control systems can be broken down down into:

* Analysis of feedback control systems

* Design (or synthesis) of feedback control systems

Before proceeding with these topics, it is desirable to define a general relationship between input and output of control systems. This is accomplished in Section 9.2.

Typically, three objectives are associated with the **analysis** of feedback control systems:

1) to determine the degree and extent of overall system stability

2) to determine the transient response of the system to some known input

3) to determine the steady state performance of the system to some known input

These objectives are met by the following three steps in the analysis process:

Step 1:   Determine the transfer functions of all system components

Step 2:   Construct a model which represents the flow of input, feedback and output signals. Such a model is called a block diagram

Step 3:   Determine the overall system characteristics in terms of overall system stability and response

In classical control theory five methods are used in the analysis of control systems:

Method 1: The root–locus method   Method 4: The Nichols chart method

Method 2: The Bode–plot method   Method 5: The time domain response method

Method 3: The Nyquist diagram method

In this chapter the root–locus method and the Bode–plot method are used in concert with each other to analyze and synthesize feedback control systems. Both methods are referred to as frequency domain methods. Ultimately a control system must function properly in the time domain. Therefore, in several instances it will be necessary to verify that a system analyzed in the frequency domain will function properly in the time domain. That requires inversion to the time domain or, in real world cases in the presence of nonlinearities, friction and limiters, some form of simulation. Discussion of simulation is beyond the scope of this text: the reader is referred to Reference 9.1.

The root–locus method is discussed in Section 9.3. The Bode–plot method was discussed in Chapter 8. Application of the Bode–plot method to analysis of feedback control systems is discussed in Section 9.4. The root–locus method and the Bode–plot method are both frequency domain methods. In the real world, control systems operate in the time domain. Therefore, it is essential to connect the frequency domain with the time domain. Relationships between the time–domain and the frequency domain are presented in Section 9.5.

Typically, the following objectives are associated with the **design** of a control system:

I)   Feedback control systems in airplanes must conform to certain performance specifications. These performance specifications serve as physical and/or mathematical constraints on the system and its components. In various military and civilian regulations, the following performance characteristics are usually specified:

       * Speed of response   * Relative stability

       * System accuracy (allowable error)

The role of system performance specifications is discussed in Section 9.6.

II)   Feedback control systems must be robust and as simple as possible.

       A system is called robust if its closed loop performance characteristics do not vary greatly with changes in its parameters. In this regard the reader is reminded of the fact that all stability, control and inertial characteristics used in describing the airplane transfer functions are themselves the result of an engineering estimate or a measurement. In either case errors and/or uncertainties are involved.

A system should be as simple as possible. Complex systems tend to be unreliable and therefore costly to maintain and/or repair. Lack of reliability can also cause airworthiness problems.

In Section 9.7 a number of feedback control system design applications are presented.

The theory of this chapter can be used to:

A.   Study the controllability of a given airplane by a human pilot. This application is discussed in Chapter 10.

B.   Synthesize stability augmentation and automatic flight control systems. This application is discussed in Chapter 11.

Classical control theory as presented in this chapter has a number of limitations. These limitations will be pointed out as part of the discussion. Many of these limitations can be overcome by using the so-called modern control theory. In that theory (also referred to as state–space theory) extensive use of matrix methods is made. A frequently encountered problem with these matrix methods is that it leads to loss of touch with physical reality.

The author believes that both theories should be mastered by those who intend to practice control system design. References 9.2 through 9.7 should be consulted for further reading in the area of classical control theory. References 9.8 and 9.9 are recommended for the study of modern control theory.

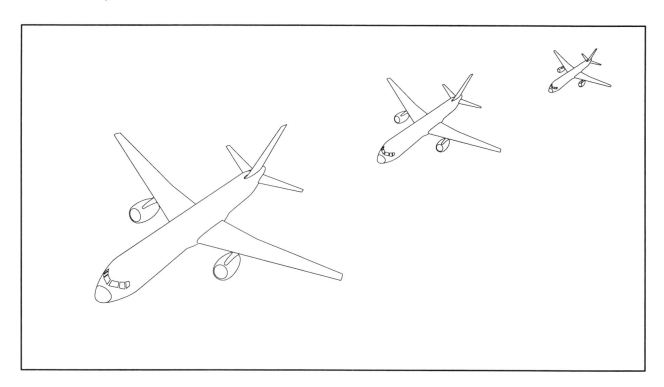

9.1 EXAMPLE OF THE POTENTIAL OF FEEDBACK CONTROL

The fundamental idea behind feedback control is to modify the stability characteristics of a given system which has unsatisfactory inherent stability behavior. For example, if a given system has insufficient damping (i.e. it responds with too much oscillatory behavior) a feedback loop is arranged to improve the damping. As a general rule, one or more of three basic types of feedback can be used:

* Position feedback (also called stiffness feedback)
* Velocity feedback (also called rate feedback)
* Acceleration feedback

A simple illustration of the potential effects of these types of feedback will be presented next. Consider the spring–mass–damper system of Figure 9.1. The reader will recognize this as identical to the system of Figure 5.3.

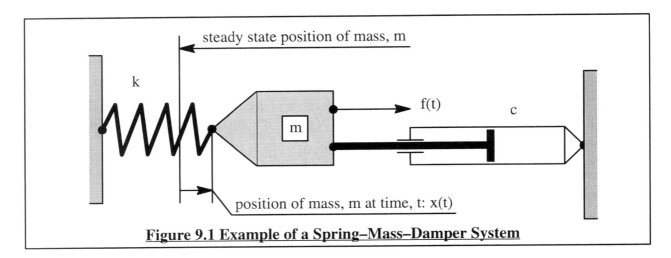

Figure 9.1 Example of a Spring–Mass–Damper System

The equation of motion for the system of Figure 9.1 can be written as follows:

$$m\ddot{x} + c\dot{x} + kx = f(t) \tag{9.1}$$

Taking the Laplace transform for zero initial conditions yields:

$$ms^2 x(s) + csx(s) + kx(s) = f(s) \tag{9.2}$$

From this it is possible to determine the open loop system transfer function as:

$$\left(\frac{x(s)}{f(s)}\right) = \left(\frac{1}{ms^2 + cs + k}\right) \tag{9.3}$$

The dynamic stability behavior of this system is determined completely by the roots of its characteristic equation (also called the "system equation"):

$$ms^2 + cs + k = 0 \tag{9.4}$$

The roots of this equation take the following form:

$$s_{1,2} = \frac{-c \pm \sqrt{c^2 - 4mk}}{2m} \qquad (9.5)$$

Note that the system will be stable as long as c>0. System stability by itself does not mean that the system has acceptable response behavior.

In Chapter 5, the frequency and damping characteristics of this system were shown to be:

$$\omega_n = \sqrt{\frac{k}{m}} \qquad \zeta = \frac{c}{2\sqrt{km}} \qquad \omega = \omega_n\sqrt{1 - \zeta^2} \qquad (9.6)$$

Assume that some or all of these characteristics are unsatisfactory. Assume also that making inherent changes in m, c and k is judged to be not feasible. The dynamic characteristics represented by Eqns (9.5) and (9.6) can be altered by arranging for the three types of feedback of page 688. A scheme for accomplishing that is shown in Figure 9.2.

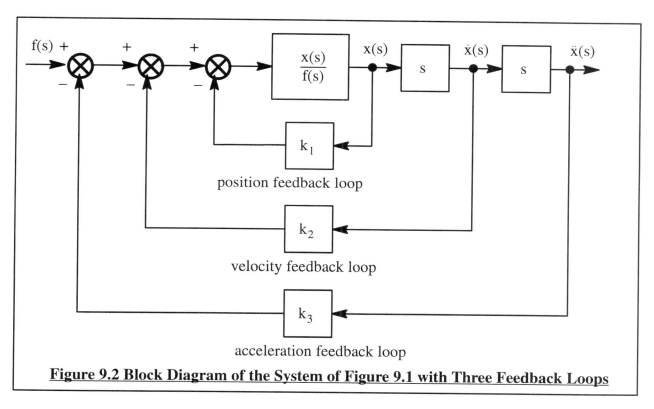

Figure 9.2 Block Diagram of the System of Figure 9.1 with Three Feedback Loops

The equation of motion of the system of Figure 9.2 is obtained by modifying Eqn (9.1) to:

$$m\ddot{x} + c\dot{x} + kx = f(t) - k_1 x - k_2 \dot{x} - k_3 \ddot{x} \qquad (9.7)$$

Taking the Laplace transformation for zero initial conditions and rearranging yields:

$$\left\{ (m + k_3)s^2 + (c + k_2)s + (k + k_1) \right\} x(s) = f(s) \qquad (9.8)$$

The corresponding system transfer function can be written as:

$$\left(\frac{x(s)}{f(s)}\right) = \left(\frac{1}{(m + k_3)s^2 + (c + k_2)s + (k + k_1)}\right) \tag{9.9}$$

The characteristic equation for this feedback system is:

$$(m + k_3)s^2 + (c + k_2)s + (k + k_1) = 0 \tag{9.10}$$

The roots of this characteristic equation may be expressed as:

$$s_{1,2} = \frac{-(c + k_2) \pm \sqrt{(c + k_2)^2 - 4(m + k_3)(k + k_1)}}{2(m + k_3)} \tag{9.11}$$

Eqn (9.10) is referred to as the 'augmented system equation'. It is clear that the role of the feedback gains, k_1, k_2 and k_3, is to alter the root locations in the s–plane from those represented by Eqn (9.5) to those represented by Eqn (9.11). How this occurs is most readily demonstrated with the help of the root–locus diagram of Figure 9.3. This root–locus diagram applies to the system of Figure 9.2 for the following open loop case:

$$m = 5 \text{ slugs} \qquad c = 50 \text{ lbs/ft/sec} \qquad k = 250 \text{ lbs/ft} \tag{9.12}$$

One of the corresponding open loop system poles is shown in Figure 9.3. The effect of varying the position, velocity and acceleration feedback gains, k_1, k_2 and k_3, on an individual basis are shown in Figure 9.3. It is seen that:

1) Position (or stiffness) feedback, k_1, affects both the undamped natural frequency and the damping ratio of the closed loop system. The root locus in this case is a straight line which passes through the open loop system pole(s). Observe that the real part of the closed loop system root remains constant as k_1 is varied, while the constants k_2 and k_3 are kept at a value of zero.

2) Velocity (or rate) feedback, k_2, affects the damping ratio of the closed loop system only. The root locus in this case is a circle around the origin of the s–plane. Observe that the undamped natural frequency of the closed loop system remains constant as k_2 is varied, while the constants k_1 and k_3 are kept at a value of zero.

3) With k_1 and k_2 kept at a value of zero, acceleration feedback, k_3, affects both the undamped natural frequency and the damping ratio of the closed loop system. The root locus is a circle with origin at the point n=−5 rad/sec. Note that as k_3 is varied toward infinity, the undamped natural frequency tends toward zero. The reason is clear from the fact that in such a case: $\omega_n = \sqrt{k/(m + k_3)}$.

4) By selecting any combination of values for k_1, k_2 and k_3 it is possible to place the poles of the closed loop system at an arbitrary desired location in the s–plane. This thought is referred to as: pole assignment.

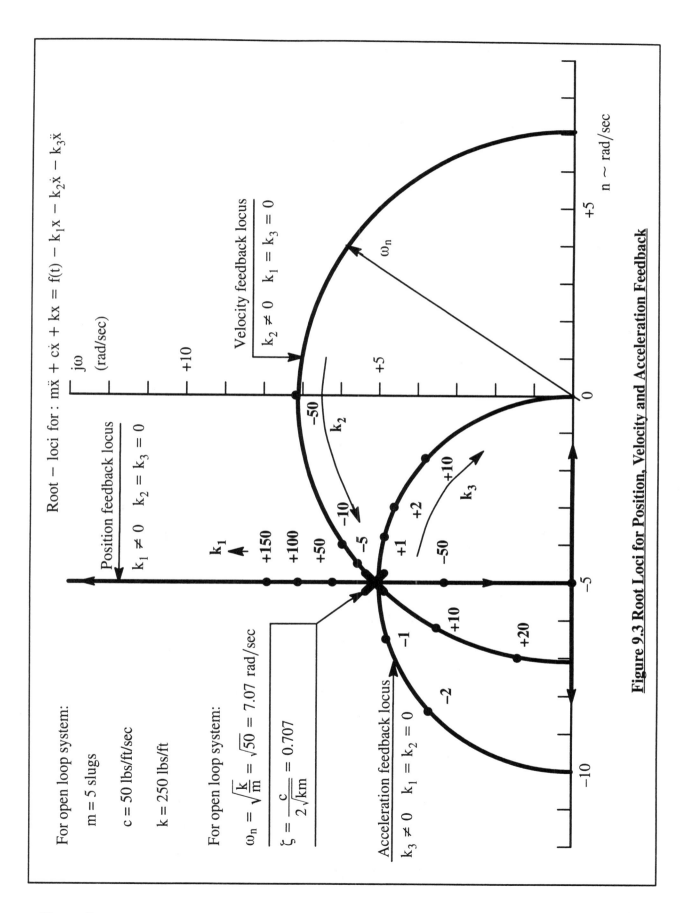

Figure 9.3 Root Loci for Position, Velocity and Acceleration Feedback

9.2   BASIC RELATIONSHIPS AND DEFINITIONS USED IN FEEDBACK CONTROL SYSTEMS

In the design and analysis of feedback control systems, block diagrams are used to convey the general way a given feedback system operates. Figure 9.4 shows an example of such a block diagram for a typical yaw damper installation in an airplane.

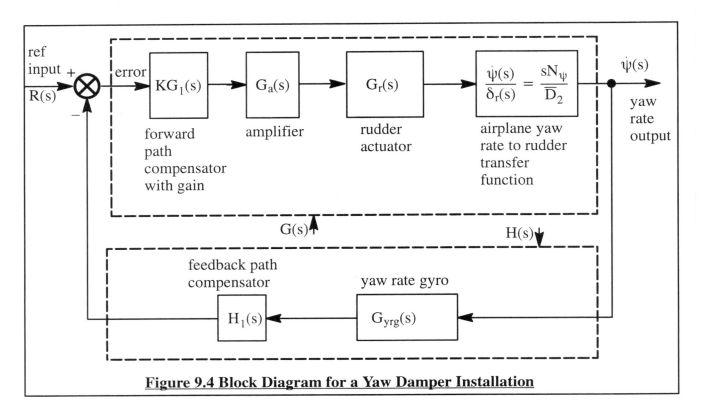

Figure 9.4 Block Diagram for a Yaw Damper Installation

When an airplane flies through turbulence, it is subjected to motion perturbations relative to steady state flight. One of these perturbations is the yaw rate. If the airplane open loop yaw–rate–to–rudder transfer function has a poorly damped dutch roll root, the ensuing yaw rate perturbations of the airplane can be very annoying to crew and passengers. The function of the yaw damper is to oppose and eliminate any yaw rate perturbations which arise because of flight through turbulence. It was shown in Chapter 5 (pages 397–398) that a yaw damper can be thought of as a device which artificially enhances the negative magnitude of the open loop yaw damping derivative, C_{n_r} , thereby

increasing the dutch roll damping ratio. Figure 9.4 shows what is needed from a systems viewpoint to accomplish this. Assume that the rudder is deflected a small amount. The airplane open loop yaw–rate–to–rudder transfer function, $\dot{\psi}(s)/\delta_r(s)$, is used to predict the ensuing yaw rate. This yaw

rate is sensed by a yaw rate gyro which in Figure 9.4 is located in the so–called feedback loop of the yaw damper installation. The output signal of the yaw rate gyro is sent to a device known as the feedback path compensator. The output of this compensator is sent to a comparator which serves to subtract the feedback path signal from the overall system input signal. In steady state level flight, this overall system input signal would normally be zero: this commands a zero yaw rate. The output of the comparator (also known as the system error signal) is sent to a device known as the forward path compensator. This compensator normally contains a multiplying constant known as the system feedback gain. The output of the compensator is sent to an amplifier. The function of the amplifier is to boost the signal level up to a power level which is compatible with the input power requirements of the rudder actuator. The output of the amplifier commands the actuator to deflect the rudder a certain amount.

It is clear that the yaw damper loop of Figure 9.4 serves to drive the error signal to zero. When that state of affairs has been reached, the airplane yaw rate will be zero and the yaw damper has done its job.

To analyze the system stability and response it is necessary to find the overall system transfer function. This is done with the help of block diagram algebra after simplifying the block diagram of Figure 9.4. That simplification is accomplished by first replacing the product of all transfer functions in the forward path by G(s). Second, the same is done in the feedback loop, which yields H(s). The block diagram of Figure 9.4 is now replaced by the generic block diagram of Figure 9.5. The following definitions are used:

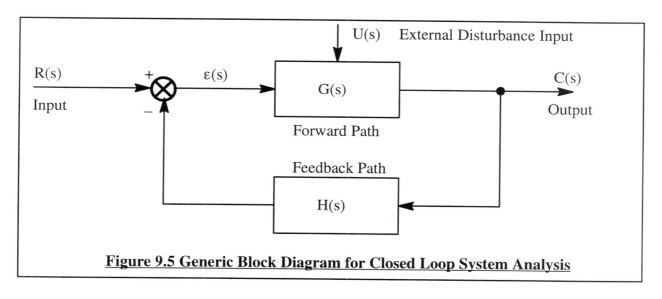

Figure 9.5 Generic Block Diagram for Closed Loop System Analysis

Definitions:

R(s)   is the Laplace transform of the system input. This input is also called the system reference input.

G(s)   is the forward path transfer function.

C(s)   is the Laplace transform of the output of the system.

H(s)   is the feedback path transfer function.

$\epsilon(s)$ is the Laplace transform of the error signal: $\epsilon(s) = R(s) \pm H(s)C(s)$.

The +/– depends on whether the system has positive or negative feedback.

As shown in Figure 9.5 the feedback is negative, meaning that the feedback path signal is subtracted from the reference input signal.

U(s)   is the Laplace transform of the external disturbance input to the system.

From these definitions the following equations can be written for the error signal, $\varepsilon(s)$, and for the output signal, C(s):

$$\varepsilon(s) = R(s) - H(s)C(s) \tag{9.13}$$

$$C(s) = \{\varepsilon(s) + U(s)\}G(s) \tag{9.14}$$

Substitution of Eqn (9.13) into Eqn (9.14) yields:

$$C(s) = \{R(s) - H(s)C(s) + U(s)\}G(s) \tag{9.15}$$

Solving for the system output, C(s):

$$C(s) = \frac{\{R(s) + U(s)\}G(s)}{\{1 + G(s)H(s)\}} \tag{9.16}$$

Note that for zero disturbance input:

$$\frac{C(s)}{R(s)} = \frac{G(s)}{\{1 + G(s)H(s)\}} \tag{9.17}$$

This is called the output–to–reference–input closed loop transfer function of the system.

Note also that for zero reference input:

$$\frac{C(s)}{U(s)} = \frac{G(s)}{\{1 + G(s)H(s)\}} \tag{9.18}$$

This is called the output–to–disturbance–input closed loop transfer function of the system.

Apparently these two closed loop transfer functions are identical! Several additional definitions are now introduced.

Definitions:

1)   The right hand side of Eqns (9.17) and (9.18) is defined as the
closed loop system transfer function, W(s):

$$W(s) = \frac{G(s)}{\{1 + G(s)H(s)\}} \tag{9.19}$$

Note again that this transfer function applies to both reference inputs and disturbance inputs to the system.

2)   The product of all transfer function around the loop, G(s)H(s), is called the **open loop system transfer function**.

3)   When H(s) = 1 (output is fed back directly to the comparator) the system is referred to as a **unity negative feedback system**.

It should be clear to the reader that the dynamic stability and response behavior of the closed loop system depends entirely on the characteristics of the closed loop transfer function, W(s). Furthermore, the dynamic stability characteristics of the closed loop system depend entirely on the roots of its characteristic equation:

$$\{1 + G(s)H(s)\} = 0 \tag{9.20}$$

Usually, the forward path transfer function is written as KG(s), instead of merely G(s). The constant K is called the system feedback gain. Thus, the closed loop system transfer function is:

$$W(s) = \frac{KG(s)}{\{1 + KG(s)H(s)\}} \tag{9.21}$$

while the system characteristic equation becomes:

$$\{1 + KG(s)H(s)\} = 0 \tag{9.22}$$

The behavior of the roots of this characteristic equation as a function of K is crucial to the understanding of feedback systems. The stability behavior of feedback systems, as a function of varying gain K, will be discussed with the help of two methods:

9.3 The root–locus method

9.4 The Bode method

Before starting the discussion of these methods, it is desirable to apply the derivation of the closed loop system transfer function to the yaw–damper system of Figure 9.4. The closed loop transfer function of that yaw–damper system is:

$$W(s) = \left\{ \frac{KG_1(s)G_a(s)G_r(s)\dfrac{\psi(s)}{\delta_r(s)}}{1 + KG_1(s)G_a(s)G_r(s)\dfrac{\psi(s)}{\delta_r(s)}H_1(s)G_{yrg}(s)} \right\} \tag{9.23}$$

The airplane open loop yaw–rate–to–rudder transfer function, $\psi(s)/\delta_r(s) = sN_\psi/ \overline{D}_2$, is

obtained from Eqn (5.104) in Part I of this text. It was shown in Chapter 5 that the denominator of this transfer function contains a poorly damped dutch roll quadratic. The idea behind the yaw damper is to select K, $G_1(s)$ and $H_1(s)$ in such a way that the closed loop poles yield a closed loop damping ratio which is larger than the open loop system damping ratio. How this can be done will become clear after studying the material in Sections 9.3 and 9.4 and applying it to the yaw damper. That application is discussed in Chapter 11.

9.3   THE ROOT LOCUS METHOD

In this section four aspects of the root locus method will be discussed:

9.3.1 Root locus fundamentals
9.3.2 Root locus asymptotes
9.3.3 Breakaway angle from a complex pole
9.3.4 Step–by–step construction of a root locus diagram

9.3.1   ROOT LOCUS FUNDAMENTALS

Consider again the closed loop system transfer function $W(s)$ of Equation (9.21):

$$W(s) = \frac{C(s)}{R(s)} = \frac{KG(s)}{\{1 + KG(s)H(s)\}} \tag{9.24}$$

This transfer function has as characteristic equation:

$$\{1 + KG(s)H(s)\} = 0 \tag{9.25}$$

The open loop system transfer function, $KG(s)H(s)$, will in general consist of numerator and denominator polynomials in the Laplace variable s. As a general rule, it will be possible to express $KG(s)H(s)$ as follows:

$$KG(s)H(s) = \frac{K \prod\limits_{i=1}^{i=m} (s + Z_i)}{\prod\limits_{j=1}^{j=n} (s + P_j)} \tag{9.26}$$

The roots of the numerator characteristic equation are $-Z_i$. The Z_i's are referred to as the open loop zeros of the system. The roots of the denominator characteristic equation are $-P_j$. The P_j's are called the open loop poles of the system.

Another way of writing the characteristic equation (9.25) is:

$$\{1 + KG(s)H(s)\} = \left\{1 + K\frac{N_1(s)N_2(s)}{D_1(s)D_2(s)}\right\} = 0 \tag{9.27a}$$

where: $G(s) = N_1(s)/D_1(s)$ \hfill (9.27b)

$$H(s) = N_2(s)/D_2(s) \tag{9.27c}$$

Clearly, the zeros Z_i of Eqn (9.26) are all the zeros of $N_1(s)$ and $N_2(s)$ combined. Similarly, the poles P_j of Eqn (9.26) are all the poles of $D_1(s)$ and $D_2(s)$ combined.

Now consider Eqn (9.25) rewritten with Eqns (9.27b) and (9.27c):

$$D_1(s)D_2(s) + KN_1(s)N_2(s) = 0 \tag{9.28}$$

Consider what happens under the following two scenarios:

Scenario 1: K = 0

Under this scenario, the roots of the characteristic equation degenerate to the open loop system poles which are given by:

$$D_1(s)D_2(s) = 0 \tag{9.29}$$

The roots of this equation are exactly the open loop system poles!

Scenario 2: K = ∞

Under this scenario, the roots of the characteristic equation degenerate to the open loop system zero's which are given by:

$$KN_1(s)N_2(s) = 0 \tag{9.30}$$

The roots of this equation are exactly the open loop system zeros!

The following very important conclusion can now be drawn:

CONCLUSION: **If, in a closed loop system, the gain, K, is varied from 0 to ∞ , the closed loop system poles will migrate from the open loop system poles toward the open loop system zero's.**

The paths in the s–plane, taken by the closed loop system poles are called the closed loop system root loci. In the following, rules will be developed from which it is possible to visualize the paths taken by the closed loop system poles as K is varied from 0 to ∞ .

For practical systems n>m or n=m. If n>m it will be shown that n–m of the system open loop zeros are located at infinity.

Consider the generic system block diagram of Figure 9.6.

The closed loop system transfer of this system is given by:

$$W(s) = \frac{C(s)}{R(s)} = \frac{KG(s)}{\{1 + KG(s)H(s)\}} \tag{9.31}$$

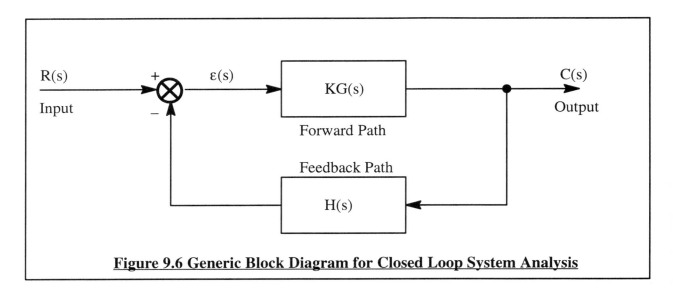

Figure 9.6 Generic Block Diagram for Closed Loop System Analysis

The characteristic equation for this system (which totally determines its dynamic stability behavior) can be written as:

$$1 + KG(s)H(s) = 0 \qquad (9.32)$$

The roots of this characteristic equation are the closed loop poles of W(s).

Eqn (9.32) can be rewritten as:

$$KG(s)H(s) = -1 \qquad (9.33)$$

Because s is a complex number, the expression KG(s)H(s) also represents a complex number. Such a complex number can be written as:

$$KG(s)H(s) = |KG(s)H(s)| \ @ \ \measuredangle\{KG(s)H(s)\} \qquad (9.34)$$

Eqn (9.33) states that the complex number KG(s)H(s) must equal the real number −1. Using Eqn (9.34) it is seen that the only way this can be satisfied is, if the following two conditions are **simultaneously satisfied**:

$$\boxed{|\ KG(s)H(s)\ | = 1} \qquad (9.35)$$

and:

$$\boxed{\measuredangle\{KG(s)H(s)\} = \pm 180^0, \ \pm 540^0, \ etc.} \qquad (9.36)$$

where, in the latter, it is assumed, that K is a positive constant which contributes zero phase angle.

Note well: * Equation (9.35) is known as the magnitude requirement.

    * Equation (9.36) is known as the angle requirement.

As indicated before, for a point in the s–plane to be on the root locus it must **SATISFY BOTH REQUIREMENTS SIMULTANEOUSLY**.

Applying the notation of Eqn (9.26) it is possible to write Eqn (9.35) as follows:

$$|KG(s)H(s)| = \frac{K|(s + Z_1)||(s + Z_2)|.......|(s + Z_m)|}{|(s + P_1)||(s + P_2)|........|(s + P_n)|} = 1 \qquad (9.37)$$

Similarly, it is possible to write Eqn (9.36) as:

$$\angle\{KG(s)H(s)\} = \angle K + \angle(s + Z_1) + \angle(s + Z_2) + ...\angle(s + Z_m) + \qquad (9.38)$$

$$- \angle(s + P_1) - \angle(s + P_2) - ......\angle(s + P_n) =$$

$$= \pm 180^0 , \pm 540^0 , \text{ etc.}$$

The angle expressions in Eqn (9.38) can be visualized with the help of Figure 9.7 for a pole on the real axis. The reader is asked to redraw Figure 9.7 for the case of a complex pole.

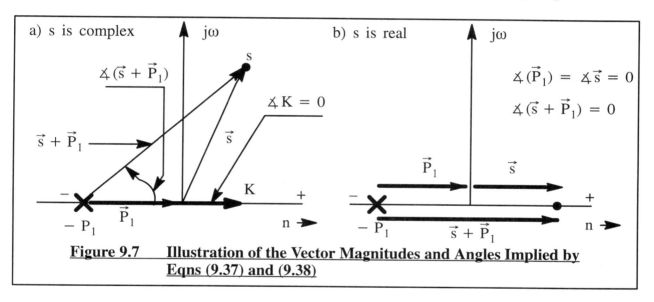

Figure 9.7   Illustration of the Vector Magnitudes and Angles Implied by Eqns (9.37) and (9.38)

These properties can be used to determine the paths taken by the poles of the closed loop system W(s) as they migrate from the open loop poles of W(s) toward the open loop zero's of W(s) while K varies from 0 to ∞. How this is done is now demonstrated with a numerical example.

Consider the system of Figure 9.6 with:

$$KG(s)H(s) = \frac{K(s + 8)}{s(s + 3)(s + 6)(s + 12)} \qquad (9.39)$$

To determine where the root–loci of the system are, assume that the s–plane has been divided into two regions:

* region 1: the real axis   * region 2: the entire s–plane except the real axis

Each region is considered separately.

* Region 1: the real axis

The angle requirement of Eqn (9.36) will be used to determine which parts of the real axis qualify as part of the root loci and which parts don't.

To find the solution to this problem, assume that a point s is located at point A in Figure 9.8. Figure 9.8 shows the pole and zero vectors drawn to point A. It is clear that all vectors have an angle equal to 0 degrees with the real axis. Therefore, the angle requirement as expressed by Eqn (9.36) cannot possibly be met. Thus, point A cannot be part of a root locus of this system. But this implies that no point on the real axis which lies to the right of the pole at the origin can be on the root locus. Therefore, as K becomes positive, the pole at the origin must move to the left!

Next, consider the point B in Figure 9.8. As seen from Figure 9.9, the pole and zero vectors drawn to point B all have an angle equal to 0 degrees, except the one drawn from the pole at the origin. That pole vector makes an angle of +/− 180 degrees with the real axis. Therefore, point B does satisfy the angle requirement. However, that means that any point located between s=0 and s=−3 meets the angle requirement. Therefore, as K becomes positive, the pole at the origin (s=0) moves to the left, while the pole at s=−3 moves to the right.

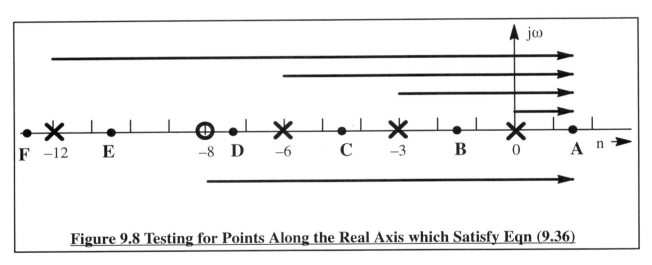

Figure 9.8 Testing for Points Along the Real Axis which Satisfy Eqn (9.36)

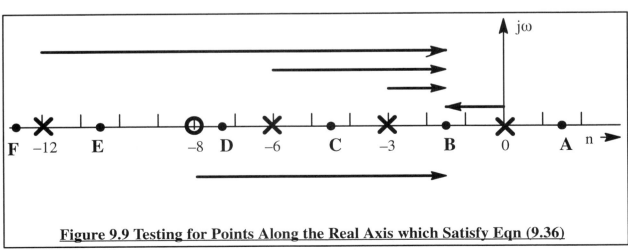

Figure 9.9 Testing for Points Along the Real Axis which Satisfy Eqn (9.36)

The reader is asked to show in a similar manner that the following is true:

* Point(s) C cannot be on the root locus of this system.
* Point(s) D are on the root locus of this system.
* Point(s) E cannot be on the root locus of this system.
* Point(s) F are on the root locus of this system.

The picture which emerges for the root loci in region 1 is shown in Figure 9.10. Note that the system pole at s=−12 moves toward −∞. The pole at s=−6 moves toward the zero at s=−8. The poles at s=0 and s=−3 move toward each other. At some value of K they meet (two equal real roots) and, as K increases further, these poles form an oscillatory (complex) pair of roots. These complex roots then move into region 2.

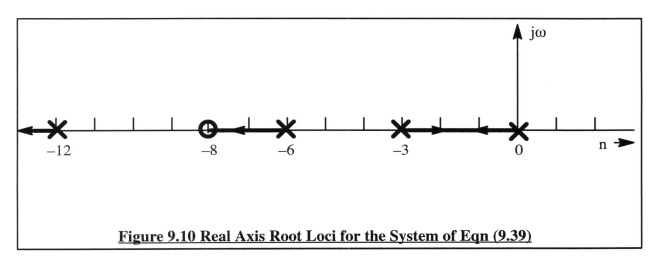

Figure 9.10 Real Axis Root Loci for the System of Eqn (9.39)

* Region 2: the entire s–plane except the real axis

To determine where in region 2 the root loci of the system of Eqn (9.39) might be, consider any point s as shown in Figure 9.11.

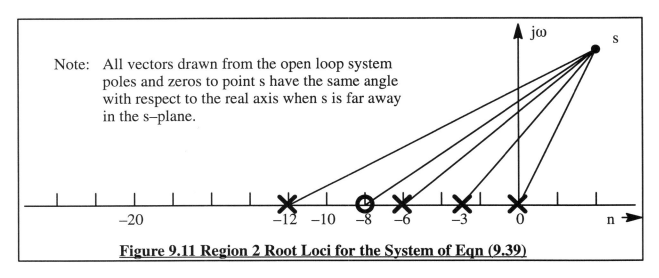

Note: All vectors drawn from the open loop system poles and zeros to point s have the same angle with respect to the real axis when s is far away in the s–plane.

Figure 9.11 Region 2 Root Loci for the System of Eqn (9.39)

As long as the point s is far away into the s–plane, all pole and zero vectors drawn to point s have the same angle with respect to the real axis. Call that angle: Θ. The angle requirement in this case demands that:

$$\Theta(\text{number of zeros}) - \Theta(\text{number of poles}) = \pm 180^0, \pm 540^0, \text{ etc.} \tag{9.40}$$

For the current example it is found that:

$$\Theta = \frac{\pm 180^0}{1 - 4} = \pm 60^0 \tag{9.41}$$

and:

$$\Theta = \frac{\pm 540^0}{1 - 4} = \pm 180^0 \tag{9.42}$$

and:

$$\Theta = \frac{\pm 900^0}{1 - 4} = \pm 300^0 = \mp 60^0 \tag{9.43}$$

The latter result is a repetition of Eqn (9.41). Apparently, there are (far–away) directions in the s–plane at +/– 60 deg and +/– 180 degrees where there are root loci. These far–away root–loci are referred to as the **root locus asymptotes**.

Apparently the real axis itself is such an asymptote. Because of what happened to point F in Figure 9.8 this was already known! The asymptotes at +/–60 degrees are shown in the complete system root locus diagram in Figure 9.12. How to construct the intercept of the asymptotes with the real axis will be discussed in Section 9.3.2.

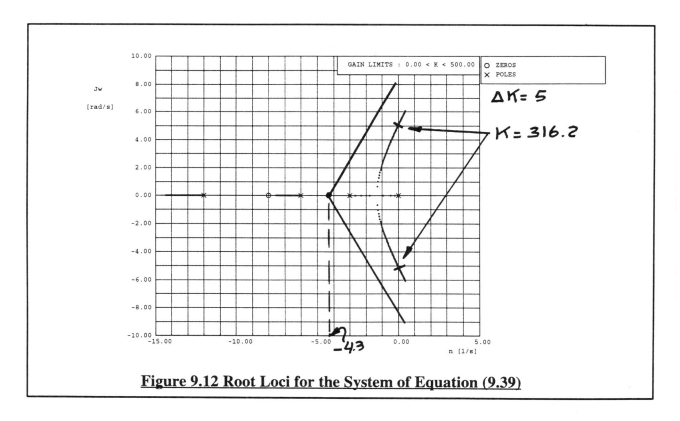

Figure 9.12 Root Loci for the System of Equation (9.39)

To determine where, for a given value of K, specific points are on the root locus it is necessary to solve the magnitude requirement of Eqn (9.35). Observe from Figure 9.12 that the system becomes unstable for K>316.2. The latter is most readily determined with the help of a Bode plot as shown in Section 9.4: see Figure 9.19.

9.3.2 ROOT LOCUS ASYMPTOTES

Consider a system with the following open loop transfer function:

$$KG(s)H(s) = \frac{K(s^m + a_1 s^{m-1} + ... + a_m)}{(s^n + b_1 s^{n-1} + ... + b_n)} \tag{9.44}$$

Note that this is merely a different way of writing Eqn (9.26).

The system has n poles and m zeros. These poles and zeros are also called the finite poles and zeros. As s→∞ it is seen that KG(s)H(s) behaves as K/s^{n-m}. Therefore, as K increases from 0 to ∞ the closed loop system poles migrate from the finite open loop system poles to the open loop system zeros, m of which are finite and n–m of which are located at infinity in the direction of the root locus asymptotes.

The objective of the following derivation is to show how these asymptotes can be located.

First, recall from algebra the following properties:

$$a_1 = Z_1 + Z_2 + ... + Z_m \tag{9.45}$$

$$a_m = (Z_1)(Z_2).....(Z_m) \tag{9.46}$$

$$b_1 = P_1 + P_2 + ... + P_n \tag{9.47}$$

$$b_n = (P_1)(P_2).....(P_n) \tag{9.48}$$

Second, divide the numerator and the denominator of Eqn (9.44) by its numerator. This yields:

$$KG(s)H(s) = \frac{K}{s^{n-m} + (b_1 - a_1)s^{n-m-1} + ... + \dfrac{R(s)}{(s^m + a_1 s^{m-1} + ... + a_m) = P(s)}} \tag{9.49}$$

All points on the root loci of the system must satisfy the system characteristic equation. Therefore, these points must meet the requirement of Eqn (9.33). This results in:

$$s^{n-m} + (b_1 - a_1)s^{n-m-1} + ... + \frac{R(s)}{P(s)} = -K \tag{9.50}$$

On the asymptotes the corresponding values of s are very large. For very large s the remainder, R(s)/P(s) → 0. Furthermore, for large values of s, only the first two terms in the s–polynomial of Eqn (9.50) are important. Therefore, Eqn (9.50) on the asymptotes, reduces to:

$$s^{n-m} + (b_1 - a_1)s^{n-m-1} = s^{(n-m)}\left\{1 + \frac{(b_1 - a_1)}{s}\right\} = -K \tag{9.51}$$

Raising both sides to the 1/(n–m) power yields:

$$s\left\{1 + \frac{(b_1 - a_1)}{s}\right\}^{1/(n-m)} = (-K)^{1/(n-m)} \tag{9.52}$$

Expanding the l.h.s. term in a power series results in:

$$s\left\{1 + \frac{(b_1 - a_1)}{(n-m)s} + \ldots\right\} = (-K)^{1/(n-m)} \tag{9.53}$$

Neglecting higher order terms in this expansion it is found that:

$$\left\{s + \frac{(b_1 - a_1)}{(n-m)}\right\} \approx (-K)^{1/(n-m)} \tag{9.54}$$

Because s is a complex number it can be written as:

$$s = \sigma + j\omega \tag{9.55}$$

It is to be noted that the r.h.s. of Eqn (9.54) represents a complex number with a magnitude of: $K^{1/(n-m)}$ making an angle of $\frac{(2k+1)\pi}{(n-m)}$ with the real axis.

Substitution of Eqn (9.55) into Eqn (9.54) and using De Moivre's Theorem yields:

$$\sigma + j\omega + \frac{(b_1 - a_1)}{(n-m)} = |K^{1/n-m}|\left[\cos\left\{\frac{(2k+1)\pi}{(n-m)}\right\} + j\sin\left\{\frac{(2k+1)\pi}{(n-m)}\right\}\right] \tag{9.56}$$

Equation (9.56) is satisfied **if and only if** the real parts on the l.h.s. equal the real parts on the r.h.s. AND if the imaginary parts on the l.h.s. equal the imaginary parts on the r.h.s. Therefore, Eqn (9.56) splits into two equations:

$$\sigma + \frac{(b_1 - a_1)}{(n-m)} = |K^{1/n-m}|\left[\cos\left\{\frac{(2k+1)\pi}{(n-m)}\right\}\right] \tag{9.57}$$

and

$$\omega = |K^{1/n-m}|\left[\sin\left\{\frac{(2k+1)\pi}{(n-m)}\right\}\right] \tag{9.58}$$

Dividing Eqn (9.57) into Eqn (9.58) results in:

$$\frac{\omega}{\sigma + \frac{(b_1 - a_1)}{(n - m)}} = \tan\left\{\frac{(2k + 1)\pi}{(n - m)}\right\} \quad (9.59)$$

The latter equation can be rewritten as follows:

$$\omega = \left\{\sigma + \frac{(b_1 - a_1)}{(n - m)}\right\} \tan\left\{\frac{(2k + 1)\pi}{(n - m)}\right\} \quad (9.60)$$

Clearly, Eqn (9.60) represents the far–away root–loci or asymptotes of the system. The reader will recognize that Eqn (9.60) represents a straight line in the s–plane with its intercept point at: $\sigma = \frac{-(b_1 - a_1)}{(n - m)}$ and a slope equal to $\arctan\left\{\frac{(2k + 1)\pi}{(n - m)}\right\}$. The following conclusions can now be drawn:

Conclusion 1: The root locus asymptotes intersect the real axis at a point defined by:

$$s = \frac{-(b_1 - a_1)}{(n - m)} \quad (9.61)$$

Conclusion 2: The root locus asymptotes make angles with the real axis given by:

$\arctan\left\{\frac{(2k + 1)\pi}{(n - m)}\right\}$ where k is a positive integer.

Remember from Eqn (9.45) and (9.47) that the constant a_1 represents the sum of the open loop system zeros, while the constant b_1 represents the sum of the open loop system poles. The point s as given by Eqn (9.61) is referred to as the **center of gravity of the root locus diagram**. The reason for this nomenclature is the following. If positive unit masses were assigned to each pole and negative unit masses were assigned to each zero, the combined center of gravity of these masses would be at point s as computed from Eqn (9.61).

Figure 9.13 illustrates the implication of Conclusions 1 and 2 in the s–plane.

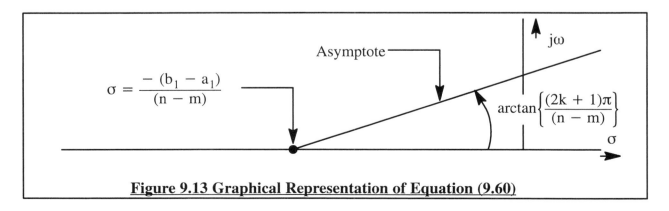

Figure 9.13 Graphical Representation of Equation (9.60)

9.3.3 BREAKAWAY ANGLE FROM A COMPLEX POLE

A useful property of the root locus method is the so–called break–away angle property. Consider a root locus branch which emanates from a complex pole, P_2 , as shown in Figure 9.14.

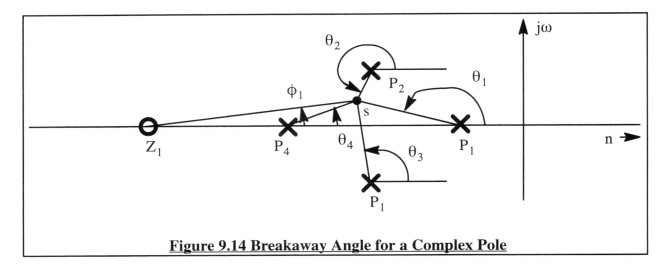

Figure 9.14 Breakaway Angle for a Complex Pole

Let point s in Figure 9.14 be a point on the root locus. In that case, s must satisfy the angle requirement of Eqn (9.36). This angle requirement demands that:

$$\phi_1 - \theta_1 - \theta_2 - \theta_3 - \theta_4 = \pm 180^0 \tag{9.62}$$

If point s is very close to P_2 , the angle θ_2 in fact represents the breakaway angle of the root locus from the pole P_2 . The other angles in Eqn (9.62) are the pole and zero vector angles to the point s= P_2 . These can be read directly of Figure 9.15. The breakaway angle for the pole at P_2 is therefore given by:

$$\theta_2 = \theta_{\text{breakaway}} = \phi_1 - \theta_1 - \theta_3 - \theta_4 \mp 180^0 \tag{9.63}$$

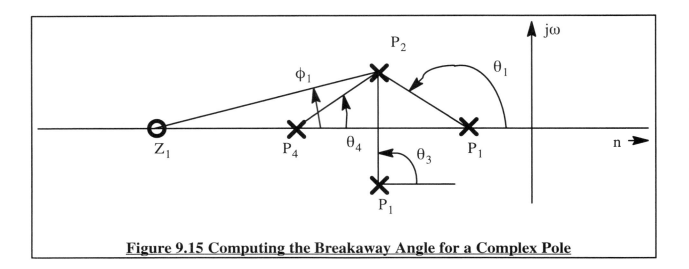

Figure 9.15 Computing the Breakaway Angle for a Complex Pole

At this point it is useful to summarize the "rules" for root locus construction as developed so far. This is done in Sub–section 9.3.4 in the form of a step–by–step procedure for construction of a root locus diagram.

9.3.4 STEP-BY-STEP CONSTRUCTION OF A ROOT LOCUS DIAGRAM

A step–by–step procedure for root locus construction for a system which can be represented by the generic block diagram of Figure 9.6 is given next.

Step 1)   Determine the open loop transfer function of the system: KG(s)H(s).

Step 2)   Plot the open loop poles and zeros of KG(s)H(s) in the s–plane.

Step 3)   Locate the asymptotes of the root loci by computing their point of intersection with the real axis from:

$$\sigma = \frac{\left[\Sigma\{\text{Poles of KG(s)H(s)}\} - \Sigma\{\text{Zeros of KG(s)H(s)}\}\right]}{(n - m)} \qquad (9.64)$$

where: n is the number of (finite) poles of KG(s)H(s)

   m is the number of (finite) zeros of KG(s)H(s), where n>m is assumed.

Step 4)   The angles which these asymptotes make with the real axis are:

$$\Theta = \frac{\pm 180^0}{(n - m)} ; \frac{\pm 540^0}{(n - m)} ; \text{ etcetera} \qquad (9.65)$$

The asymptotes can now be drawn in.

Step 5)   Root locus branches of W(s) start at the poles of KG(s)H(s) when K=0. They terminate at the zeros of KG(s)H(s) when K=∞ . Note that n–m of these zeros are located along the asymptotes at infinity.

Step 6)   Root locus branches on the real axis lie to the left of an odd number of poles and zeros, starting with the pole or zero farthest to the right.

Step 7)   A branch of the root loci between two poles on the real axis will, at some value of K, break away from the real axis and form two complex, conjugate branches. These complex branches terminate at one each of the zeros of KG(s)H(s). Again, n–m of these zeros are located at infinity.

Step 8) For any given value of K, the location of one or more poles of the closed loop system, W(s) may be found from the magnitude requirement of Eqn (9.37):

$$K = \frac{(s + P_1)(s + P_2)......(s + P_m)}{(s + Z_1)(s + Z_2).....(s + Z_n)} \tag{9.66}$$

Step 9) The angle at which a root locus branch leaves a complex pole may be computed from the angle requirement as shown in Eqn (9.63).

The AAA program of Appendix A, Part I can be used to calculate and plot root–loci for systems for which the s–polynomial order satisfies the condition: (m+n)<50.

An application of this procedure will now be discussed.

Consider a system with the block diagram of Figure 9.6 such that:

$$G(s) = \frac{K}{s(s^2 + 4s + 25)} \tag{9.67}$$

and

$$H(s) = \frac{(s + 4)}{(s + 2)} \tag{9.68}$$

The root loci for this system will be determined by following the 9 steps enumerated before.

Step 1) The open loop transfer function of the system is:

$$G(s)H(s) = K\left\{\frac{1}{s(s^2 + 4s + 25)}\right\}\frac{(s + 4)}{(s + 2)} \tag{9.69}$$

Step 2) The open loop (finite) poles and zeros of this system are found at:

Poles at : s = 0   s = − 2   s = − 2 ± j4.58 $\tag{9.70}$

Zero at : s = − 4 $\tag{9.71}$

Figure 9.16 shows a pole–zero plot (not to scale) of this system.

Step 3) The intersection point of the asymptotes with the real axis is found from Eqn (9.64) as follows:

$$\sigma = \frac{-\{(0) + (2) + (2 + j4.58) + (2 - j4.58) - (4)\}}{(4 - 1)} = \frac{-2}{3} = -0.67 \tag{9.72}$$

This intercept point is indicated in Figure 9.16 by the heavy dot.

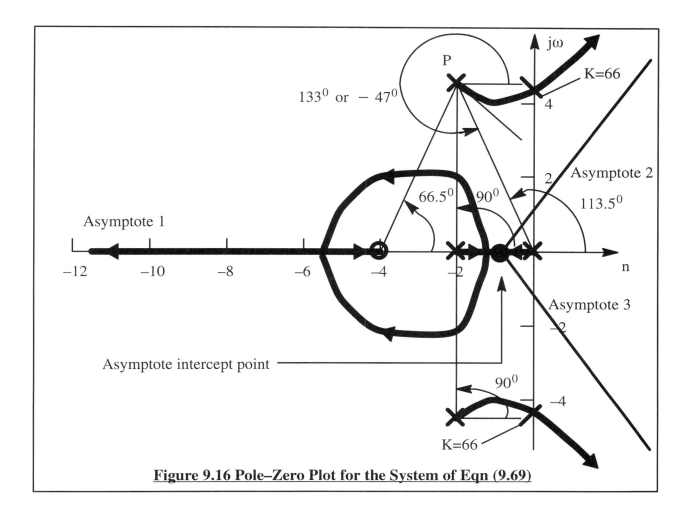

Figure 9.16 Pole–Zero Plot for the System of Eqn (9.69)

Step 4)   The asymptotes make the following angles with the real axis:

$$\Theta = \frac{\pm\,180^0}{(3)} = \pm\,60^0 \;;\; \frac{\pm\,540^0}{(3)} = \pm\,180^0 \qquad (9.73)$$

The 60 degree asymptotes are shown in Figure 9.16. Clearly the negative real axis is also an asymptote.

Steps 5) – 7)   The root loci are shown in heavy lines in Figure 9.16. The system becomes unstable for K>66. How this result is obtained will be explained in Section 9.4.

Step 8)   Figure 9.17 shows the location of the closed loop system poles for K=66. The AAA program of Appendix A was used to determine the location of these poles. In Section 9.4 it will be shown that the Bode method can be used to achieve the same result.

Step 9)   The breakaway angle of the complex root locus branch which emanates from the pole labeled P in Figure 9.16 is determined with Eqn (9.63):

$$\theta_P = \theta_{\text{breakaway}} = 66.5^0 - 90^0 - 90^0 - 113.5^0 - 180^0 = -47^0 \qquad (9.74)$$

The angles are illustrated in Figure 9.16.

The AAA program of Appendix A was used to draw the root locus diagram of the system to the proper scale in Figure 9.17.

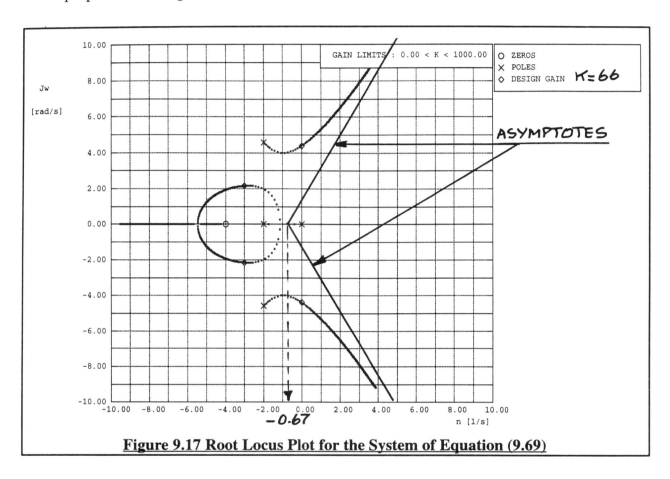

Figure 9.17 Root Locus Plot for the System of Equation (9.69)

9.4 APPLICATION OF THE BODE PLOT METHOD TO CONTROL SYSTEM ANALYSIS

It was shown in Section 9.3 that a control system can become unstable at some value of the feedback gain, K. The purpose of this section is to show that the value of K beyond which instability occurs can be easily determined from a Bode plot. It will also be shown that certain systems cannot become unstable at any gain. The condition for which this is true will be determined.

Consider the generic, unscaled Bode plot of Figure 9.18.

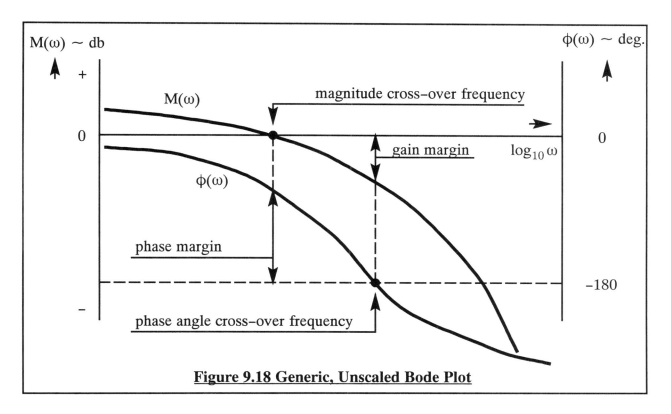

Figure 9.18 Generic, Unscaled Bode Plot

The following four definitions are important to remember:

Definition 1: The frequency at which the Bode magnitude plot $M(\omega)$ crosses the 0 db line is referred to as the magnitude cross-over frequency.

Definition 2: The frequency at which the Bode phase angle plot $\phi(\omega)$ crosses the –180 db line is referred to as the phase angle cross-over frequency.

Definition 3: At the magnitude cross-over frequency, the phase angle obtained by taking $\{\phi(\omega) + 180^0\}$ is referred to as the phase margin. As drawn in Figure 9.18 the phase margin is positive.

Definition 4: At the phase angle cross–over frequency, the magnitude obtained by taking $\{0 - M(\omega)\}$ is referred to as the gain margin. As drawn in Figure 9.18 the gain margin is positive.

Assuming that $M(\omega)$ in Figure 9.18 was drawn in for K=1.0, the system will become unstable

when: $K > \text{invlog}_{10}\left(\dfrac{\text{gain margin}}{20}\right)$. That this is the case can be explained as follows:

1) when K becomes larger than 1.0, the phase plot, $\phi(\omega)$, in Figure 9.18 will not be affected.

2) when K becomes larger than 1.0, the magnitude plot, $M(\omega)$, shifts up (vertically) over a distance $20\log_{10} K$.

3) when $K = \text{invlog}_{10}\left(\dfrac{\text{gain margin}}{20}\right)$ both the phase margin and the gain margin are simultaneously equal to zero. For any value of K larger than this, the system will become unstable.

It should be clear from this discussion that when the phase plot of a system does not cross -180 degrees, the system cannot become unstable at any gain. Therefore, systems for which (n–m) is 1 or 2 cannot become unstable. But systems for which (n–m)>2 do become unstable beyond some value of gain, K.

Two examples will now be presented.

Example 1: Consider a system with the open loop transfer function given by Eqn (9.39). In the standard format this transfer function takes on the form:

$$KG(s)H(s) = \left(\frac{K}{27}\right)\left(\frac{1}{s}\right)\left(\frac{3}{s+3}\right)\left(\frac{6}{s+6}\right)\left(\frac{s+8}{8}\right)\left(\frac{12}{s+12}\right) \tag{9.75}$$

The root locus plot for this system was shown in Figure 9.12. Its corresponding Bode plot is shown in Figure 9.19. Note that at the phase cross–over frequency the gain margin is 50 db. The

corresponding value of K is found from: $K = \text{invlog}_{10}\left(\frac{50}{20}\right) = 316.2$.

It is of interest to see what the answer would have been if the asymptotic Bode approximations would have been used in the prediction of the stable operating range of K for this system. To that end, consider the approximate Bode plot given in Figure 9.19.

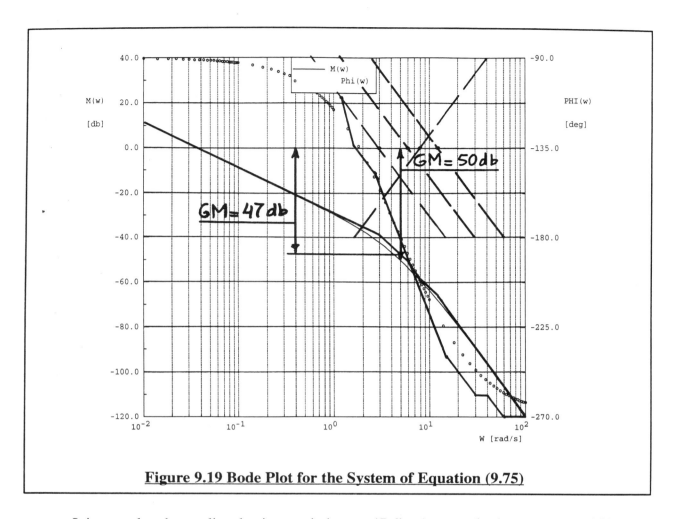

Figure 9.19 Bode Plot for the System of Equation (9.75)

It is seen that the predicted gain margin is now 47 db. As a result, the system would be predicted to become unstable for values of K found from: $K = \text{invlog}_{10}\left(\frac{47}{20}\right) = 223.9$. This would seem to be a significant error until it is realized that:

A) The break frequencies in real world systems are not known very accurately to begin with. In the case of the airplane, all break frequencies are the result of estimating stability derivatives and inertias, all of which are not accurately known.

B) Systems must operate at a reasonable gain and phase margin. Typical gain margins used in systems design are: 10 db and 45 degrees respectively.

The system under consideration has plenty of gain and phase margin either way.

Example 2: Consider a system with the open loop transfer function given by Eqn (9.69). In the standard format this transfer function takes on the form:

$$G(s)H(s) = K\left(\frac{2}{25}\right)\left(\frac{1}{s}\right)\left(\frac{2}{s+2}\right)\left(\frac{s+4}{4}\right)\left(\frac{25}{s^2+4s+25}\right) \qquad (9.76)$$

The root locus plot for this system was shown in Figure 9.17. Its corresponding Bode plot is shown in Figure 9.20. Note that at the phase cross–over frequency the gain margin is 36.4 db.

The corresponding value of K is found from: $K = invlog_{10}\left(\dfrac{36.4}{20}\right) \approx 66$.

Again, it is of interest to see what the answer would have been if the asymptotic Bode approximations would have been used in the prediction of the stable operating range of K for this system. To that end, consider the approximate Bode plot also given in Figure 9.20. It is seen, that the predicted gain margin is now 42 db. As a result, the system would be predicted to become unstable for

values of K found from: $K = invlog_{10}\left(\dfrac{42}{20}\right) = 125.8$. This error is larger than the one in the previous example. This is caused by the fact, that the quadratic in Eqn (9.76) has a damping ratio of 0.4. This results in a magnitude error of about 2 db. Add to this the error of about 2–3 db because of the first order break at 4 rad/sec and, as a result, the gain margin would be reduced to approximately 38 db which, for K yields: 79.4. That is a lot closer to the actual K=66.1.

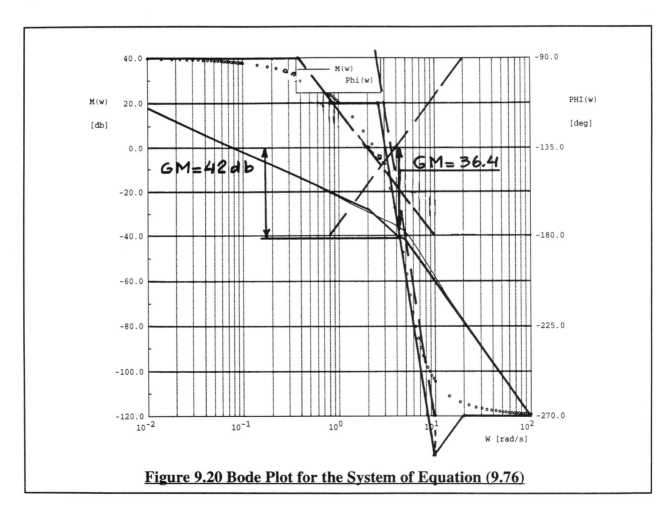

<u>Figure 9.20 Bode Plot for the System of Equation (9.76)</u>

9.5   CONNECTION BETWEEN THE FREQUENCY DOMAIN AND THE TIME DOMAIN

The root–locus method and the Bode–plot method are both frequency domain methods. Actual control systems operate in the time domain. It is desirable to learn to 'visualize' how closed loop system behavior in the frequency domain is related to the time domain behavior of such a system. The objective of this section is to provide some basic insights into the connection between pole–zero locations (specific points on the root–loci) in the s–domain and time domain response.

The connection between pole–zero locations in the s–domain and the corresponding time domain response of open and closed loop systems is illustrated in Tables 9.1 and 9.2 respectively.

Table 9.1 illustrates the following items for simple systems in open loop situations:

* open loop system transfer function

* pole–zero plot of the open loop system transfer function

* output Laplace transform for a unit step input

* output formula and output plot in the time domain

* application

Six different open loop transfer functions ranging from a differentiator and an integrator to more complicated transfer functions are listed in Table 9.1. The reader is encouraged to learn to visualize the time domain response which is associated with certain open loop pole configurations.

Table 9.2 illustrates the consequence of adding a feedback loop around an open loop system. Note that in the closed loop case all responses in the time domain become functions of the feedback gain, K. The (not–to–scale) example time domain responses in Tables 9.1 and 9.2 are labelled with numbers. These numbered responses will be discussed in the following. When reading the discussion, the reader should pay particular attention to the relationship between s–domain pole locations and time domain response behavior.

Response 1 of Table 9.1

Note that response number 1 in Table 1 is simply the unit impulse function.

Response 2 of Table 9.1

Response number 2 in Table 1 is the ramp function.

For the responses numbered 3 through 11, there is a corresponding, scaled time domain response plot in Figures 9.21 through 9.30. Note, that as a general rule, the farther a pole is away from the origin, the faster is the response. A discussion of these responses is given next.

Table 9.1 Connection between Frequency Domain and Time Domain for Open Loop Systems

Input $\frac{1}{s}$ → G(s) → Output C(s)

System Response to Step Inputs

OPEN LOOP	G(s)	Pole–Zero Plot	C(s)	Mathematical C(t)	Graphical C(t)	Application
1	s	zero at origin	1	Unit impulse at t=0		Differentiator
2	$\dfrac{1}{s}$	pole at origin	$\dfrac{1}{s^2}$	t		Integrator
3	$\dfrac{a}{(s+a)}$	pole at $-a$	$\dfrac{a}{s(s+a)}$	$1 - e^{-at}$		* Roll Rate Response * Actuator Response
4	$\dfrac{a}{s(s+a)}$	poles at 0, $-a$	$\dfrac{a}{s^2(s+a)}$	$\dfrac{1}{a}\left(e^{-at} + at - 1\right)$		Bank Angle Response
5	$\dfrac{ab}{(s+a)(s+b)}$	poles at $-a$, $-b$	$\dfrac{ab}{s(s+a)(s+b)}$	$1 + \dfrac{ab}{a-b}\left(\dfrac{1}{a}e^{-at} + -\left(\dfrac{1}{b}e^{-bt}\right)\right)$		Altitude response at constant speed
6	$\dfrac{ab}{s(s+a)(s+b)}$	poles at 0, $-a$, $-b$	$\dfrac{ab}{s^2(s+a)(s+b)}$	$t - \dfrac{1}{a} - \dfrac{1}{b} - \dfrac{ab}{a-b} \times\left(\dfrac{1}{b^2}e^{-bt} - \dfrac{1}{a^2}e^{-at}\right)$		Open loop bank angle response with servo

Table 9.2 Connection between Frequency Domain and Time Domain for Closed Loop Systems

System Response to Step Inputs

Block diagram: Input $1/s$ → $+$ ⊗ $-$ → $G(s)$ → Output $C(s) = (1/s)W(s)$

CLOSED LOOP (unity negative feedback) $W(s)$	Pole–Zero Plot	$C(s)$	Mathematical $C(t)$	Graphical $C(t)$	Application
(7) $\dfrac{Ks}{1+Ks}$	zero at origin, pole at $-1/K$ ($+j\omega$ / $+\sigma$)	$\dfrac{K}{1+Ks}$	$e^{-t/K}$	$C(t)$, 1.0 down to 0, K	Washout
(8) $\dfrac{K}{s+K}$	pole at $-K$ ($+j\omega$ / $+\sigma$)	$\dfrac{K}{s(s+K)}$	$1 - e^{-Kt}$	$C(t)$, 1.0, rising to K	Rate command
(9) $\dfrac{Ka}{s+a(1+K)}$	pole at $-a(1+K)$ ($+j\omega$ / $+\sigma$)	$\dfrac{Ka}{s[s+a(1+K)]}$	$\dfrac{K}{1+K}\left(1 - e^{-a(1+K)t}\right)$	$C(t)$, $K/(1+K)$, rising to K	Rate command with variable final value
(10) $\dfrac{Ka}{s^2+sa+Ka}$	complex poles near $-a$, arrows K ($+j\omega$ / $+\sigma$)	$\dfrac{Ka}{s(s^2+sa+Ka)}$	$1 + \left[\dfrac{1}{\sqrt{1-\zeta^2}}\,e^{-\zeta\omega_1 t}\right] \times$ $\sin\left\{\left(\omega_1\sqrt{1-\zeta^2}\,t\right) - \psi\right\}$	$C(t)$, 1.0, oscillating to K	Pure gain wing leveler $\omega_1^2 = Ka$ $2\zeta\omega_1 = a$ $\psi = \arctan\dfrac{\sqrt{1-\zeta^2}}{-\zeta}$
(11) $\dfrac{Kab}{\{s^2+s(a+b)+ab(1+K)\}}$	poles ($+j\omega$ / $+\sigma$), arrow K	$\dfrac{Kab}{s\{s^2+s(a+b)+ab(1+K)\}}$	as above, but: $\omega_1^2 = ab(1+K)$ $2\zeta\omega_1 = a + b$	As above, but: instead of 1.0, final value is: $K/(1+K)$	Roll damper
(12) $\dfrac{Kab}{\{s(s+a)(s+b)+Kab\}}$	poles at $-a$, $-b$ ($+j\omega$ / $+\sigma$)	$\dfrac{Kab}{s\{s(s+a)(s+b)+Kab\}}$	No explicit formula given	$C(t)$, Strong dependence on K	Wing leveler with servo in the loop

Response 3 of Table 9.1

As shown in Figure 9.21, as the open loop system pole at s=−a moves further away to the left from the origin (larger 'a') the responses become more rapid. That this should be the case is obvious by inspection of the corresponding C(t) in Table 9.1.

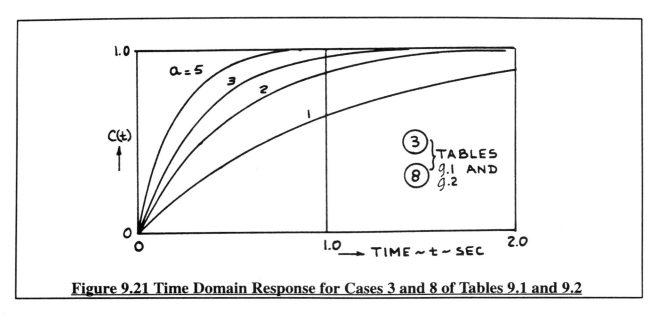

Figure 9.21 Time Domain Response for Cases 3 and 8 of Tables 9.1 and 9.2

Response 4 of Table 9.1

As shown in Figure 9.22, the observation made for Response 3 also applies here.

Response 5 of Table 9.1

Figure 9.23 indicates that for a given pole position at −b, the farther the pole at −a moves to the left, the faster the response. However, it should be observed that as 'a' grows toward infinity, the response becomes dominated by the pole location at −b.

Response 6 of Table 9.1

As shown in Figure 9.24, the observation made for Response 5 also applies here.

Response 7 of Table 9.2

It is seen from Figure 9.25 that as K is increased (i.e. the pole moves closer to the origin) the time−domain response slows down.

Response 8 of Table 9.2

It is noted that this case is similar to Response 3.

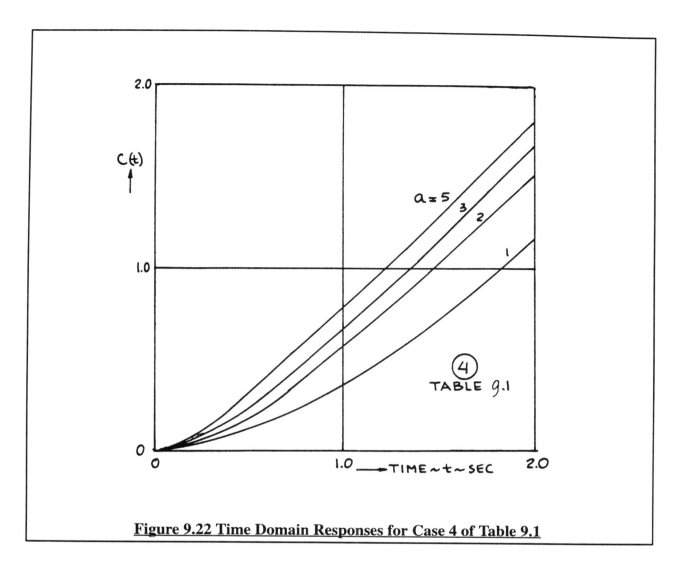

Figure 9.22 Time Domain Responses for Case 4 of Table 9.1

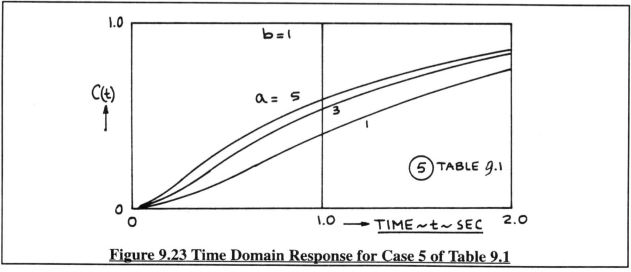

Figure 9.23 Time Domain Response for Case 5 of Table 9.1

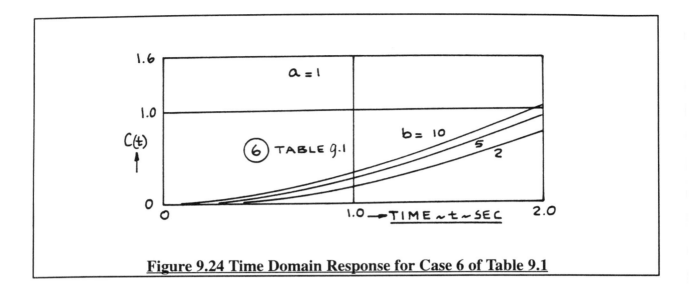

Figure 9.24 Time Domain Response for Case 6 of Table 9.1

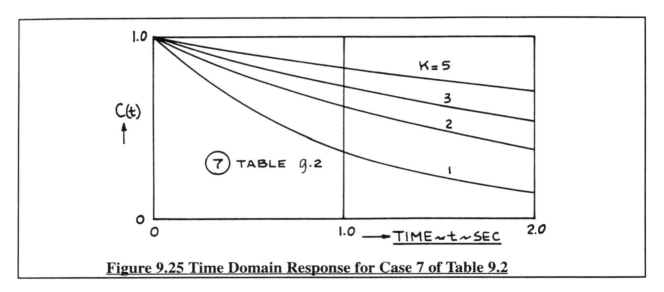

Figure 9.25 Time Domain Response for Case 7 of Table 9.2

Response 9 of Table 9.2

Figure 9.26 indicates the fact that for a given value of 'a', as K increases, so does the rapidity of the response. Note that at the same time the magnitude of the final response also increases with increasing K.

Response 10 of Table 9.2

Figure 9.27 indicates the fact that for a given value of 'a', the system exhibits more oscillatory overshoots (less damping) as K increases. Also, as K increases, the frequency of the oscillation increases. For a given value of K, the oscillatory overshoots increase for lower 'a'. The frequency of oscillation decreases with decreasing value of 'a'.

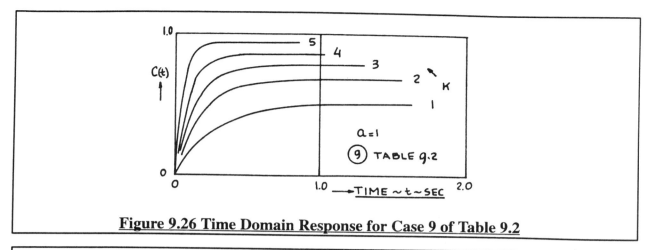

Figure 9.26 Time Domain Response for Case 9 of Table 9.2

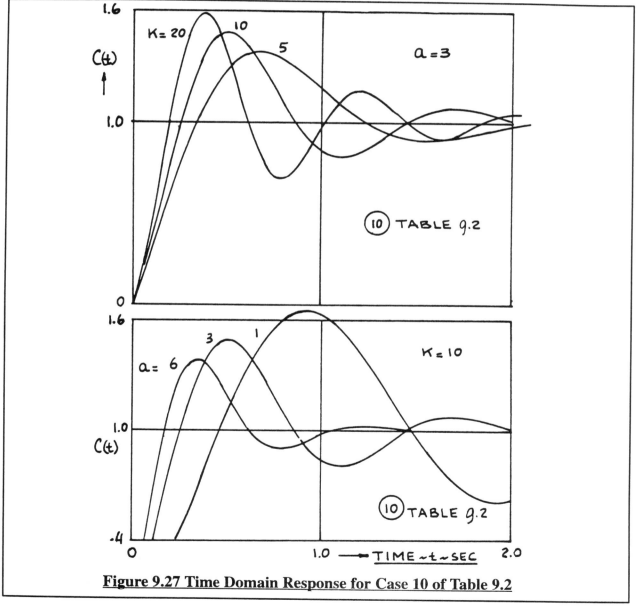

Figure 9.27 Time Domain Response for Case 10 of Table 9.2

Response 11 of Table 9.2

Figure 9.28 indicates that for a given value of 'a' and 'b' the system becomes more oscillatory (less damped) when K increases. Also, for a given combination of 'a' and K, as 'b' decreases, the system shows an increase in oscillatory overshoots.

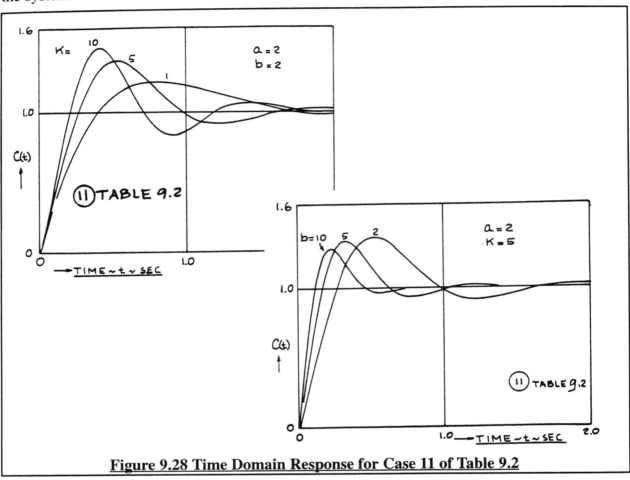

Figure 9.28 Time Domain Response for Case 11 of Table 9.2

The connection between pole–zero locations in the s–domain for systems with second order open loop poles will be made by examining the following output transfer function:

$$C(s) = K\omega_n^2 \left\{ \frac{(1 + as)}{s(s^2 + 2\zeta\omega_n s + \omega_n^2)} \right\} \tag{9.77}$$

Note that this output differs from the output pictured in Figure 5.8 (Part I) because of the zero at $-1/a$. Figure 9.29 shows the pole–zero locations of the output defined by Eqn (9.77). The reader is reminded of the fact that large undamped natural frequency, ω_n, means large pole distance from the origin. The corresponding time–domain responses are shown in Figure 9.30. Note that for given values of "a", K and damping ratio, ζ, the overshoot of the response depends strongly on the undamped natural frequency, ω_n. The effect of varying the zero location at $-1/a$ is illustrated in Figure 9.31 for the case of zero damping ratio, ζ. Observe, that as the zero is moved from negative infinity (a=0) to close to the origin (a=2) the response exhibits larger overshoots. For a given value of "a", the same statement applies to increase in the undamped natural frequency, ω_n.

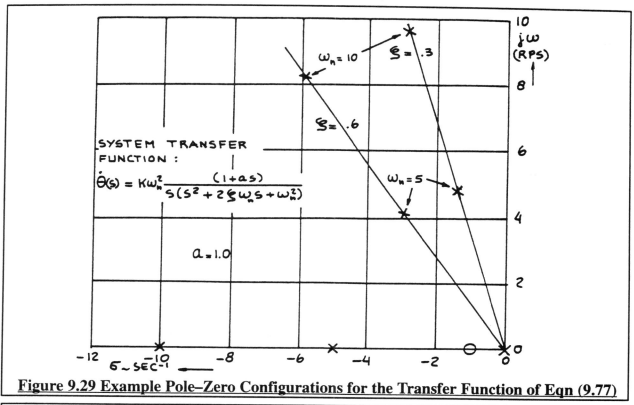

Figure 9.29 Example Pole–Zero Configurations for the Transfer Function of Eqn (9.77)

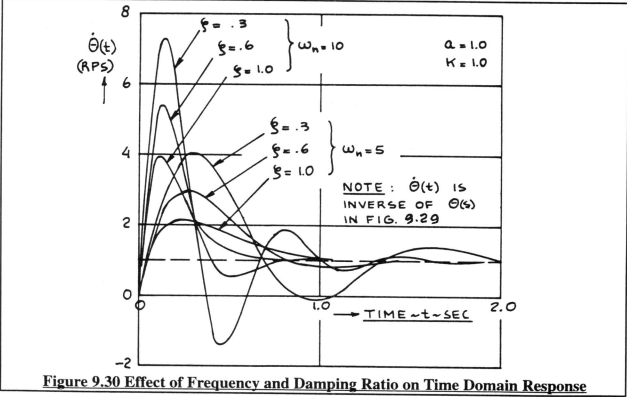

Figure 9.30 Effect of Frequency and Damping Ratio on Time Domain Response

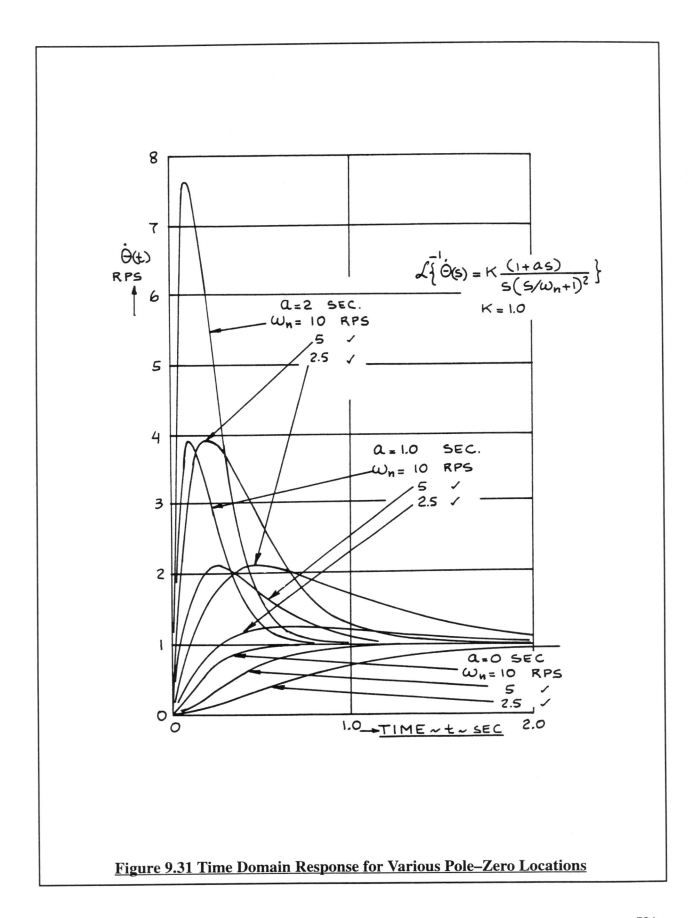

Figure 9.31 Time Domain Response for Various Pole–Zero Locations

9.6   SYSTEM PERFORMANCE SPECIFICATIONS

Three types of system performance specifications will be considered:

9.6.1 Frequency domain specifications

9.6.2 Time domain specifications

9.6.3 Error specifications

The role played by these three types of system performance specifications will be discussed. In addition, the sensitivity of systems to changes in some system parameter are of interest in systems design. A general definition of system sensitivity to changes in an arbitrary parameter is given in Sub–section 9.6.4.

9.6.1   FREQUENCY DOMAIN SPECIFICATIONS

Frequency domain specifications can be cast in the following forms:

1) Specifications of frequencies, damping ratios and/or time constants.

2) Specifications of Bode plot characteristics.

1) Specifications of frequencies, damping ratios and/or time constants were already encountered in the case of the open loop flying quality specifications discussed in Chapter 6 of Part I. For closed loop systems such specifications are also used in terms of the so–called 'equivalent system' characteristics. In such cases, the location of closed loop system poles (at some level of system gain) are restricted by specifying the implied levels of frequencies, damping ratios and/or time constants.

2) For Bode plot specifications the reader should refer to Figures 9.32 through 9.34.

Typically, the following quantities are specified:

a) Gain Margin   b) Phase Margin   c) Delay Time

d) Bandwidth   e) Cutoff Rate   f) Resonance Peak

g) Resonance Frequency

These specifications will be discussed using Figures 9.32 through 9.34.

a) Gain Margin

See Figure 9.32 for a graphical interpretation of gain margin. The gain margin of a system is defined as the magnitude of the constant K by which the magnitude of $GH(j\omega_{pcf})$ must be shifted up to obtain the following conditions:

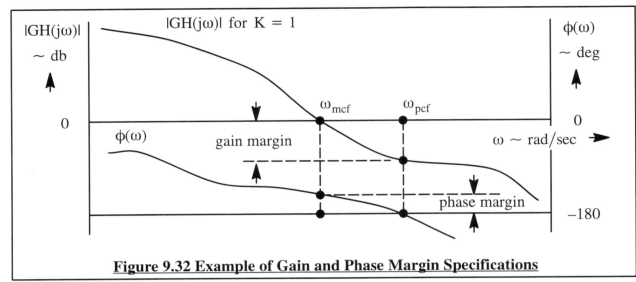

Figure 9.32 Example of Gain and Phase Margin Specifications

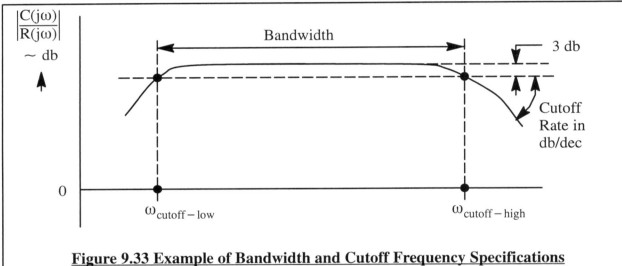

Figure 9.33 Example of Bandwidth and Cutoff Frequency Specifications

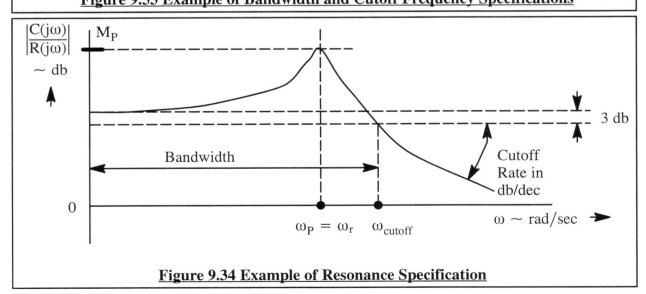

Figure 9.34 Example of Resonance Specification

$$\left|KGH(j\omega_{pcf})\right| = 0 \text{ db} \qquad \text{with} \qquad \angle\, GH(j\omega_{pcf}) = -180^0 \tag{9.78}$$

The phase–cross–over–frequency, ω_{pcf}, is the frequency at which the phase angle of $GH(j\omega)$ first crosses the -180 degrees line.

As a general rule, the higher the gain margin, the better is the relative stability of a system. For many systems, a de–facto gain margin of a factor of 3 is adequate to prevent annoying oscillatory overshoots. A factor 3 gain margin amounts to roughly 9.5 db on the Bode plot.

b) Phase Margin

See Figure 9.32 for a graphical interpretation of phase margin. The phase margin of a system is defined as 180 degrees plus the phase angle of the open loop transfer function at unity gain. In other words:

$$\phi_{PM} = 180^0 + \angle\, GH(j\omega_{mcf}) \tag{9.79}$$

where: $\left|GH(j\omega_{mcf})\right| = 1$ or 0 db

ω_{mcf} is the magnitude cross–over frequency

As a general rule, the greater the phase margin, the better is the relative stability of the system. In many systems a good rule of thumb is to accept only phase margins which are larger than 35 degrees.

c) Delay Time

The delay time of a system is defined as follows:

$$T_{delay}(\omega) = -\frac{d\angle\left(\dfrac{C(j\omega)}{R(j\omega)}\right)}{d\omega} \tag{9.80}$$

This slope can be viewed as the increase of phase lag with frequency over a certain frequency range. Observe, that the units of this expression are indeed time in seconds because the frequency, ω is given in rad/sec. In many systems the average value of $T_d(\omega)$ is specified over a range of frequencies. As a general rule, the shorter the delay time, $T_d(\omega)$, the faster the response of the system to an input (command) signal. There is an alternate definition for delay time in the time–domain. That definition is given under in Sub–section 9.6.2.

d) Bandwidth

The bandwidth of a system is defined as that range of frequencies (between the so–called cut–off frequencies) over which the system responds satisfactorily. A 'flat' frequency response implies that the magnitude of the output to input amplitude ratio is constant over the bandwidth. See Figure 9.33 for a graphical interpretation.

e) Cutoff Rate

The cutoff rate of a system is defined as the drop in magnitude with frequency (in db/decade) beyond the cutoff frequency of a system. Figure 9.33 provides a graphical interpretation. In many systems a typical cutoff rate is less than 10 db/decade. In many airplane system applications it is found necessary to include filters. The purpose of filters is to prevent high frequency signals from passing through the system. This can be important in the case of acceleration or rate sensors which are located close to a vibration source (gun or engine). In the case of filters a minimum acceptable cutoff rate would be specified.

f) Resonance Peak

The resonance peak, M_P of a system is defined as the maximum value of the magnitude of the closed loop system response. Using the symbology of Figure 9.34 it is seen that:

$$M_P = \max \left| \frac{C(j\omega)}{R(j\omega)} \right| \qquad (9.81)$$

The reader should review the discussion of Example 3) in Chapter 8 (page 643). The magnitude of the resonance peak is a measure of relative system stability: large peaks imply large oscillatory overshoots. As a general rule as long as M_P is between 1 and 1.7 db the time–domain performance of a system will be acceptable.

g) Resonance Frequency

The resonance frequency of a system, ω_P or ω_r is that frequency at which the peak of the magnitude response, M_P, occurs. The reader should review the discussion of Example 3) which is presented in Chapter 8 (page 643).

9.6.2   TIME DOMAIN SPECIFICATIONS

System time domain specifications are normally given in terms of the response of the system to a unit step input, a ramp input and (or) a parabolic input. As discussed in Chapter 8, system response can be split into two components: the transient response and the steady state response.

The steady state response of systems is defined mostly in terms of some allowable steady state error which is a measure of the accuracy of the system output for a given input. These errors are often specified in terms of the so–called error–constants discussed in Sub–section 9.6.3.

The transient response of a system is often described in terms of the response to a unit step input. The reader should refer to Figure 9.35 for a graphical interpretation of the following specifications:

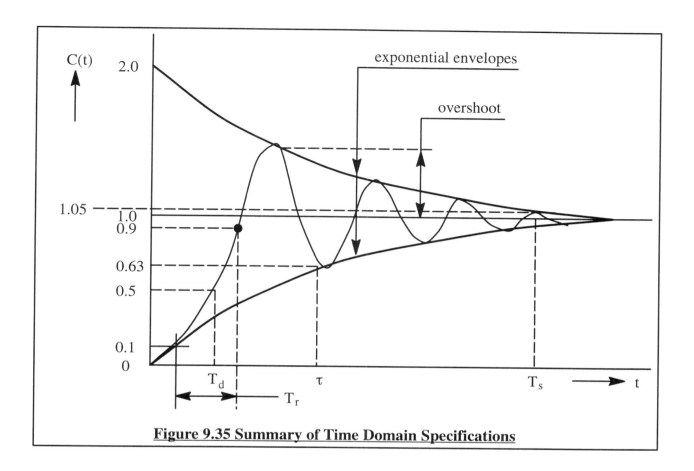

Figure 9.35 Summary of Time Domain Specifications

a) Overshoot   b) Delay Time   c) Rise Time

d) Apparent Time Constant   e) Settling Time

a) Overshoot

The overshoot of a system is defined as the maximum difference between the transient response and the steady state response of a system to a unit step input. Overshoot should be seen as a measure of relative system stability. It is frequently specified as an allowable percentage of the steady state output.

b) Delay Time

The delay time, T_d, of a system is the time required for the output response to reach 50% of its final (i.e. steady state) value. It is to be noted that overshoot and delay time are both measures for the 'rapidity' of the response of a system.

c) Rise Time

The rise time of a system is the time required for the response to rise from 10% to 90% of its final (i.e. steady state) value.

d) Apparent Time Constant

The apparent time constant, τ, of a system is the time it takes for the envelope of the transient response to decay to 37% of its final (i.e. steady state) value. For a stable (but under–damped) system, the time domain solutions typically contain the following terms:

$$Ae^{-\alpha t} \text{ for first order system components} \tag{9.82}$$

$$Ae^{-\alpha t}\cos(\omega t + \theta) \text{ for second order system components} \tag{9.83}$$

In such situations the apparent time constant, τ, is defined as the time it takes for the exponent, $-\alpha t$ to reach the value -1 or:

$$\tau = \frac{1}{\alpha} \tag{9.84}$$

e) Settling Time

The settling time, T_s, is the time required for the response to reach and remain within a specified percentage (2% and 5% are often used) of its final value.

Note: both the time constant and the settling times are measures for the rapidity of the response as well as for the relative stability of a system.

9.6.3 ERROR AND ERROR–CONSTANT SPECIFICATIONS

Before introducing the definition and meaning of several error specifications it is useful to recall that the open loop transfer function of a feedback system, according to Eqn (9.26), can be written as:

$$KG(s)H(s) = \frac{K \prod_{i=1}^{i=m} (s + Z_i)}{\prod_{j=1}^{j=n} (s + P_j)} \tag{9.85}$$

where: K is a constant

m and n are real positive integers with m<n or m=n

P_j and Z_i are the finite poles and zeros of the system

It will be tacitly assumed that all finite poles of the system are stable.

It is possible that some of the finite poles and zeros are located at the origin. Assume that "a" zeros and "b" poles are located at the origin. Now define:

$$l = b - a \tag{9.86}$$

Therefore, if the system has a zeros and b poles located at the origin, Eqn (9.85) can be written as:

$$KG(s)H(s) = \frac{Ks^a\left\{\prod_{i=1}^{i=m-a}(s + Z_i)\right\}}{s^b\left\{\prod_{j=1}^{j=n-b}(s + P_j)\right\}} \qquad \text{with}: \quad (b - a) = 1 \qquad (9.87)$$

The following definition will be used in the error specifications of this Sub–section:

Definition:

> A control system with open loop transfer function given by Eqn (9.87) is called a type 1 system

In the following, the error characteristics of two types of system will be discussed:

9.6.3.1 Error characteristics of unity negative feedback systems

9.6.3.2 Error characteristics of general systems

9.6.3.1 Error Characteristics of Unity Negative Feedback Systems

The following three errors and associated error constants are often used in the judgement of the effectiveness of a control system:

a) position error and position error constant

b) velocity error and velocity error constant

c) acceleration error and acceleration error constant

These will now be discussed.

a) position error and position error constant

The steady state position error, $\varepsilon(\infty)$, for a stable, unity negative system **subject to a unit step input**, is defined by:

$$\varepsilon(\infty) = 1 - C(\infty) \qquad (9.88)$$

where: $C(\infty)$ is the system output for t=∞

It will be shown that this position error is related to its position error constant, K_P. This position error constant is defined as:

Definition:

> The position (step) error, K_P, of a stable, unity negative feedback system of type l is defined as:
>
> $$K_P = \lim_{s \to 0} G(s) = \lim_{s \to o} \frac{K\left\{\prod_{i=1}^{i=m-a}(s + Z_i)\right\}}{s^l\left\{\prod_{j=1}^{j=n-b}(s + P_j)\right\}} = \frac{K\left\{\prod_{i=1}^{i=m-a}(s + Z_i)\right\}}{\left\{\prod_{j=1}^{j=n-b}(s + P_j)\right\}} \quad \text{when } l = 0 \quad (9.89)$$
>
> $$= \infty \quad \text{when} \quad l > 0$$

In general, the error of the system at any time, t can be written as:

$$\varepsilon(t) = 1 - C(t) \tag{9.90}$$

In the s–domain this becomes:

$$\varepsilon(s) = \frac{1}{s} - C(s) \tag{9.91}$$

With the help of Eqn (9.31), for a unity negative feedback system it follows that:

$$C(s) = \frac{1}{s}\left[\frac{G(s)}{\{1 + G(s)\}}\right] \tag{9.92}$$

Note, that the gain constant, K, is included in G(s) as defined by Eqn (9.89). Substitution into Eqn (9.91) yields:

$$\varepsilon(s) = \frac{1}{s\{1 + G(s)\}} \tag{9.93}$$

Application of the final value theorem now yields:

$$\varepsilon(t = \infty) = \lim_{s \to 0} s\varepsilon(s) = \lim_{s \to 0}\left\{\frac{1}{\{1 + G(s)\}}\right\} = \frac{1}{1 + K_P} \tag{9.94}$$

It is seen from the definition of position error, K_P, that for type 1 and above systems the position error will be zero.

b) velocity error and velocity error constant

The steady state error, $\varepsilon(\infty)$, for a stable, unity negative system subject to a unit ramp input, is defined by:

$$\varepsilon(\infty) = t - C(\infty) \tag{9.95}$$

where: $C(\infty)$ is the system output for t=∞

It will be shown that this position error is related to its velocity error constant, K_V. This velocity error constant is defined as:

Definition:

The velocity (ramp) error, K_V of a stable, unity negative feedback system of type l is defined as:

$$= 0 \quad \text{when} \quad l = 0$$

$$K_V = \lim_{s \to 0} sG(s) = \lim_{s \to o} \frac{K\left\{ \prod_{i=1}^{i=m-a} (s + Z_i) \right\}}{s^{l-1}\left\{ \prod_{j=1}^{j=n-b} (s + P_j) \right\}} = \frac{K\left\{ \prod_{i=1}^{i=m-a} (s + Z_i) \right\}}{\left\{ \prod_{j=1}^{j=n-b} (s + P_j) \right\}} \quad \text{when} \quad l = 1 \quad (9.96)$$

$$= \infty \quad \text{when} \quad l > 1$$

The steady state error, in the s–domain can be expressed as:

$$\varepsilon(s) = \frac{1}{s^2} - C(s) \tag{9.97}$$

The output C(s) using the unit ramp input is:

$$C(s) = \frac{1}{s^2}\left[\frac{G(s)}{\{1 + G(s)\}} \right] \tag{9.98}$$

The error, also in the s–domain is now:

$$\varepsilon(s) = \frac{1}{s^2}\left[\frac{1}{\{1 + G(s)\}} \right] \tag{9.99}$$

With the final value theorem it is found that:

$$\varepsilon(t = \infty) = \lim_{s \to 0} s\varepsilon(s) = \lim_{s \to 0}\left\{ \frac{1}{(s + sG(s))} \right\} = \frac{1}{K_V} \tag{9.100}$$

c) acceleration error and acceleration error constant

The steady state error, $\varepsilon(\infty)$, for a stable, unity negative system subject to a unit parabolic input, is defined by:

$$\varepsilon(\infty) = \frac{1}{2}t^2 - C(\infty) \tag{9.101}$$

where: $C(\infty)$ is the system output for $t = \infty$

It will be shown that this position error is related to its acceleration error constant, K_A. This velocity error constant is defined as:

Definition:

The acceleration (parabolic) error, K_A, of a stable, unity negative feedback system of type l is defined as:

$$= 0 \quad \text{when} \quad l = 0 \text{ or } l = 1$$

$$K_A = \lim_{s \to 0} s^2 G(s) = \lim_{s \to 0} \frac{K \left\{ \prod_{i=1}^{i=m-a} (s + Z_i) \right\}}{s^{l-2} \left\{ \prod_{j=1}^{j=n-b} (s + P_j) \right\}} = \frac{K \left\{ \prod_{i=1}^{i=m-a} (s + Z_i) \right\}}{\left\{ \prod_{j=1}^{j=n-b} (s + P_j) \right\}} \quad \text{when } l = 2$$

$$= \infty \quad \text{when} \quad l > 2$$

(9.102)

The reader is asked to show that steady state error, in the s–domain can be expressed as:

$$\varepsilon(s) = \frac{1}{s^3} \left\{ \frac{1}{\{1 + G(s)\}} \right\}$$

(9.103)

With the final value theorem it is found that:

$$\varepsilon(t = \infty) = \lim_{s \to 0} s\varepsilon(s) = \lim_{s \to 0} \left\{ \frac{1}{\{s^2 + s^2 G(s)\}} \right\} = \frac{1}{K_A}$$

(9.104)

A summary of the error characteristics of a unity negative feedback system for these three types of input signals is given in Table 9.3.

9.6.3.2 Error Characteristics of General Systems

The error constants which were defined in Sub–section 9.6.3.1 apply only to stable, negative unity feedback systems. Their definitions can be easily extended to more general (but still stable) systems. This is done by comparing the output of the actual system to that of an ideal system.

Figure 9.36 shows how the error of a more general system is defined by comparing the output of that more general system, $C(s)$ with the output of some ideal system which has the transfer function $I(s)$. For the case of Figure 9.36 the three error constants are defined in the following.

Input	Unit Step		Unit Ramp		Unit Parabola	
	$R(t)$ $R(t) = 1.0$ 1.0 0 t $s - domian \ 1/s$		$R(t)$ $R(t) = t$ 1.0 0 1.0 t $s - domian \ 1/s^2$		$R(t)$ $R(t) = t^2/2$ 2.0 0 2.0 t $s - domian \ 1/s^3$	
Error and error constant System Type	K_P	Steady state error	K_V	Steady state error	K_A	Steady state error
Type 0	$K \dfrac{\left\{ \prod\limits_{i=1}^{i=m-a} (s + Z_i) \right\}}{\left\{ \prod\limits_{j=1}^{j=n-b} (s + P_j) \right\}}$	$\dfrac{1}{1 + K_P}$	0	∞	0	∞
Type 1	∞	0	$K \dfrac{\left\{ \prod\limits_{i=1}^{i=m-a} (s + Z_i) \right\}}{\left\{ \prod\limits_{j=1}^{j=n-b} (s + P_j) \right\}}$	$\dfrac{1}{K_V}$	0	∞
Type 2	∞	0	∞	0	$K \dfrac{\left\{ \prod\limits_{i=1}^{i=m-a} (s + Z_i) \right\}}{\left\{ \prod\limits_{j=1}^{j=n-b} (s + P_j) \right\}}$	$\dfrac{1}{K_A}$

Table 9.3   **Summary of Error Behavior of a Unity Negative Feedback System to Three Types of Unit Inputs**

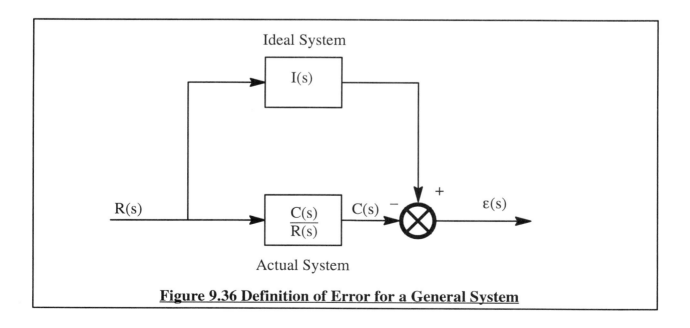

Figure 9.36 Definition of Error for a General System

Definition:

> The position error constant, K_s, of a stable feedback system is defined as:
>
> $$K_s = \frac{1}{\lim_{s \to 0}\left\{ I(s) - \frac{C(s)}{R(s)} \right\}}$$

(9.105)

The reader is asked to show that the steady state error for the general system for a unit step input is related to this step error constant by:

$$\varepsilon(\infty) = \lim_{t \to \infty} \varepsilon(t) = \frac{1}{K_s}$$

(9.106)

Definition:

> The ramp error constant, K_r, of a stable feedback system is defined as:
>
> $$K_r = \frac{1}{\lim_{s \to 0}\frac{1}{s}\left\{ I(s) - \frac{C(s)}{R(s)} \right\}}$$

(9.107)

The reader is asked to show that the steady state error for the general system for a unit step input is related to this ramp error constant by:

$$\varepsilon(\infty) = \lim_{t \to \infty} \varepsilon(t) = \frac{1}{K_r}$$

(9.108)

Definition:

> The parabolic error constant, K_p, of a stable feedback system is defined as:
>
> $$K_p = \frac{1}{\lim_{s \to 0}\frac{1}{s^2}\left\{ I(s) - \frac{C(s)}{R(s)} \right\}}$$

(9.109)

The reader is asked to show that the steady state error for the general system for a unit step input is related to this parabolic error constant by:

$$\varepsilon(\infty) = \lim_{t \to \infty} \varepsilon(t) = \frac{1}{K_p}$$

(9.110)

9.6.4 SYSTEM SENSITIVITY

It has been noted on several occasions that the locations of open loop system poles and zeros of airplanes are not precisely known. In many cases an accuracy greater than +/– (10% to 15%) should not be expected. The same statement can be made relative to pole–zero locations of various system components in an airplane. For that reason it is of interest to be able to determine what the sensitivity is of any system to an arbitrary change in some system parameter.

Consider a system with the transfer function G(s). In general, such a system can be considered to be a complex number at some frequency vale of s=jω. When written in polar form:

$$G(s) = | G(s) | e^{j\phi} \qquad (9.111)$$

Assume that k is a parameter inside G(s). The following sensitivity definition can be used to evaluate how sensitive the system is to a change in the parameter k:

Definition:

The sensitivity of G(s) to a change in a parameter k is:

$$S_k^{G(s)} = \frac{d\ \ln\{G(k)\}}{d\ \ln\ k} = \frac{\frac{1}{G(s)}dG(s)}{\frac{1}{k}\ln\ k} = \frac{k}{G(s)}\left\{\frac{dG(k)}{dk}\right\} \qquad (9.112)$$

Definition:

The sensitivity of the magnitude of G(s) to a change in a parameter k is:

$$S_k^{|G(s)|} = \frac{d\ \ln\{G(k)\}}{d\ \ln\ k} = \frac{\frac{d|G(k)|}{|G(k)|}}{\frac{dk}{k}} = \frac{k}{|G(k)|}\left\{\frac{d|G(k)|}{dk}\right\} \qquad (9.113)$$

Definition:

The sensitivity of the phase angle, ϕ of G(s) to a change in a parameter k is:

$$S_k^{\phi} = \frac{d\ \ln\ \phi}{d\ \ln\ k} = \frac{\frac{d\phi}{\phi}}{\frac{dk}{k}} = \frac{k}{\phi}\frac{d\phi}{dk} \qquad (9.114)$$

The greater these sensitivities, the greater care must be taken to assure that production articles of airplane plus system will behave as intended.

9.7   SOME FEEDBACK CONTROL SYSTEM DESIGN APPLICATIONS

The following examples will be discussed:

9.7.1 A multiple feedback loop system: pole assignment
9.7.2 Setting system gain to achieve a specified damping ratio
9.7.3 Setting gain to achieve a specified gain margin and position error constant
9.7.4 Finding a lag compensator to alter the breakaway angle from complex poles
9.7.5 Finding a lead–lag compensator to increase system gain margin
9.7.6 Using cancellation compensation to achieve better closed loop characteristics
9.7.7 Root contours for variable poles
9.7.8 Root contours for variable zeros

9.7.1   A MULTIPLE FEEDBACK LOOP SYSTEM: POLE ASSIGNMENT

It will be shown in Chapter 11 that many situations arise where more than one type of feedback is required. For example, it will be shown that in the design of pitch attitude control loops for autopilots of high performance airplanes it will be necessary to feedback not only pitch attitude angle but also pitch rate. Such a situation calls for a multiple loop system. Figure 9.37 shows an example of a double loop feedback system.

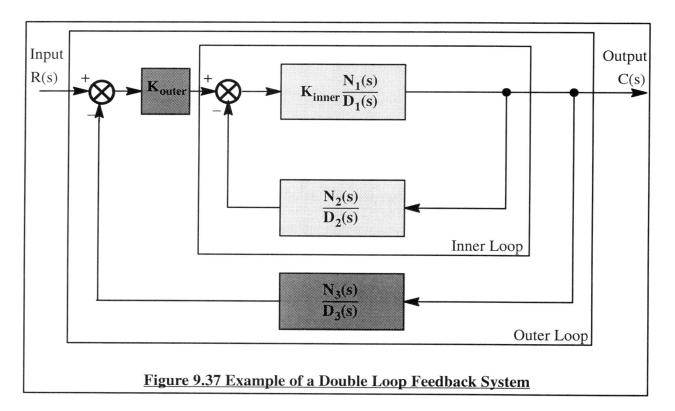

Figure 9.37 Example of a Double Loop Feedback System

Note, that the system loops are labelled "inner loop" and "outer loop" respectively. The reader is asked to verify that the closed loop transfer function of the inner loop is:

$$W(s)_{inner\ loop} = \frac{K_{inner}\left\{\dfrac{N_1(s)}{D_1(s)}\right\}}{1 + K_{inner}\left\{\dfrac{N_1(s)N_2(s)}{D_1(s)D_2(s)}\right\}} \tag{9.115}$$

This can also be written as:

$$W(s)_{inner\ loop} = \frac{K_{inner}N_1(s)D_2(s)}{D_1(s)D_2(s) + K_{inner}N_1(s)N_2(s)} \tag{9.116}$$

Clearly, the characteristic equation for the closed, inner loop is:

$$D_1(s)D_2(s) + K_{inner}N_1(s)N_2(s) = 0 \tag{9.117}$$

The reader is asked to compare this with Eqn (9.28) and conclude how the closed, inner loop poles move when K_{inner} is varied from 0 to ∞. If $K_{inner} = K_1$ is selected for the inner loop, the roots of the inner loop characteristic equation are determined from:

$$D_1(s)D_2(s) + K_1N_1(s)N_2(s) = 0 \tag{9.118}$$

When the outer loop is wrapped around the inner loop, with $K_{inner} = K_1$, the closed loop transfer function of the outer loop is given by:

$$W(s)_{outer\ loop} = \frac{C(s)}{R(s)} = \frac{K_{outer}\left\{\dfrac{K_1N_1(s)D_2(s)}{D_1(s)D_2(s) + K_1N_1(s)N_2(s)}\right\}}{1 + K_{outer}\left\{\dfrac{K_1N_1(s)D_2(s)}{D_1(s)D_2(s) + K_1N_1(s)N_2(s)}\right\}\left\{\dfrac{N_3(s)}{D_3(s)}\right\}} \tag{9.119}$$

This can be cleaned up somewhat, resulting in:

$$W(s)_{outer\ loop} = \frac{K_{outer}K_1N_1(s)D_2(s)D_3(s)}{\{D_1(s)D_2(s) + K_1N_1(s)N_2(s)\}D_3(s) + K_{outer}K_1N_1(s)D_2(s)N_3(s)} \tag{9.120}$$

Clearly, the characteristic equation for the closed, outer loop is:

$$\{D_1(s)D_2(s) + K_1N_1(s)N_2(s)\}D_3(s) + K_{outer}K_1N_1(s)D_2(s)N_3(s) = 0 \tag{9.121}$$

The roots of this equation are the closed, outer loop poles. These closed, outer loop poles behave in the following manner:

1) When $K_{outer} = 0$ the closed, outer loop poles start at the roots of:

$$D_1(s)D_2(s) + K_1N_1(s)N_2(s) = 0 \tag{9.122a}$$

and:

$$D_3(s) = 0 \tag{9.122b}$$

In other words, for $K_{outer} = 0$ the outer loop poles start at the open loop poles of the outer loop feedback path and at the closed loop poles of the inner loop at $K_{inner} = K_1$. The poles defined by Ens (9.121) are referred to as the outer loop departure poles.

2) When $K_{outer} = \infty$ the closed, outer loop poles end at the roots of:

$$K_{outer}K_1N_1(s)D_2(s)N_3(s) = 0 \tag{9.123}$$

In other words, for $K_{outer} = \infty$ the outer loop poles end at the zeros of the forward path of the inner loop, at the poles of the feedback path of the inner loop and at the zeros of the feedback path of the outer loop.

Because the polynomial order of Eqn (9.121) can be substantial, solving root locus problems for multiple loop systems is normally done with a computer program. The AAA program of Appendix A (Part I) can be used to do this.

Next, consider a simple numerical example of a double loop system. Figure 9.38 shows the computational block diagram of such a system.

The open loop pole configuration of the basic system of Figure 9.38 is shown in Figure 9.39a. Note the undamped natural frequency and damping ratio of the basic system. It is now assumed that the undamped natural frequency of 10 rad/sec and the damping ratio of 0.10 of the basic system are unsatisfactory. It is further assumed that it is required to improve the undamped natural frequency to a level of 14 rad/sec and the damping ratio to a level of 0.357. This is to be achieved with a rate feedback loop (inner loop in Figure 9.38) and a position feedback loop (outer loop in Figure 9.38). The resulting system is also called the augmented system. It will be shown in Chapter 11 that this type of system is similar to an airplane with both angle of attack and pitch rate feedback.

The closed loop transfer function of the inner loop of the system of Figure 9.38 is:

$$W_1(s) = \frac{K_1 sG(s)}{1 + K_1 sG(s)} \tag{9.124}$$

where:

$$G(s) = \frac{100}{s^2 + 2s + 100} \tag{9.125}$$

The characteristic equation for the inner loop is:

$$s^2 + s(2 + 100K_1) + 100 = 0 \tag{9.126}$$

The closed loop transfer function of the outer loop of the system of Figure 9.38 is:

$$W_2(s) = \frac{K_2\frac{1}{s}W_1(s)}{1 + K_2\frac{1}{s}W_1(s)} \tag{9.127}$$

The characteristic equation for the outer loop is:

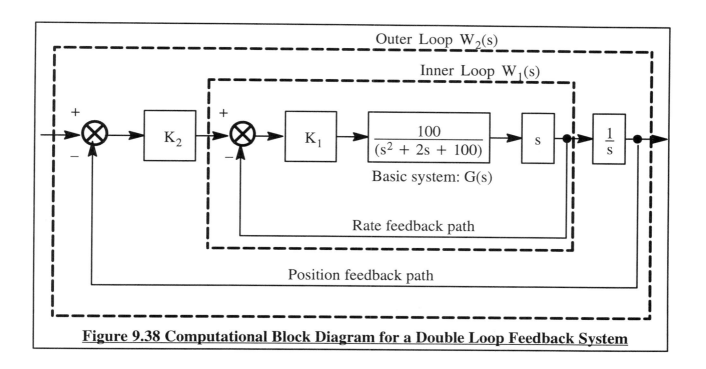

Figure 9.38 Computational Block Diagram for a Double Loop Feedback System

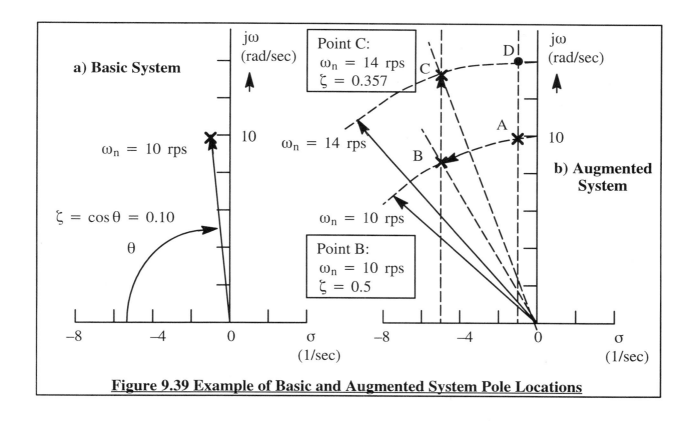

Figure 9.39 Example of Basic and Augmented System Pole Locations

$$1 + K_2 \frac{1}{s} W_1(s) = 0 \tag{9.128}$$

By substituting Eqn (9.124) for the inner loop transfer function this yields:

$$s^2 + s(2 + 100K_1) + 100(1 + K_1K_2) = 0 \tag{9.129}$$

By comparison with the standard quadratic form: $(s^2 + 2\zeta\omega_n s + \omega_n^2)$, it follows for the augmented system that:

$$2\zeta\omega_n = 2 + 100K_1 \quad \text{in this case}: 9.996 = 2 + 100K_1 \tag{9.130}$$

and:

$$\omega_n^2 = 100(1 + K_1K_2) \quad \text{in this case}: 196 = 100(1 + K_1K_2) \tag{9.130}$$

Solving for the gains K_1 and K_2 it is found that:

$$K_1 = 0.08 \quad \text{and}: \quad K_2 = 12 \tag{9.131}$$

Figure 9.39b shows the following pole locations:

* Point A represents the basic open loop system pole

* Point B represents the augmented system pole for the case of inner loop (rate feedback) only

* Point C represents the augmented system pole for the case of inner loop (rate feedback) AND outer loop (position feedback) acting simultaneously.

* Point D represents what would happen if the inner loop (rate feedback) were to fail.

This design procedure is referred to as the "pole assignment" method.

9.7.2 SETTING SYSTEM GAIN TO ACHIEVE A SPECIFIED DAMPING RATIO

Consider a single loop feedback system with the following open loop transfer function:

$$G(s)H(s) = \frac{K}{s(s + 3)(s + 7)} \tag{9.132}$$

It will be shown in Chapter 11 that this type of system is similar to a bank–angle–hold autopilot loop in an airplane. Assume that the requirement is to determine the gain, K, such that the system has a complex pair of roots with a damping ratio of 0.5. Figure 9.40 shows a root locus diagram with the gains marked in intervals of 2.0. By interpolation it can be found that when K=34.8 the closed loop damping ratio is 0.5.

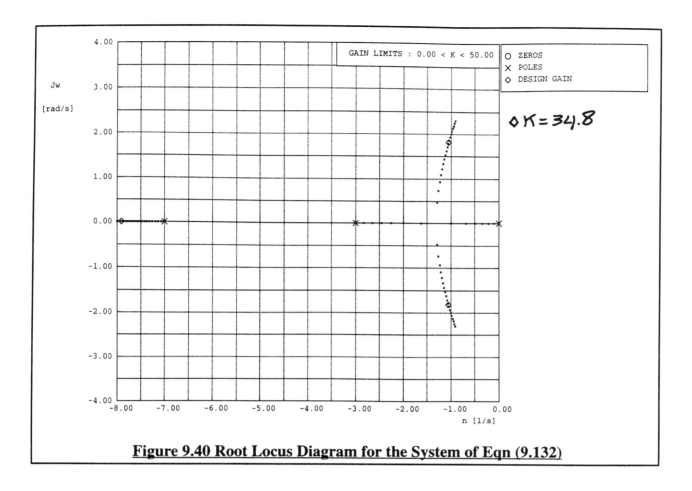

Figure 9.40 Root Locus Diagram for the System of Eqn (9.132)

9.7.3 SETTING GAIN TO ACHIEVE A SPECIFIED GAIN MARGIN AND POSITION ERROR CONSTANT

Consider a single loop feedback system with the following open loop transfer function:

$$G(s)H(s) = \frac{K}{(s+1)(s+3)(s+7)} \qquad (9.133)$$

This type of system can occur in the case of a pitch–attitude–hold autopilot for a light airplane at aft center of gravity. Assume that the requirement is to determine the gain, K, so that the steady state error is less than 0.5 and the gain margin is larger than 10 db.

Using the 'type'' definition of Sub–section 9.6.3 this is a type 0 system. Therefore, its position error constant, K_P, is given by:

$$K_P = \frac{K}{(1 \times 3 \times 7)} = 0.048K \qquad (9.134)$$

According to Table 9.3 the steady state error of this system is given by:

$$\text{steady state error} = \frac{1}{1 + K_P} = \frac{1}{1 + 0.048K} \qquad (9.135)$$

If this error is to be less than 0.5, the critical gain, K follows from:

$$0.5 = \frac{1}{1 + 0.048K} \quad \text{or:} \quad K = 21 \tag{9.136}$$

Figure 9.41 shows a Bode plot for this system. From the Bode plot it is seen that the system will become unstable for K >316 which amounts to 50 db. For a gain margin of 10db the corresponding gain would be 50 – 10 = 40 db. This gives K= 100. Therefore, both requirements are satisfied as long as: 21<K<100.

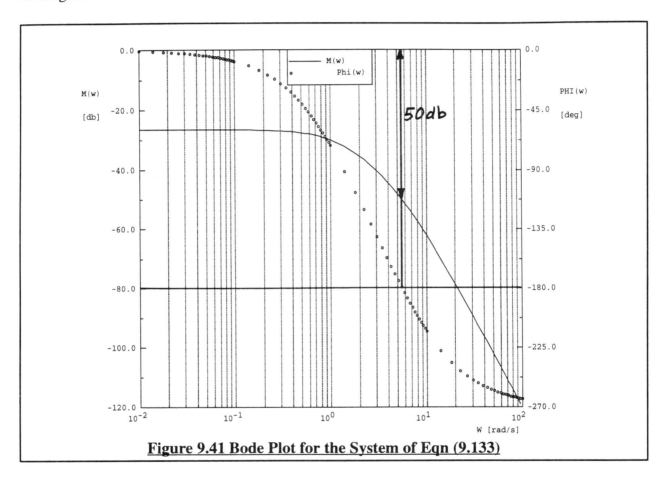

Figure 9.41 Bode Plot for the System of Eqn (9.133)

9.7.4 FINDING A LAG COMPENSATOR TO ALTER THE BREAKAWAY ANGLE FROM COMPLEX POLES

Consider a system with the following open loop transfer function:

$$G(s)H(s) = \frac{K}{(s + 2)(s + 5)(s^2 + 2s + 17)} \tag{9.137}$$

A root locus plot for this system is shown in Figure 9.42. Its corresponding Bode plot is given in Figure 9.43. Note that the system becomes unstable beyond K=224. Now, suppose it is desired

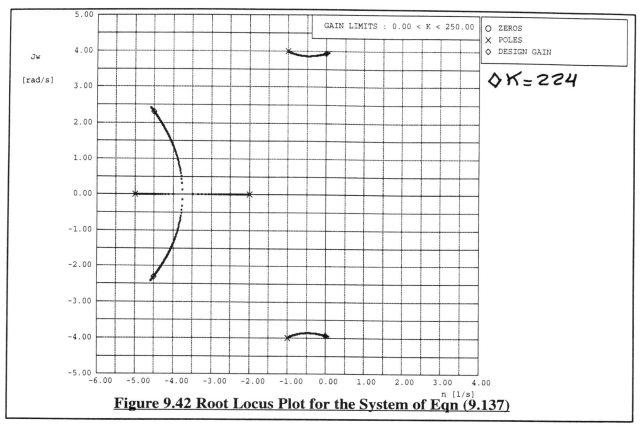

Figure 9.42 Root Locus Plot for the System of Eqn (9.137)

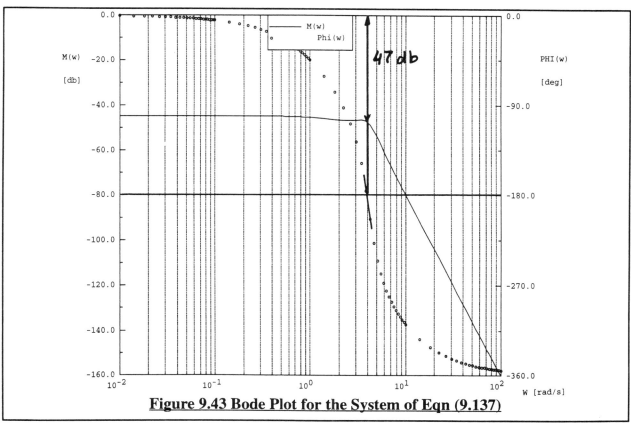

Figure 9.43 Bode Plot for the System of Eqn (9.137)

to use a lag compensator to force the quadratic open loop poles to move left instead of right. It will be shown that this can be done by adding a lag compensator with transfer function c/(s+c) to the system. This form does not alter the zero frequency gain of the system. The open loop transfer function of the system will then take the following form:

$$G(s)H(s) = \frac{Kc}{(s + c)(s + 2)(s + 5)(s^2 + 2s + 17)} \tag{9.138}$$

where: the lag compensator pole is located at s=–c. The question is, what should c be? A study indicating the effect of the magnitude of "c" is shown in Figures 9.44. Note, that as the compensator pole is moved closer to the origin, the objective is achieved and at the same time, the gain range for stable operation is increased.

9.7.5 FINDING A LEAD–LAG COMPENSATOR TO INCREASE SYSTEM GAIN MARGIN

Consider a system with the following open loop transfer function:

$$G(s)H(s) = \frac{20K}{s(s + 2)(s + 10)} \tag{9.139}$$

Figure 9.45 shows a root locus plot of this system. Figure 9.46 shows the Bode plot. Note that the system becomes unstable beyond K=12.5. At K=1 the system gain margin is: 22 db and the system phase margin is 60 deg. The question now is to find a lead–lag compensator which makes the gain margin 31 db while also improving the phase margin.

The lead–lag compensator will be assumed to have the form: {(s+a)/a}{b/(s+b)}. This form does not alter the zero frequency gain of the system. The new open loop transfer function now is:

$$G(s)H(s) = \left(K\frac{b}{a}\right)\left(\frac{20(s + a)}{s(s + 2)(s + 10)(s + b)}\right) \tag{9.140}$$

By inspecting the root locus diagram it is seen that by placing the lead (zero) close to the pole at –2 and the lag (pole) to the left of the pole at –10 it should be possible to force the branch of the root locus which goes unstable to the left. That should enhance the relative stability of the system.

On a Bode plot of the system the effect of the lead–lag compensation is to introduce a phase lead of +45 degrees at a frequency of "a" rad/sec and a phase lag of –45 degrees at a frequency of "b" rad/sec. To delay the occurrence of the extra phase lag, the lag pole will be placed at –20 and the lead zero will be placed at s=–2.5. The consequence of doing this is shown in the root loci of Figure 9.47. The corresponding Bode plot is shown in Figure 9.48. Note that the gain margin is now 31 db and the phase margin is 70 degrees. The design objective has therefore been met.

The reader is asked to plot the system phase and gain margin as a function of the lead zero placement over a range of –4.5 to –0.5.

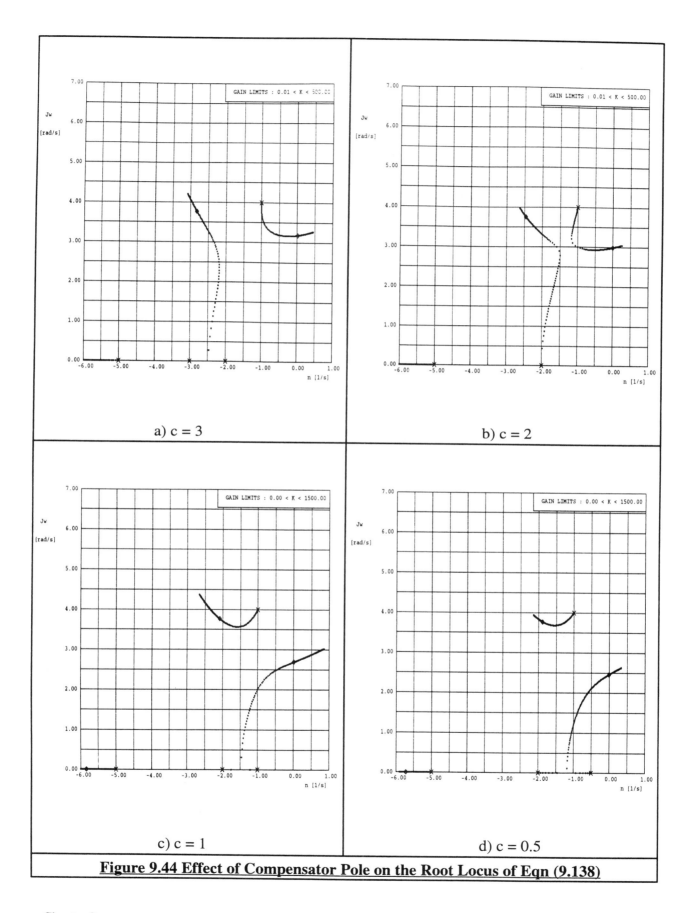

a) c = 3

b) c = 2

c) c = 1

d) c = 0.5

Figure 9.44 Effect of Compensator Pole on the Root Locus of Eqn (9.138)

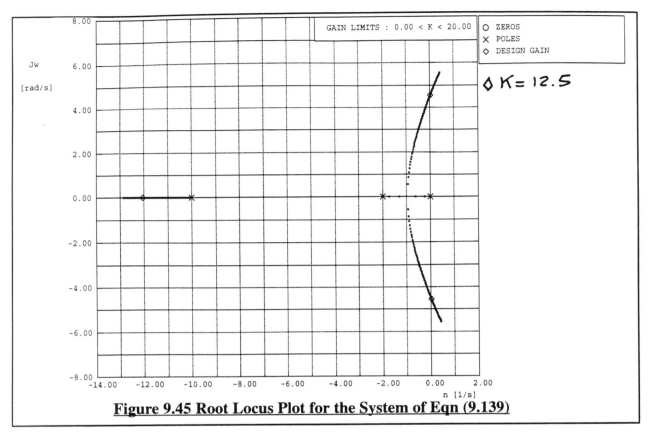

Figure 9.45 Root Locus Plot for the System of Eqn (9.139)

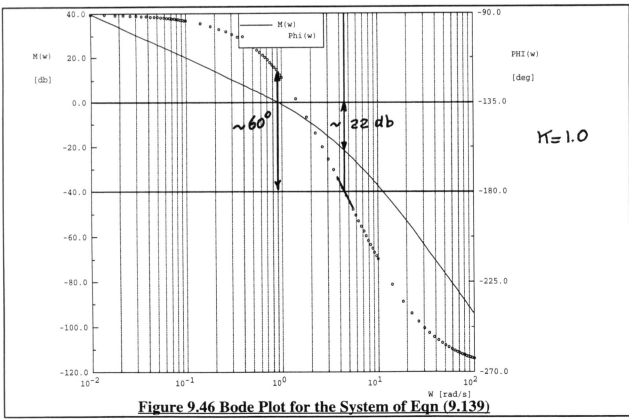

Figure 9.46 Bode Plot for the System of Eqn (9.139)

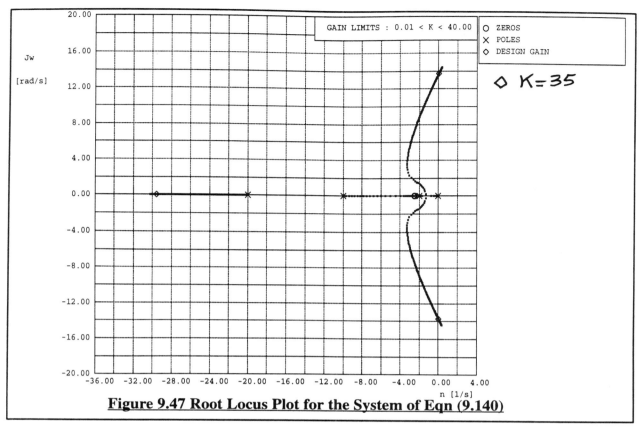

Figure 9.47 Root Locus Plot for the System of Eqn (9.140)

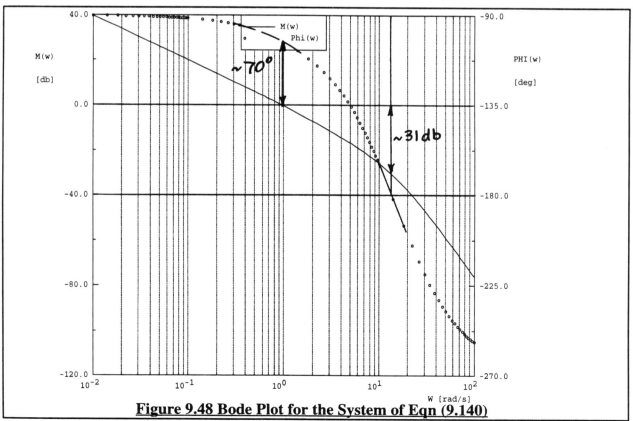

Figure 9.48 Bode Plot for the System of Eqn (9.140)

9.7.6 USING CANCELLATION COMPENSATION TO ACHIEVE BETTER CLOSED LOOP CHARACTERISTICS

Consider a system with the following open loop transfer function:

$$G(s)H(s) = \frac{2K}{(s - 2)} \tag{9.141}$$

The reader is asked to show analytically that this system is unstable for K<1. The root locus plot of Figure 9.49 and the Bode plot of Figure 9.50 (drawn for K=1) also show this.

Assume that a lead–lag compensator of the form $3(s - 2 + \varepsilon)/2(s + 3)$ is added in the forward path of the system. As a result the new open loop transfer function is:

$$G(s)H(s) = \frac{3K(s - 2 + \varepsilon)}{(s - 2)(s + 3)} \tag{9.142}$$

The quantity ε is added to the transfer function to give recognition to the fact that production tolerances and/or other uncertainties make it impossible to guarantee the location of either the open loop system pole at +2 or the cancellation zero at +2. For H(s)=1 the closed loop transfer function of the compensated system is:

$$W(s) = \frac{3K(s - 2 + \varepsilon)}{\{s^2 + s(1 + 3K) - 6 - 6K + 3K\varepsilon\}} \tag{9.143}$$

The condition for closed loop system stability is:

$$- 6 - 6K + 3K\varepsilon > 0 \tag{9.144}$$

Therefore, the system is stable for: $\varepsilon > \dfrac{6(1 + K)}{3K}$ and unstable for $\varepsilon < \dfrac{6(1 + K)}{3K}$. The problem is that this will generally be the case for almost any value of K, since ε is a small number. It is therefore concluded that this type of cancellation compensation will probably not work very satisfactorily. The root locus diagrams of Figures 9.51 and 9.52 back up this conclusion: the system stays unstable for $\varepsilon = +/- 0.10$.

By using a lead–lag compensator of the form $5(s + 2)/(s + 10)$ the system will work. Now the modified open loop transfer function is:

$$G(s)H(s) = \frac{10K(s + 2)}{(s - 2)(s + 10)} \tag{9.145}$$

The closed loop transfer function for this compensated system is:

$$W(s) = \frac{10K(s + 2)}{s^2 + s(8 + 10K) - 20 + 20K} \tag{9.146}$$

This system is stable for K>1. The root locus diagram of Figure 9.53 shows this.

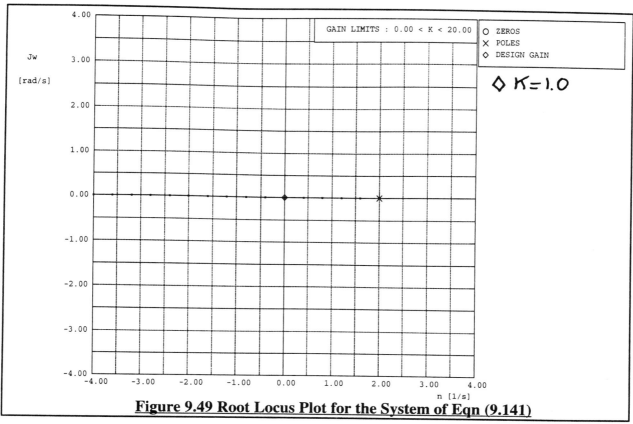

Figure 9.49 Root Locus Plot for the System of Eqn (9.141)

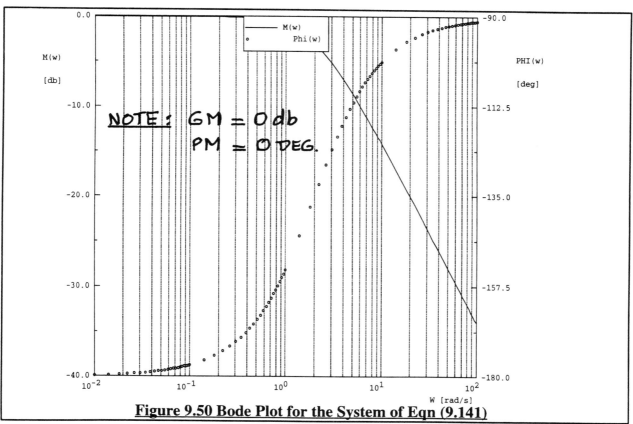

Figure 9.50 Bode Plot for the System of Eqn (9.141)

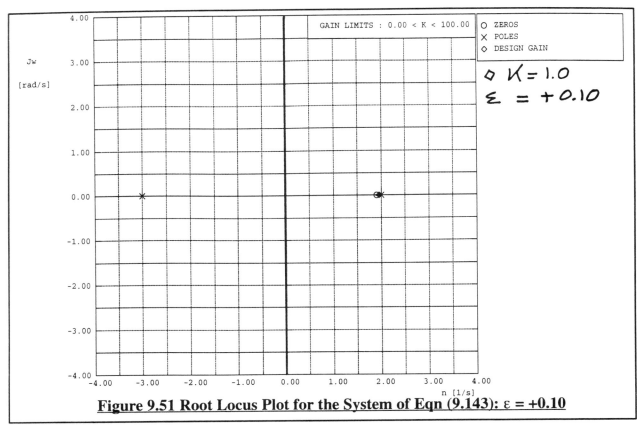

Figure 9.51 Root Locus Plot for the System of Eqn (9.143): ε = +0.10

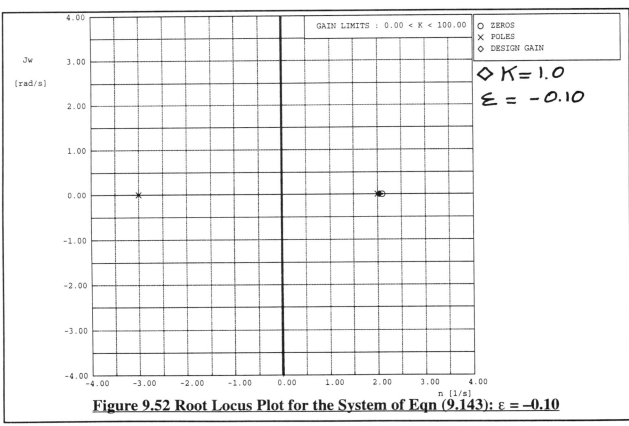

Figure 9.52 Root Locus Plot for the System of Eqn (9.143): ε = –0.10

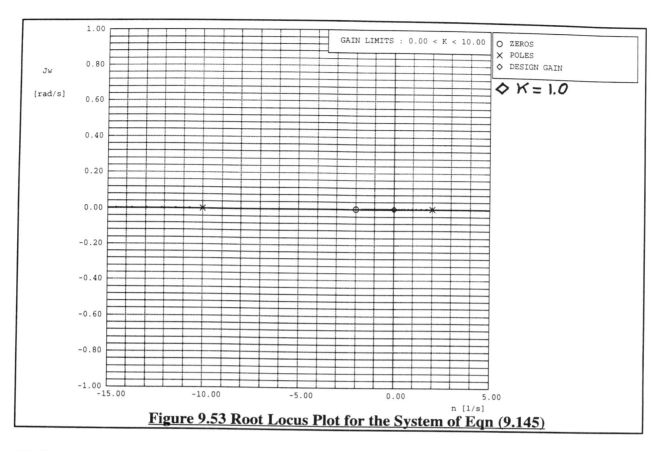

Figure 9.53 Root Locus Plot for the System of Eqn (9.145)

9.7.7 ROOT CONTOURS FOR VARIABLE POLES

Consider a single loop feedback system of the type shown in Figure 9.54.

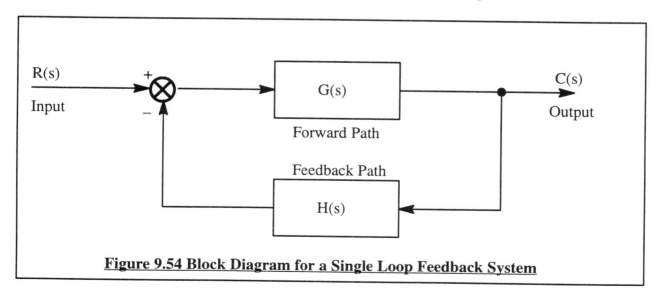

Figure 9.54 Block Diagram for a Single Loop Feedback System

The open loop system transfer function is G(s)H(s). If one of the poles in this open loop transfer function is considered to be a variable it is possible to write the open loop transfer function as:

$$G(s)H(s) = \left(\frac{1}{1 + T_x s}\right) Q(s) \qquad (9.147)$$

In this form, $s = -\frac{1}{T_x}$ represents the variable pole. The closed loop transfer function for the entire system may be written in the usual manner as:

$$W(s) = \frac{C(s)}{R(s)} = \frac{G(s)}{1 + G(s)H(s)} = \frac{G(s)(1 + T_x s)}{1 + sT_x + Q(s)} \qquad (9.148)$$

By dividing numerator and denominator of Eqn (9.148) by $\{1 + Q(s)\}$ it follows that:

$$W(s) = \frac{\frac{G(s)}{1 + Q(s)}(1 + sT_x)}{1 + \frac{sT_x}{1 + Q(s)}} \qquad (9.149)$$

Next, the following new transfer functions are defined:

$$G_1(s) = \frac{G(s)}{1 + Q(s)}(1 + sT_x) \qquad (9.150)$$

and

$$G_1(s)H_1(s) = \frac{sT_x}{1 + Q(s)} \qquad (9.151)$$

Therefore:

$$H_1(s) = \frac{sT_x}{G(s)(1 + sT_x)} \qquad (9.152)$$

However, by now using Eqn (9.149) it is found that:

$$W(s) = \frac{C(s)}{R(s)} = \frac{G_1(s)}{1 + G_1(s)H_1(s)} \qquad (9.153)$$

Therefore, the root locus behavior of the system with a variable pole can be analyzed by using as the open loop transfer function:

$$G_1(s)H_1(s) = \frac{sT_x}{1 + Q(s)} \qquad (9.154)$$

with T_x as the variable gain.

As an example, consider a system with the following open loop transfer function:

$$G(s)H(s) = \frac{4K}{\{s(s + 4)(1 + sT_x)\}} \qquad (9.155)$$

In this case, Q(s) takes on the following form:

$$Q(s) = \frac{4K}{s(s + 4)} \tag{9.156}$$

The effect of the variable pole at $s = -\frac{1}{T_x}$ is evaluated at a given gain, K, by constructing the root locus of a system with the following open loop transfer function:

$$G_1(s)H_1(s) = \frac{sT_x}{\left\{1 + \frac{4K}{s(s+4)}\right\}} = \frac{s^2T_x(s + 4)}{s^2 + 4s + 4K} \tag{9.157}$$

where: K now has a given, constant value.

The root locus diagram corresponding to Eqn (9.157) is shown in Figure 9.55 for four values of K: 1, 2, 3 and 4. The root loci in this case are referred to as root contour lines for varying $s = -\frac{1}{T_x}$. The system designer can use this information to decide which combination of K and $s = -\frac{1}{T_x}$ should be used to achieve certain closed loop system characteristics.

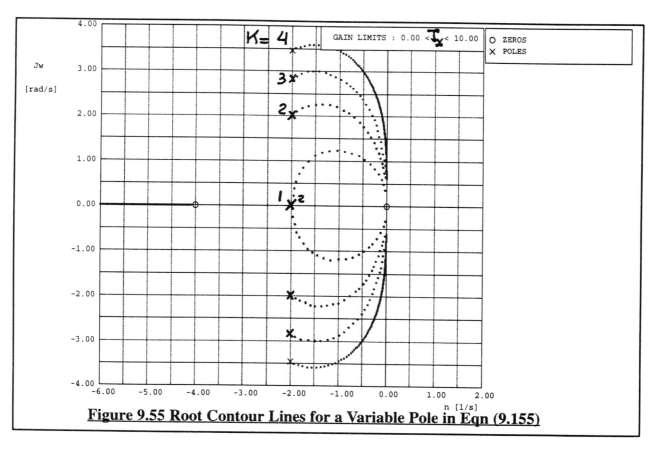

Figure 9.55 Root Contour Lines for a Variable Pole in Eqn (9.155)

9.7.8 ROOT CONTOURS FOR VARIABLE ZEROS

Consider a single loop feedback system of the type shown in Figure 9.54. The open loop system transfer function is G(s)H(s). If one of the zeros in this open loop transfer function is considered to be a variable it is possible to write the open loop transfer function as:

$$G(s)H(s) = (1 + sT_y)P(s) \qquad (9.158)$$

In this form, $s = -\dfrac{1}{T_y}$ represents the variable zero. The closed loop transfer function for the entire system may be written in the usual manner as:

$$W(s) = \frac{C(s)}{R(s)} = \frac{G(s)}{1 + G(s)H(s)} = \frac{G(s)}{1 + (1 + sT_y)P(s)} \qquad (9.159)$$

By dividing numerator and denominator of Eqn (9.159) by $\{1 + P(s)\}$ it follows that:

$$W(s) = \frac{\dfrac{G(s)}{1+P(s)}}{1 + \dfrac{sT_yP(s)}{1+P(s)}} \qquad (9.160)$$

Next, the following new transfer functions are defined:

$$G_2(s) = \frac{G(s)}{1 + P(s)} \qquad (9.161)$$

and

$$H_2(s) = sT_y\frac{P(s)}{G(s)} \qquad (9.162)$$

Equation (9.160) can now be rewritten as:

$$W(s) = \frac{G_2(s)}{1 + G_2(s)H_2(s)} \qquad (9.163)$$

with:

$$G_2(s)H_2(s) = \frac{sT_yP(s)}{1 + P(s)} \qquad (9.164)$$

Therefore, the root locus behavior of the system with a variable zero can be analyzed by using as the open loop transfer function Eqn (9.164) with T_y as the variable gain.

As an example, consider a unity negative feedback system $\{H(s)=1\}$ with the following open loop transfer function:

$$P(s) = \frac{8K}{s(s + 2)(s + 4)} \qquad (9.165)$$

A conventional root locus diagram for this system is shown in Figure 9.56. The reader is asked to use the Bode method to show that the system will be unstable for K>6. Now assume that it is desired to operate this system at an undamped natural frequency above 3.5 rad/sec. Figure 9.56 shows that this requires a gain level of about 10. Obviously, the system is unstable at this gain. One way to solve this problem is to add a "proportional plus differentiator" network to the system. What that really amounts to is adding a zero to the system. The question now is to determine that zero location which meets the frequency design objective but which also provides a reasonable damping ratio for the closed loop system. With the variable zero added to the system its open loop transfer function is:

$$G(s) = \frac{8K(1 + sT_y)}{s(s + 2)(s + 4)} = (1 + sT_y)P(s)$$ (9.166)

According to Eqn (9.164) the open loop transfer function of the equivalent system is:

$$G_2(s)H_2(s) = \frac{8KsT_y}{\{s(s + 2)(s + 4) + 8K\}}$$ (9.167)

Figure 9.57 shows the root contours for varying T_y at the various gain levels for K. Note, by interpolation, that the desired performance can be attained for K=2 and $T_y = 0.6$. Figure 9.58 shows the system root locus diagram for $T_y = 0.6$ and varying K. Note, that at K=2 the undamped natural frequency meets the specification while the damping ratio is 0.63 which is acceptable.

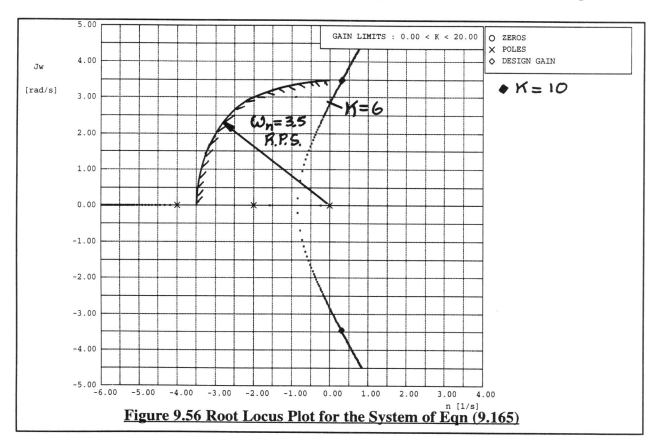

Figure 9.56 Root Locus Plot for the System of Eqn (9.165)

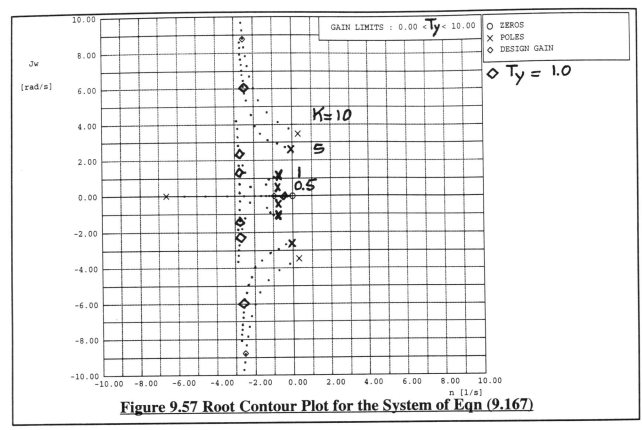

Figure 9.57 Root Contour Plot for the System of Eqn (9.167)

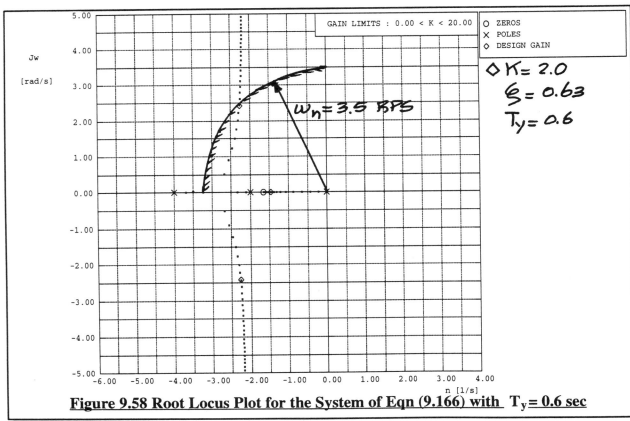

Figure 9.58 Root Locus Plot for the System of Eqn (9.166) with $T_y = 0.6$ sec

9.8   SUMMARY FOR CHAPTER 9

In this chapter the reader is introduced to the root locus method for analyzing feedback systems. It is shown how the Bode method and the root locus method are used in concert with each other. Relationships between the root locus method, the Bode method and the time domain were pointed out. In addition, the role of system frequency and time domain specifications is discussed.

Several methods for specifying system errors were also pointed out. Finally, a number of example design procedures which apply the root locus method and the Bode method to a number of problems are discussed. A brief introduction to the problem of varying pole and zero locations (pole and zero contours) is also presented.

9.9   PROBLEMS FOR CHAPTER 9

9.1   Redraw Figure 9.7 for the case of a complex pole P_1.

9.2   A unity negative feedback system has the following open loop transfer function:

$$G(s) = \frac{K}{s(s + 1)(s + P)}$$

An engineer found that the system is unstable for 0<K<2.0 but he forgot to document the corresponding value of P. Find P from a root locus diagram and check the result by using Routh's stability criteria.

9.3   A unity negative feedback system has the following open loop transfer function:

$$G(s) = \frac{K(s + 1)}{s(s + 2)(s + 4)(s^2 + 2s + 10)}$$

Construct a root locus diagram for this system and determine from it that value of gain, K, beyond which the system becomes unstable. At what frequency does the root locus cross the imaginary axis? Verify your answers with a Bode diagram.

9.4   A unity negative feedback system has the following open loop transfer function:

$$G(s) = \frac{K}{s(s + P)(s^2 + 4s + 15)}$$

Construct a root locus diagram for the following cases: P=3, P=4 and P=5. Discuss the observed trends as P is varied around the value 4.

9.5   A negative feedback system has the following transfer functions:

$$G(s) = \frac{2}{s^2 + 2} \quad \text{and} \quad H(s) = (s + 2)$$

Assume that the desired (ideal) transfer function of the system is $I(s) = 0.333$, compute the steady state error of the system for a unit step input. See Figure 9.36 for the corresponding block diagram. Determine in what frequency range does the system approach the desired transfer function?

9.6 Find the maximum value of gain, K, which yields a gain margin of 6 db (or more) and a phase margin of 45 degrees (or more) for a closed loop system with the following open loop transfer

function: $G(s) = \dfrac{K}{s(1 + 0.20s^2)}$

9.7 A feedback control system has the following open loop transfer function:

$G(s)H(s) = \dfrac{K(s + a)}{(s^2 - 1)(s + 5)}$

Determine the values of K and a such that the damping ratio is 0.5 and the undamped natural frequency is 2.0 rad/sec.

9.8 The open loop transfer function of a system is:

$G(s)H(s) = \dfrac{A}{s(1 + sT)}$

By what factor should A be multiplied to increase the closed loop system damping ratio from 0.2 to 0.6?

9.9 A system has the following closed loop transfer function (K and Z are variable parameters):

$W(s) = \dfrac{K(s + Z)}{s^2 + 2\zeta\omega_n s + \omega_n^2}$

Assume that the input is a ramp function: R(t) = At. Find the values of K and Z if C(t) is

to

approach R(t) as t approaches infinity.

9.10 Determine the position, velocity and acceleration error constants for unity negative feedback systems with the following open loop transfer functions:

$G(s) = \dfrac{50}{(1 + 0.1s)(1 + 3s)}$

$G(s) = \dfrac{K}{s(1 + 0.2s)(1 + 0.5s)}$

$G(s) = \dfrac{K}{s^2(s^2 + 4s + 180)}$

$G(s) = \dfrac{K(1 + 2s)(1 + 4s)}{s^2(s^2 + 2s + 12)}$

9.11 For the example problem of Sub–section 9.7.2 (page 742) find an analytical solution to the problem of determining the gain. Also, use the Bode method to find the gain beyond which the system becomes unstable.

9.12 A system has the following open loop transfer function:

$G(s)H(s) = \dfrac{-32}{(1 + s)(s^2 - 1.6s - 16)}$

Design a compensator for this system so that the gain margin is at least 6 db and the phase margin at least 40 degrees.

9.10 REFERENCES FOR CHAPTER 9

9.1   Rolfe, J.M. and Staples, K.J.; Flight Simulation; Cambridge University Press, Cambridge, United Kingdom, 1986.

9.2   McRuer, D., Ashkenas, I. and Graham, D.; Aircraft Dynamics and Automatic Control; Princeton University Press; Princeton, New Jersey, 1973.

9.3   DiStefano III, J.J., Stubberud, A.R. and Williams, I.J.; Theory and Problems of Feedback and Control Systems; Schaum Publishing Company, New York, 1967.

9.4   Clark, R.N.; Introduction to Automatic Control Systems; J.Wiley & Sons, New York, 1962.

9.5   Newton, J.C., Jr., Gould, L.A. and Kaiser, J.F.; Analytical Design of Linear Feedback Controls; J.Wiley & Sons, New York, 1961.

9.6   Truxall, J.B.; Control System Synthesis; McGraw Hill, New York, 1955.

9.7   Kuo, B.C.; Automatic Control Systems; Prentice Hall, Inc., New Jersey, 1962.

9.8   Oehman, W.E. and Suddath, J.H.; State–Vector Control Applied to Lateral Stability of High Performance Aircraft; NASA TN D–2894, 1965.

9.9   Bryson, A.E. and Ho, Y.C.; Applied Optimal Control; Hemisphere, Washington, D.C., 1975.

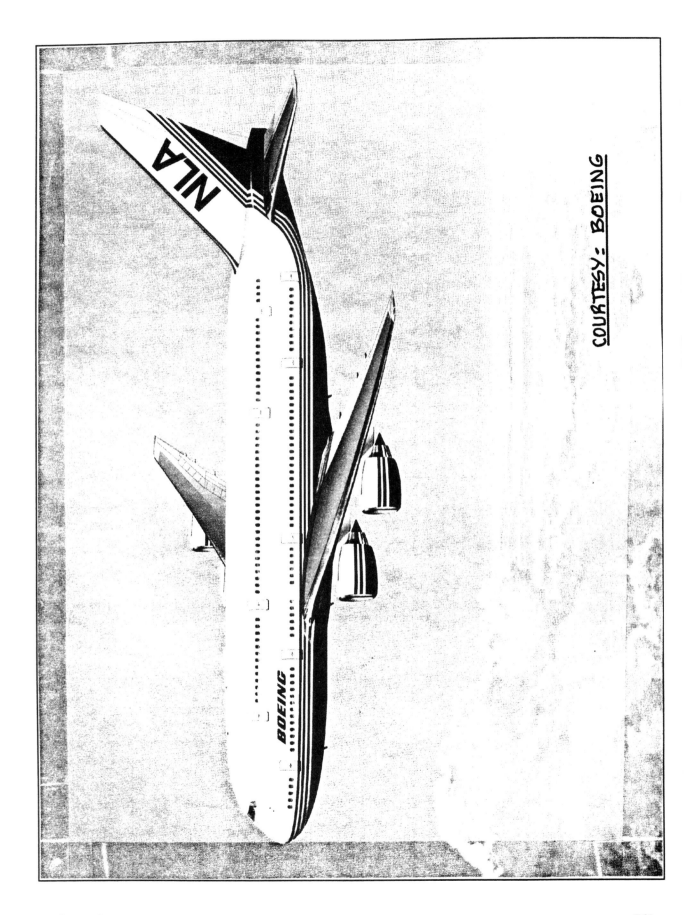

COURTESY: BOEING

CHAPTER 10: ANALYSIS OF AIRPLANE PLUS PILOT AS A CLOSED LOOP CONTROL SYSTEM

In this chapter the methods of Chapters 8 and 9 will be applied to the analysis of airplane plus pilot as a closed loop control system.

To apply classical control theory to airplane plus human pilot in closed loop situations it is required that a transfer function be defined for the pilot. The transfer function model for a human pilot will be presented and discussed in Section 10.1.

This model is then used to analyze several airplane plus pilot in the loop situations. In Section 10.2 the bank angle controllability of an airplane by a human pilot is discussed for a business jet in cruise. For the same airplane, the pitch attitude controllability by a human pilot is discussed in Section 10.3.

10.1 THE HUMAN PILOT TRANSFER FUNCTION

Figure 10.1 shows a block diagram which indicates the functions associated with a pilot closing the loop with an airplane under instrument flight conditions.

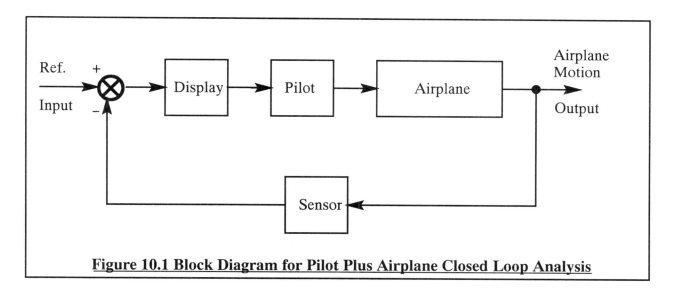

Figure 10.1 Block Diagram for Pilot Plus Airplane Closed Loop Analysis

The general manner in which this system works is as follows. Assume that the pilot's task is to control airplane bank angle such that wings level flight is maintained. The display shows the actual airplane bank angle. The pilot looks at this display and detects an error between the desired bank angle (considered to be the reference input here) and the actual bank angle sensed by a vertical gyro (shown as the sensor in the feedback path). This process of pilot detection consists of:

1) the pilot's eyes seeing the bank angle error on the display
2) the pilot's brain operates on that signal and establishes the magnitude of the error
3) the pilot's brain decides what needs to be done about this and sends a signal to that part of the brain which triggers the motion of the arms
4) the pilot's arm(s) moves the control wheel (or stick) to oppose the bank angle error
5) the control wheel moves the lateral controls
6) the airplane reacts by a change in bank angle
7) the vertical gyro sends the new bank angle magnitude to the display,

etc., etc. The operation depicted in Figure 10.1 is referred to as a compensatory control situation: the pilot tries to maintain a steady state by driving the bank angle error to zero.

There are various other manners in which a pilot can be asked to control an airplane. One other way is shown in Figure 10.2: the so–called pursuit mode of pilot operation.

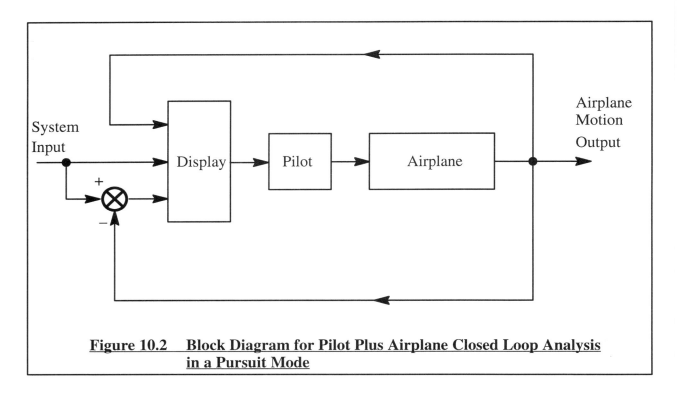

Figure 10.2 Block Diagram for Pilot Plus Airplane Closed Loop Analysis in a Pursuit Mode

In the pursuit mode of operation a pilot chases a dynamic error situation portrayed for him on the display. One symbol on the display may represent his own airplane plus perhaps a weapons launch envelope which surrounds his airplane symbol. The other symbol may represent a target which he is trying to surround with his weapons launch envelope. Of course, the target will attempt to maneuver away setting the stage for dynamic error chasing. The simple pilot model to be discussed in this chapter does not apply to such dynamic control situations. Instead, the following human pilot model applies only to compensatory control tasks (involving no more than two simultaneous degrees of freedom) as represented by Figure 10.1. It is shown in Ref. 10.1 that for those control tasks the human pilot transfer function model may be represented by:

$$Y_p(s) = \frac{K_p e^{-\tau s}(T_{lead}s + 1)}{(T_{lag}s + 1)(T_n s + 1)} \qquad (10.1)$$

where: K_p is the pilot gain.

This gain can have several different meanings. Examples are:
a) the amount of aileron deflection per degree of perceived bank angle error
b) the amount of cockpit longitudinal control deflection per degree of perceived pitch attitude angle
c) the amount of lateral cockpit control force per degree of perceived bank angle error.
The reader is asked to visualize other possible meanings.

A very important aspect of pilot gain is that its magnitude **is consciously alterable**. The pilot can, at any time, decide to act as a high gain or low gain operator. As a general rule, in normal flying tasks relatively low gains should be required. If high gain does become a requirement to maintain control, pilots will penalize the airplane with a less favorable Cooper–Harper rating. The Cooper–Harper rating scale and its application to flying qualities was discussed in Chapter 6.

$e^{-\tau s}$ represents the pilot reaction time delay. It takes the brain a finite amount of time

between reception of the display situation by the eye nerves and the sending of a signal to the muscles of the arm or leg. That amount of time is given by τ seconds. For test pilots a τ value of 0.10 can be assumed. For most other pilots this reaction time delay takes on values of 0.12 to 0.20 seconds.

A very important point is that τ **cannot be consciously altered** by the pilot. By frequent training it is possible to achieve lower τ values. The magnitude of τ will be significantly increased after alcohol enters the bloodstream. The dangerous effect of this will be illustrated with examples in Sections 10.2 and 10.3.

$\dfrac{(T_{lead}s + 1)}{(T_{lag}s + 1)}$ is the so–called pilot equalization characteristic. The reader will recognize

this as a lead–lag compensator. Depending on the open loop dynamics of the controlled element (the airplane in this case) the pilot has the ability to alter his lead/lag to achieve good closed loop control response. It is important to recognize that a pilot **can consciously decide to lead or to lag an airplane** in a given flight situation. It has been observed that if too much lead or lag is required to achieve good closed loop response, the pilot will again penalize the airplane with a less favorable Cooper–Harper rating. Ref. 10.2 discusses a relationship between Cooper–Harper ratings and lead/lag requirements.

$(T_n s + 1)$ represents the so–called neuro–muscular lag characteristic of the pilot. It is

caused by the fact that the muscles, once commanded (by the brain) to move, are in fact "fighting' a certain amount of mass or inertia. For well rested, reasonably athletic individuals the effect of neuro–muscular lag can be neglected. For heavy set and/or for non–athletic people this neuro–muscular lag may not be negligible. It is important to recognize that at any given point in time the value of the neuro–muscular lag time constant **cannot be consciously altered** by the pilot.

With the transfer function form of Eqn (10.1) the following working hypothesis is used to analyze pilot–plus–airplane closed loop situations:

Hypothesis:

In the form of Eqn (10.1) the pilot adapts gain, lead and lag {the $K_p \dfrac{(T_{lead}s + 1)}{(T_{lag}s + 1)}$ term}, to obtain good low frequency closed loop system response compatible with system stability.

Another way of expressing this is that the adaptive characteristic is selected in the form of a lag–lead, a lead–lag, a pure lead, a pure lag and/or a pure gain as appropriate to the complete system. The numerical values associated with each equalization parameter are then adjusted by the pilot to obtain good closed loop response characteristics. The criteria used by the pilot in arriving at the actual equalization characteristic are not known.

Experiments on human pilots in simulators have indicated that the pilot will try to achieve a system phase margin of somewhere between 50 and 110 degrees. The phase margin used here is defined as the difference between open loop system phase and –180 degrees at the frequency where the open loop gain is unity.

There is a practical problem with the $e^{-\tau s}$ term in the pilot transfer function model. To perform s–domain analyses it is desirable to have all transfer function components expressed in terms of poles and zeros. One way to achieve this with $e^{-\tau s}$ is to first write this term as:

$$e^{-\tau s} = \frac{e^{-\tau s/2}}{e^{\tau s/2}} \tag{10.2}$$

Next, power expansions are applied to the numerator as well as to the denominator:

$$e^{-\tau s} = \frac{1 - \frac{\tau s}{2} + \text{H.O.T.}}{1 + \frac{\tau s}{2} + \text{H.O.T.}} \tag{10.3}$$

H.O.T. stands for higher order terms. For frequencies below about 4–5 rad/sec it is reasonable to neglect these higher order terms. This yields the so–called Pade approximation to the pilot reaction time delay term:

$$e^{-\tau s} \approx \frac{1 - \frac{\tau s}{2}}{1 + \frac{\tau s}{2}} \tag{10.4}$$

Whether or not this Pade approximation is indeed reasonable depends on the magnitude of the reaction time delay, τ. This is shown in Figure 10.3 where Bode plots of $e^{-\tau s}$ are shown for first and third order approximations and for τ values ranging from 0.10 to 0.60 seconds.

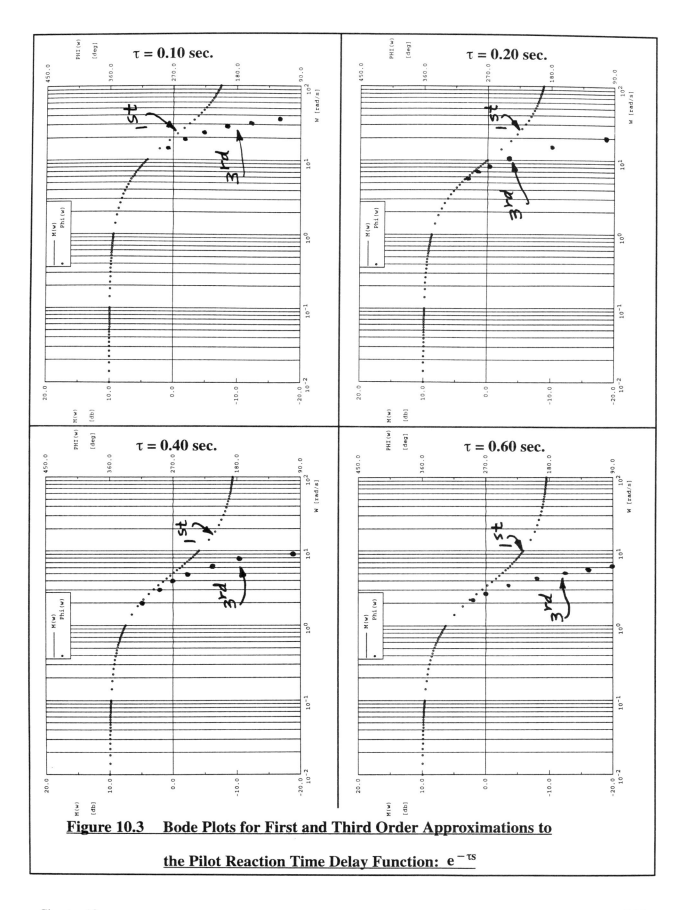

Figure 10.3   Bode Plots for First and Third Order Approximations to

the Pilot Reaction Time Delay Function: $e^{-\tau s}$

It is seen that for $0.10 < \tau < 0.20$ the Pade approximation is acceptable up to about 5 rad/sec. For $\tau = 0.40$ the Pade approximation is acceptable up to about 3 rad/sec whereas for $\tau = 0.60$ it is good only up to about 2 rad/sec. Human pilots begin to have great difficulty controlling disturbances with frequency content above about 4–5 rad/sec. Therefore, the Pade approximation is acceptable for most practical purposes.

10.2 PILOT CONTROL OF BANK ANGLE

In this Section the human pilot transfer function model will be used to determine the controllability of an airplane in bank.

Consider the business jet example of Table 5.10. In the 40,000 ft, cruise flight condition the approximate bank–angle–to–aileron transfer function is:

$$\frac{\phi(s)}{\delta_a(s)} = \frac{L_{\delta_a}}{s(s - L_p)} = \frac{6.8}{s(s + 0.44)} \tag{10.5}$$

First, consider a pure gain pilot. The transfer function of a pure gain pilot is simply:

$$Y_p(s) = K_p \tag{10.6}$$

In this case the open loop transfer function of pilot–plus–airplane is:

$$K_p \frac{\phi(s)}{\delta_a(s)} = K_p \frac{L_{\delta_a}}{s(s - L_p)} = K_p \frac{6.8}{s(s + 0.44)} \tag{10.7}$$

Because n–m=2 for this transfer function, instability cannot occur at any value of pilot gain. Figure 10.4 shows a root–locus plot of this system. It is seen that very low pilot gains (below 0.05) result in acceptable closed loop performance.

Second, consider a pilot with a reaction time delay of 0.10 seconds, negligible neuro–muscular lead and no lead–lag compensation. In that case the open loop transfer function of pilot–plus–airplane is:

$$Y_p(s) \frac{\phi(s)}{\delta_a(s)} = K_p \frac{(1 - \frac{\tau s}{2})}{(1 + \frac{\tau s}{2})} \frac{L_{\delta_a}}{s(s - L_p)} = -K_p \frac{(s - 20)}{(s + 20)} \left\{ \frac{6.8}{s(s + 0.44)} \right\} \tag{10.8}$$

In this case, because of the zero on the positive real axis, a sign change is introduced when this transfer function is written in its standard format. That sign change causes a 180 degree phase change. This means that Step 6 in Sub–section 9.2.4 (Step–by–step construction of a root locus diagram) changes to:

Step 6)   Root locus branches on the real axis lie to the right of an odd number of poles and zeros.

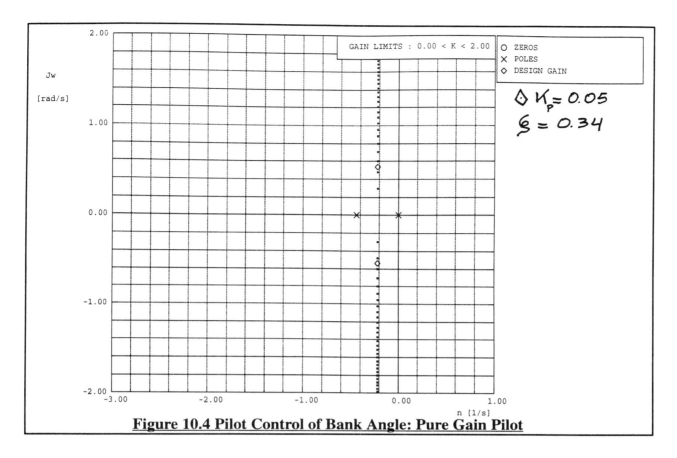

Figure 10.4 Pilot Control of Bank Angle: Pure Gain Pilot

Figure 10.5 shows the root loci for the system represented by Eqn (10.8). Also shown in Figure 10.5 are the root loci corresponding to reaction time delays of 0.2 sec., 0.4 sec. and 0.6 sec. It is seen that the system gain margin deteriorates rapidly with increasing reaction time delay.

Third, consider what happens if a pilot leads the airplane. Assuming a lead of 0.10 seconds, the corresponding pilot transfer function is:

$$Y_p(s) = K_p \frac{(1 - \frac{\tau s}{2})}{(1 + \frac{\tau s}{2})}(T_{lead}s + 1) \tag{10.9}$$

The corresponding open loop system transfer function is:

$$Y_p(s)\frac{\phi(s)}{\delta_a(s)} = -K_p \frac{(s - 20)}{(s + 20)}(0.1s + 1)\left\{\frac{6.8}{s(s + 0.44)}\right\} \tag{10.10}$$

Figure 10.6 shows the root locus diagram for this system.

It is seen that the effect of increasing pilot lead is to bend the root locus branch close to the imaginary axis over to the left. This has the effect of improving the relative system stability at constant gain. It also increases the system gain margin. The reader is asked to show the latter by drawing appropriate Bode plots.

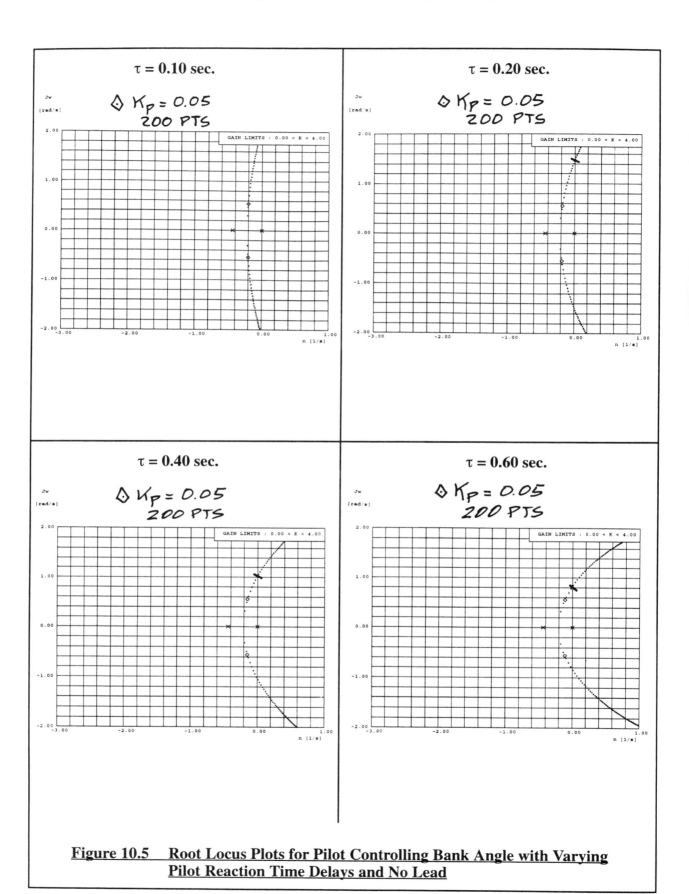

Figure 10.5   Root Locus Plots for Pilot Controlling Bank Angle with Varying Pilot Reaction Time Delays and No Lead

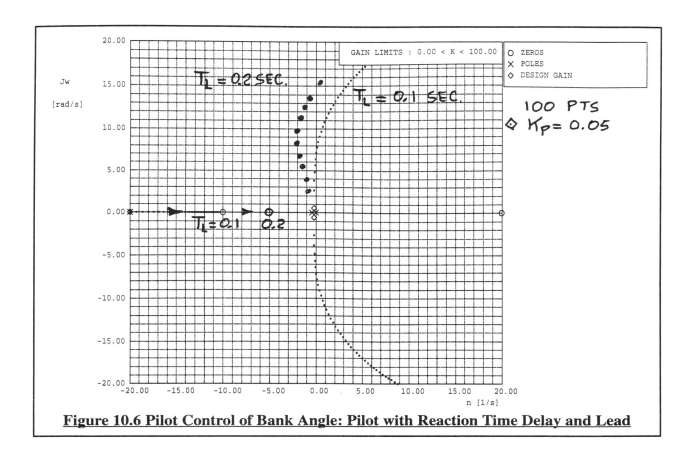

Figure 10.6 Pilot Control of Bank Angle: Pilot with Reaction Time Delay and Lead

For the business jet example at hand, there is no question about pilot–plus–airplane controllability. With a combination of low gain and very little lead, it is possible to attain very good closed loop characteristics in terms of frequency and damping.

An inebriated pilot would tend to have an increased reaction time delay and would also loose the ability to lead. Furthermore, inebriated humans tend to operate at elevated gain levels. As seen from the bottom right hand plot in Figure 10.5 such a pilot could easily P.I.O. (pilot induced oscillation) the airplane.

If an airplane has a large roll time constant (that tends to be the case for low roll damping and/or high rolling moment of inertia) the roll pole would be much closer to the origin. In that case pilot lead would definitely be required to attain good closed loop bank angle response.

It is of interest to examine what the root locus diagram would be like for pilot–plus–airplane if the complete bank–angle–to–aileron (instead of the approximation) were used. Figure 10.7 shows that root locus. The complete bank angle to aileron transfer function was taken from Table 5.10. It can be seen that the effect of the dutch roll pole and the numerator quadratic is quite negligible. Point A represents the constant gain point which is similar to the one in Figure 10.6. The effect of the extra operating point B is negligible: its time domain residue will be small as long as the quadratic pole–zero pair are close. Effectively, this amounts to the mutual cancellation of the quadratic pole–zero pair. Remember that this is a pre–assumed condition in the single degree of freedom rolling approximation in Chapter 5.

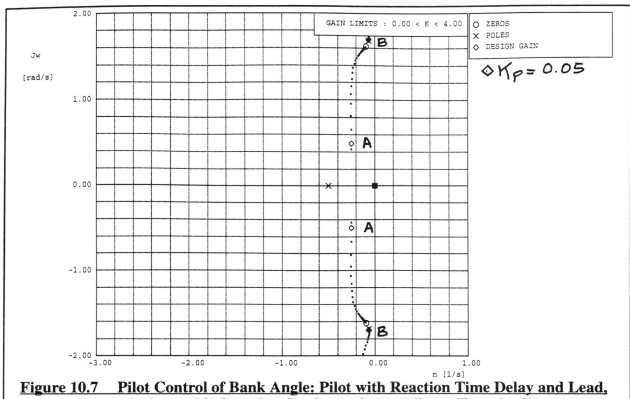

Figure 10.7   Pilot Control of Bank Angle: Pilot with Reaction Time Delay and Lead, Airplane with Complete Bank–Angle–to–Aileron Transfer Function

It was seen in Figure 10.3 that the Pade approximation becomes less accurate for larger pilot reaction time delays. In fact, for a time delay of 0.60 seconds it is seen from Figure 10.3 that the approximation is good only up to about 2 rad/sec. Of interest therefore is the question: can the accuracy of the first order Pade approximation (for a pilot with large reaction time delay and for the case of a pilot controlling bank angle) be shown on a root locus plot? To determine this, consider the open loop transfer function of pilot plus airplane:

$$Y_p(s)\frac{\phi(s)}{\delta_a(s)} = K_p e^{-\tau s}\frac{L_{\delta_a}}{s(s - L_p)} \tag{10.11}$$

where, for $\tau = 0.60$ seconds, the first order Pade approximation is:

$$Y_p(s) = K_p\frac{(1 - 0.30s)}{(1 + 0.30s)} \tag{10.12}$$

and, for $\tau = 0.60$ seconds, the third order Pade approximation is:

$$Y_p(s) = K_p\frac{(1 - 0.30s + 0.045s^2 - 0.0045s^3)}{(1 + 0.30s + 0.045s^2 + 0.0045s^3)} \tag{10.13}$$

No lead is included and the value of τ is assumed to be 0.6 seconds. Figure 10.8 shows two root loci: one for a first order Pade approximation, the other for a third order Pade approximation. It is seen that the first order approximation <u>still gives satisfactory results at the design gain level used before</u>. Note that the time domain participation corresponding to the high order Pade pole will be very small: it takes place at very high frequency and adequate damping ratio and therefore will die out in less than three cycles.

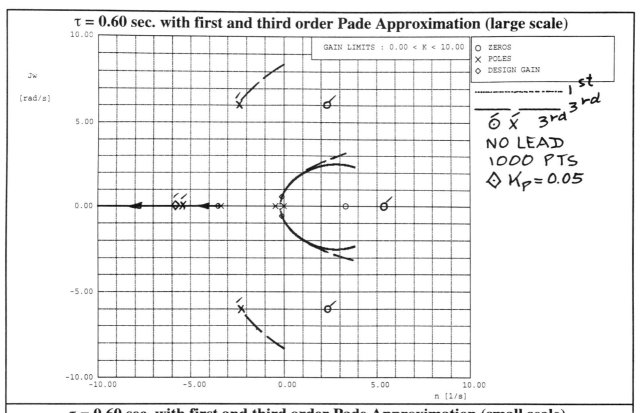

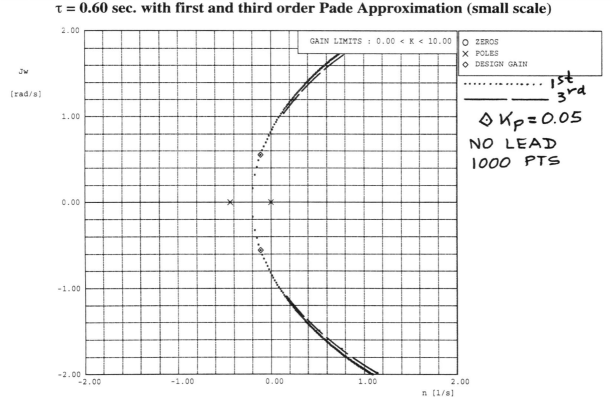

Figure 10.8   Root Locus Plots for Pilot Controlling Bank Angle with First and Second Order Pade Approximations

10.3 PILOT CONTROL OF PITCH ATTITUDE ANGLE

In this Section the human pilot transfer function model will be used to determine the controllability of an airplane in pitch.

Consider the business jet example of Table 5.4. In the 40,000 ft, cruise flight condition the complete pitch–attitude–to–elevator transfer function is:

$$\frac{\theta(s)}{\delta_e(s)} = \frac{(-11,930s^2 - 7,652s - 78.52)}{(676s^4 + 1,359s^3 + 5,440s^2 + 57.44s + 45.89)} \tag{10.14}$$

By examining the polynomial format of this transfer function (also given in Table 5.4) it is seen that the phugoid quadratic and the numerator quadratic almost cancel each other. Therefore, this transfer function will behave essentially as its corresponding short–period approximation.

First, consider a pure gain pilot. The transfer function of a pure gain pilot is simply:

$$Y_p(s) = K_p \tag{10.15}$$

In this case the open loop transfer function of pilot–plus–airplane is:

$$Y_p(s)\frac{\theta(s)}{\delta_e(s)} = K_p \frac{(-11,930s^2 - 7,652s - 78.52)}{(676s^4 + 1,359s^3 + 5,440s^2 + 57.44s + 45.89)} \tag{10.16}$$

Figure 10.9 shows the root locus for this case. Note that because n–m=2 the system cannot be driven unstable at any gain. Note also, that a negative gain was used. The reason for this is the fact that the airplane pitch–attitude–to–elevator transfer function contains a minus sign. That is caused in turn by the fact that a positive elevator deflection results in a negative change in pitch attitude angle (elevator deflection sign convention)!

Second, consider a pilot with a 0.10 second reaction time delay. In that case, the open loop system transfer function would be:

$$Y_p(s)\frac{\theta(s)}{\delta_e(s)} = -K_p\frac{(s-20)}{(s+20)}\left\{\frac{(-11,930s^2 - 7,652s - 78.52)}{(676s^4 + 1,359s^3 + 5,440s^2 + 57.44s + 45.89)}\right\} \tag{10.17}$$

The corresponding root locus diagram is given in Figure 10.10. Note that at the indicated pilot gain level (–0.10) the closed loop damping ratio of the system begins to deteriorate. The pilot will have to lead the airplane to achieve better closed loop performance.

With a 0.10 second lead, the open loop system transfer function is:

$$Y_p(s)\frac{\theta(s)}{\delta_e(s)} = -K_p\frac{(s-20)}{(s+20)}\left\{\frac{(0.1s+1)(-11,930s^2 - 7,652s - 78.52)}{(676s^4 + 1,359s^3 + 5,440s^2 + 57.44s + 45.89)}\right\} \tag{10.18}$$

The effect of lead can be seen from Figure 10.11.

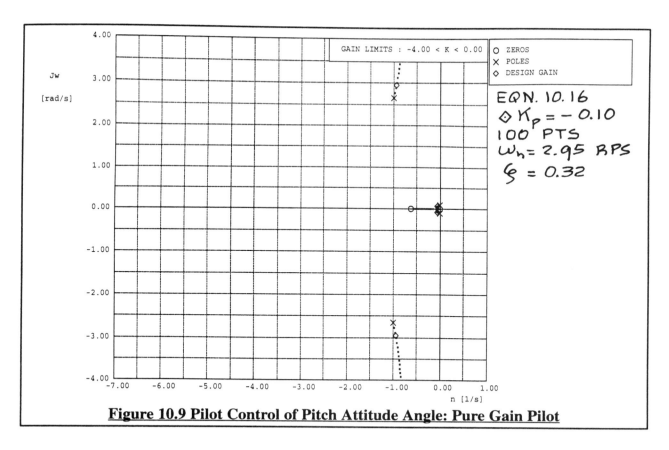

Figure 10.9 Pilot Control of Pitch Attitude Angle: Pure Gain Pilot

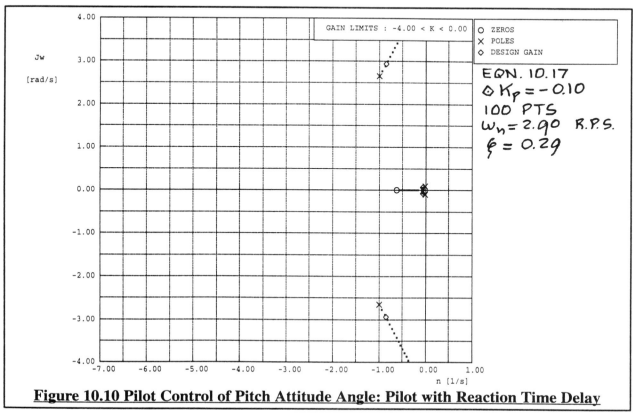

Figure 10.10 Pilot Control of Pitch Attitude Angle: Pilot with Reaction Time Delay

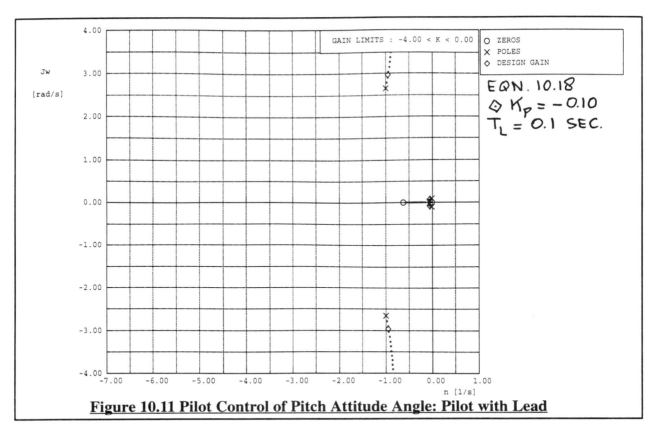

Figure 10.11 Pilot Control of Pitch Attitude Angle: Pilot with Lead

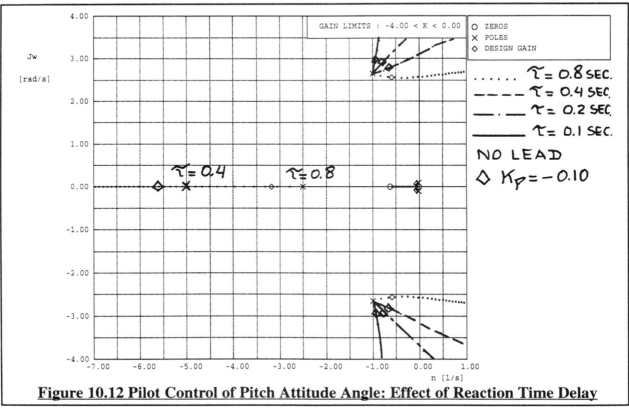

Figure 10.12 Pilot Control of Pitch Attitude Angle: Effect of Reaction Time Delay

Finally, the effect of reaction time delay on pilot plus airplane pitch attitude control is illustrated in Figure 10.12. It is seen that for increasing time delay, the pilot tends to drive his closed loop poles directly toward the imaginary axis. Couple that with the fact that an inebriated pilot would not lead and would also tend to operate at high gain, the pilot can easily P.I.O. the airplane.

10.4 SUMMARY FOR CHAPTER 10

In this chapter the reader was introduced to a mathematical model for human pilots so that closed loop control theory can be used to analyze the performance of airplane plus pilot in the loop combinations.

Applications to pilots controlling bank angle and pitch attitude angle are presented and discussed.

10.5 PROBLEMS FOR CHAPTER 10

10.1   Determine and discuss the pilot plus airplane controllability in bank and in pitch (through aileron and rudder respectively) of Airplane B on page 487 in Part I.

10.2   Determine and discuss the pilot plus airplane controllability of speed through the elevator of Airplane D on page 501 in Part I.

10.3   Determine and discuss the pilot plus airplane controllability in bank through the rudder of Airplane J on page 543 in Part I.

10.4   Determine and discuss the pilot plus airplane controllability in bank through the rudder of Airplane C on page 494 in Part I.

10.5   Show the beneficial effect of pilot lead in the case of Eqn. (10.10) by using Bode plots. Plot the effect of pilot lead time constant on the system phase and gain margins.

10.6   Show the effect of pilot neuromuscular lag time constant on closed loop system stability for the case of problem 10.1 by both root locus and Bode plots. Plot the effect of pilot neuromus–cular time constant on the system phase and gain margins.

10.6 REFERENCES FOR CHAPTER 10

10.1   McRuer, D.T. and Krendel E.S.; Dynamic Response of Human Operators; WADC Technical Report 57–524, October 1957.

10.2   Anderson, R.O.; Theoretical Pilot Rating Predictions; Air Force Flight Dynamics Laboratory; Paper presented at the AGARD Flight Mechanics Panel Specialists Meeting, September 28–October 1, 1971, Ottawa, Canada, 1968.

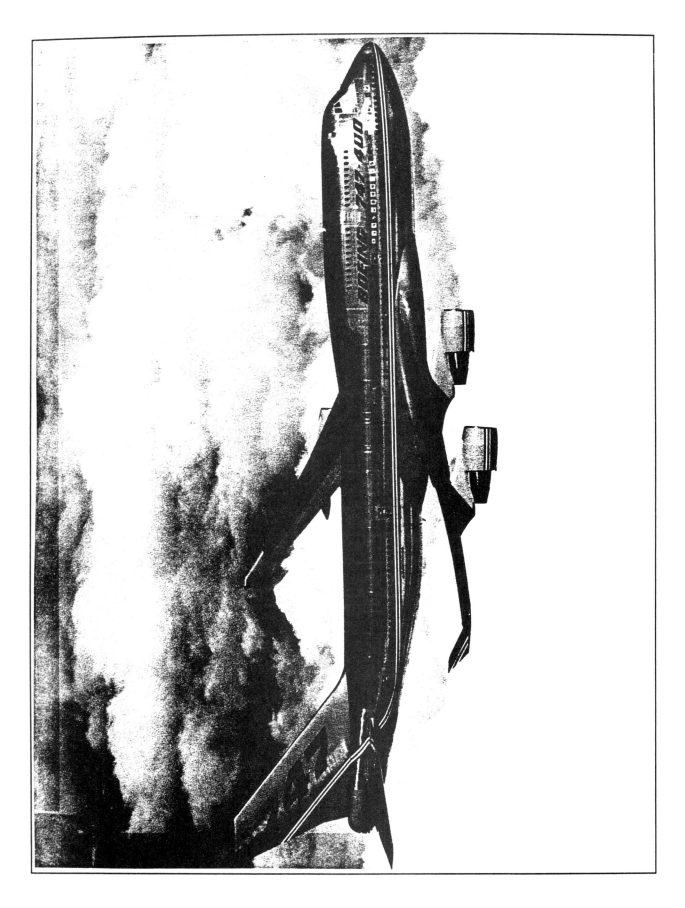

CHAPTER 11: STABILITY AUGMENTATION AND AUTOMATIC FLIGHT CONTROL SYSTEMS

In this chapter the classical control methods of Chapters 8 and 9 are used to analyze and synthesize stability augmentation systems and automatic flight control systems for airplanes.

A stability augmentation system acts to "augment" the open loop static and/or dynamic stability of an airplane. It was shown in Chapter 5 that the short period and dutch roll damping of high performance airplanes tends to deteriorate rapidly at low speed and at high altitude (i.e. at low dynamic pressure). Because yaw dampers were among the first stability augmentation systems to be used in airplanes, they are discussed first. The effect of a yaw damper on the dutch roll dynamics of airplanes is discussed in Section 11.1. Next, the effect of pitch dampers on the dynamic longitudinal stability of airplanes is discussed in Section 11.2

To enhance the maneuverability of fighter aircraft it has become commonplace to reduce the static longitudinal and static directional (inherent) stability of airplanes. In the case of longitudinal stability, many fighters are now designed with inherent negative static margins. To make such airplanes appear to the pilot as normally responding airplanes some form of stability augmentation is required. This can take the form of angle of attack feedback, angle of sideslip feedback and/or acceleration feedback. The effect of static stability augmentation systems is discussed in Section 11.3. Another interesting form of stability augmentation is found in the so-called control-wheel-steering system. This system is discussed in Section 11.4.

To lower pilot workload, particularly on long range flights, most airplanes are equipped with automatic flight control systems or autopilots. Section 11.5 shows how pilots typically interface with automatic flight control systems. Most autopilots allow for some form of automatic control of pitch attitude, bank angle, heading angle and altitude. Such features are called: autopilot modes. A number of these modes are discussed in Section 11.6.

Many autopilots also allow for some form of automatic navigation. Typical navigation modes are: glide slope intercept and hold, localizer intercept and hold, automatic landing modes and V.O.R.-hold. Longitudinal and lateral-directional navigation modes are discussed in Sections 11.7 and 11.8 respectively.

Whenever several different signals (i.e. motion variables) must be fed back to more than one controller serious mathematical complications arise in the derivation of closed loop system transfer functions. Section 11.9 introduces the reader to some typical complications which can arise.

Most airplanes still have reversible flight control systems (see Chapter 4 for a discussion of such systems). Integration of automatic feedback loops into reversible flight control systems leads to feedback of control system motions to the cockpit controls. When the system is in an autopilot mode this can be desirable. However, when the system is in a stability augmentation mode this can

Chapter 11

be very annoying. One way around this problem is to use so–called separate control surface systems. An introduction to such systems is given in Section 11.10.

For readers who want more detailed information about the hardware aspects of automatic flight control systems Appendix E has been included. Century Flight Systems, Inc. and kindly gave permission to include some of their autopilot hardware data in this text.

References 11.1 and 11.2 contain much valuable, experience based information on do's and dont's in automatic flight control system development. Reference 11.3 is an important text for more detailed study and for obtaining a historical perspective on the development of automatic flight control systems.

Methods used in this chapter for analyzing and synthesizing automatic flight control loops are essentially analog methods. The reader may well ask whether this is still relevant in an era of digital flight controls. The answer is that with the high sampling rates and high computational speeds used in modern on–board flight control computers, these systems behave much like analog systems. An elementary introduction to analysis of digital flight control systems is contained in Chapter 12.

11.1 YAW DAMPERS

Figure 9.4 (in Chapter 9) shows a generic block diagram of a yaw damper. To illustrate the basic functioning of a yaw damper this figure has been simplified in Figure 11.1. Note that the forward and feedback path compensation networks have been left out.

The transfer function of a rate gyro can generally be represented by a pure gain, measured in volts per radian per second (or in volt/deg/sec). The reason this approximation is acceptable is that the lowest break frequency in the transfer functions of rate gyros typically is larger than the highest break frequency in the airplane yaw–rate–to–rudder transfer function. Therefore, on a Bode plot, the transfer function of a rate gyro looks like a straight line at some constant db level. It is therefore acceptable to represent the yaw rate gyro transfer function in the feedback path by 1.0.

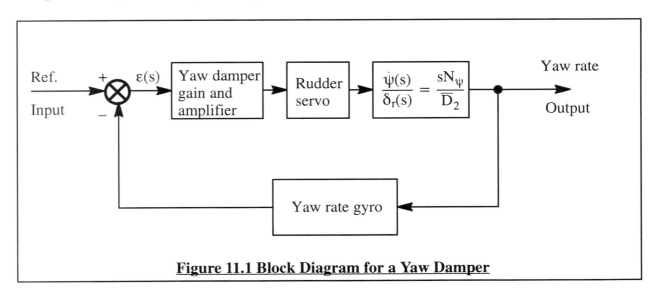

Figure 11.1 Block Diagram for a Yaw Damper

There is a problem with the yaw damper loop sketched in Figure 11.1. Since the damper will try to drive any perceived yaw rate to zero, it will work fine if the airplane is intended to be in straight line flight. In that case, the reference input in Figure 11.1 would be zero. However, the yaw damper will tend to "fight" a pilot who is trying to set up a constant bank angle turn. In such a turn the airplane has a constant (non–zero) yaw rate as indicated by Eqn (1.61c). This, of course, is not acceptable. There are two solutions to this problem:

   a) feed computed yaw rate to the yaw damper (reference) input
   b) use a washout circuit in the feedback path.

In the case of computed yaw rate, a signal given by Eqn (1.61c) is fed to the reference input:

$$R_1 = \dot{\psi}_1 \cos\theta_1 \cos\phi_1 \tag{11.1}$$

The yaw damper will then try to eliminate any yaw rate above or below the value given by Eqn (11.1). This is referred to as a "computed yaw rate" input. It evidently requires the presence of the following:

   1) a gyro to measure pitch attitude angle,
   2) a gyro to measure bank angle,
   3) a gyro to measure rate of change of heading,
   4) a computer to multiply 1), 2) and 3).

If one or more of these devices is not available, a lower cost option is to use the washout circuit of item b). A washout circuit has the following transfer function:

$$H_{washout} = \frac{\tau s}{\tau s + 1} \tag{11.2}$$

where: τ is the washout circuit time constant. The time domain response of a washout circuit can be visualized by referring to item 7 in Table 9.2. It is seen that a washout circuit drives a given input signal to zero at a pace determined by the magnitude of the time constant, τ.

When in a turn, the washout circuit will stop "fighting" yaw rate in any significant manner after a little more than τ seconds have elapsed. Clearly, if τ is very small, the yaw damper will not work at all. If τ is very large, the yaw damper will "fight" the pilot in setting up a turn. A compromise is required. Typical of such a compromise is $\tau \approx 4$ sec.

The transfer function of most amplifiers can also be represented by a simple gain. Therefore, the yaw damper gain plus amplifier block in Figure 11.1 is usually represented by a gain, also called the yaw damper gain, K_r.

With the washout circuit and a simple lag as the transfer function model for the rudder servo, the block diagram of the yaw damper is as shown in Figure 11.2.

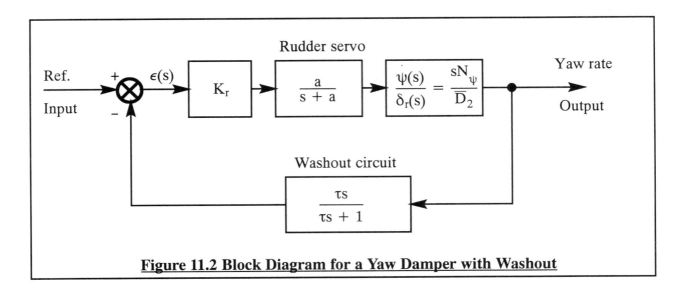

Figure 11.2 Block Diagram for a Yaw Damper with Washout

As an example, consider first the business jet as represented by the data of Table 5.10. The characteristic equation of the closed loop system for the yaw damper of Figure 11.2 is:

$$1 + K_r\left(\frac{a}{s+a}\right)\frac{sN_\psi}{\overline{D}_2}\left(\frac{\tau s}{\tau s + 1}\right) = 0 \tag{11.3}$$

The corresponding open loop airplane transfer function is obtained from Table 5.10 as:

$$\frac{sN_\psi}{\overline{D}_2} = \frac{s\{-1133(s + 0.731)(s^2 - 0.238s + 0.199)\}}{675\, s\,\{(s + 0.500)(s + 0.001)(s^2 + 0.131s + 2.85)\}} \tag{11.4}$$

Using a servo with a break frequency of 20 rad/sec and a washout circuit time constant of 4 seconds the open loop pole zero configuration is shown in Figure 11.3. To indicate the location of the servo pole, the real axis is broken to the left of the figure.

The reader should verify that all open loop poles and zeros are located appropriately in the s-plane. Figure 11.4 shows the root locus of this yaw damper. Note, that at a gain of –0.60 (degrees of rudder deflection per deg/sec of yaw rate) the closed loop system damping ratio is about 0.32 which is a significant improvement over the open loop system dutch roll damping ratio of 0.04.

As it turns out, the washout circuit has a fairly insignificant effect on the closed loop behavior of this particular yaw damper. This may be seen from Figure 11.5 where the root locus for this yaw damper without the washout circuit is shown. Note that the root locus behavior is very similar to that of Figure 11.4.

The effect of the servo break frequency on the closed loop yaw damper performance is illustrated in Figure 11.6. It is seen that for break frequencies ranging from 40 rad/sec down to 5 rad/sec the effect on the closed loop yaw damper performance is negligible. The reader should not generalize this result. The reason in this case is the fact that even with a low break frequency of 5 rad/sec, the servo break is at a much higher frequency than the open loop dutch roll mode frequency.

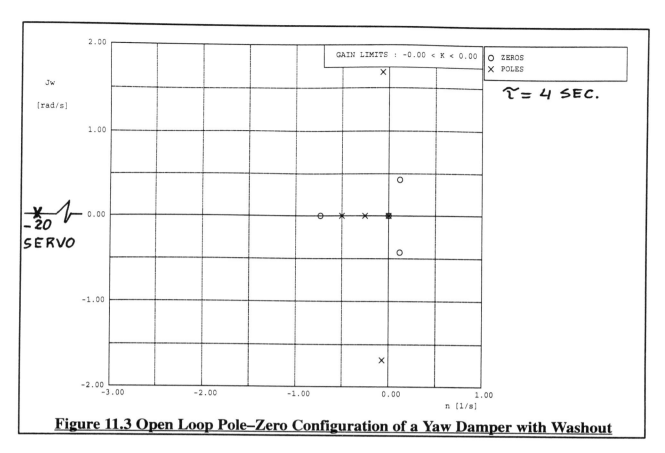

Figure 11.3 Open Loop Pole–Zero Configuration of a Yaw Damper with Washout

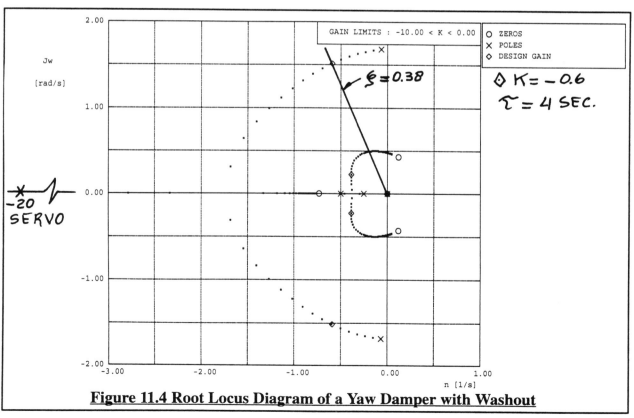

Figure 11.4 Root Locus Diagram of a Yaw Damper with Washout

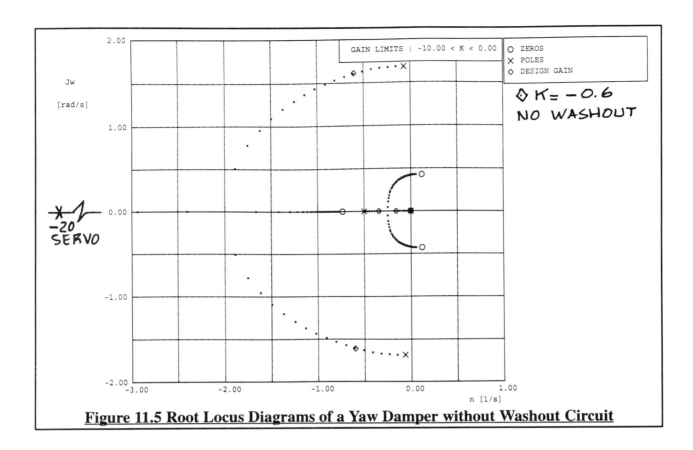

Figure 11.5 Root Locus Diagrams of a Yaw Damper without Washout Circuit

There is another problem with the yaw damper block diagram of Figure 11.1. This figure is correct only if the sensitive axis of the yaw rate gyro is perfectly aligned with the airplane Z stability axis. That will be the case in only one flight condition. For all other flight conditions, the yaw rate gyro actually senses a combination of stability axis roll and yaw rates as indicated by the vector diagram of Figure 11.7. In this figure the sensitive axis of the gyro has actually been tilted aft, relative to the airplane body–fixed Z axis. Aft tilt is defined as positive, forward tilt will be negative.

It is seen from Figure 11.7 that the signal sensed by the rate gyro can be expressed as:

$$\text{Sensed rate gyro signal}: = p \sin(\alpha + \alpha_{tilt}) + r \cos(\alpha + \alpha_{tilt}) \qquad (11.5)$$

It is the signal defined by Eqn (11.5) which is actually fed back to the comparator in the yaw damper block diagram of Figure 11.1. Figure 11.8 shows the situation in terms of a block diagram of a yaw damper without a washout. As expected, when the gyro tilt angle, $(\alpha + \alpha_{tilt})$, is equal to zero, the situation is that corresponding to Figure 11.1. Referring to Figure 11.8, the effect of summing $\dfrac{r(s)}{\delta_r(s)} \cos(\alpha + \alpha_{tilt})$ and $\dfrac{p(s)}{\delta_r(s)} \sin(\alpha + \alpha_{tilt})$ is to retain the same lateral–directional denominator in the resulting transfer function. However, the numerator is altered, depending on the magnitude of the angle $(\alpha + \alpha_{tilt})$. The consequence of this is that the three zeros of the open loop transfer function of the yaw damper are moved around in the s–plane as a function of the gyro tilt angle. Figure 11.9 shows how these zeros move as a function of the gyro tilt angle. Serious problems

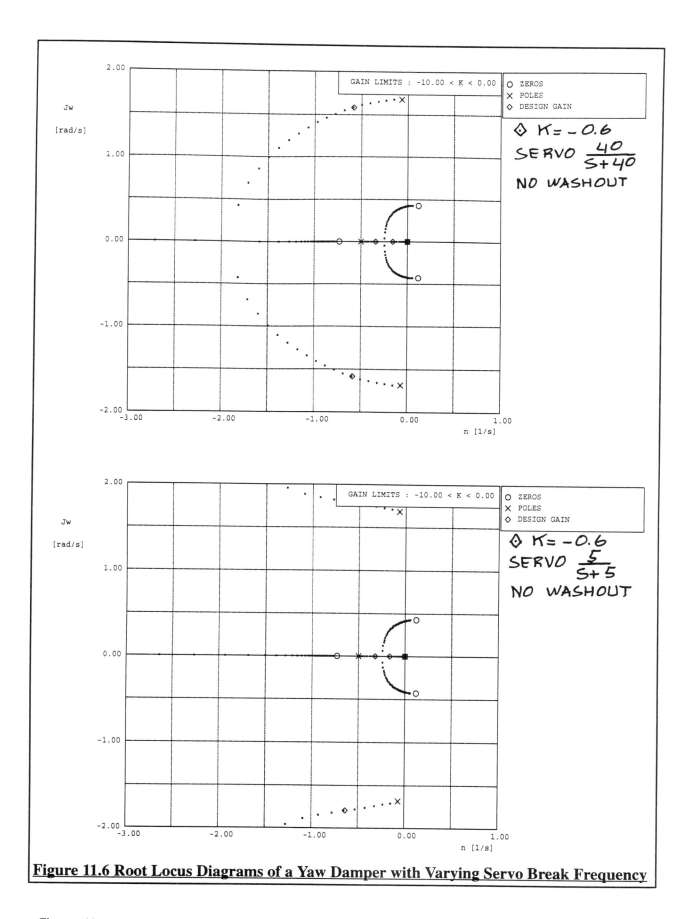

Figure 11.6 Root Locus Diagrams of a Yaw Damper with Varying Servo Break Frequency

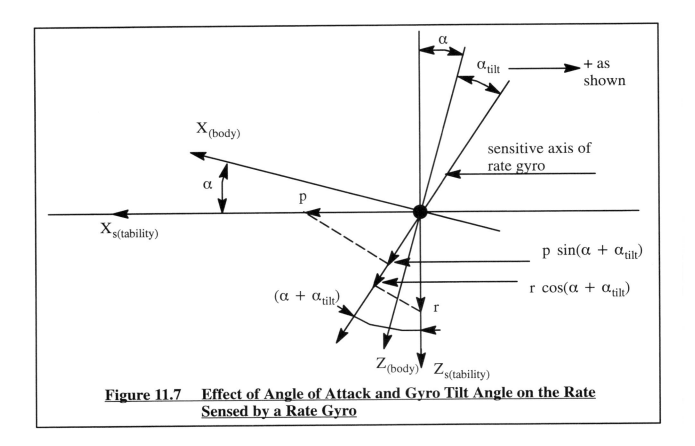

Figure 11.7   Effect of Angle of Attack and Gyro Tilt Angle on the Rate Sensed by a Rate Gyro

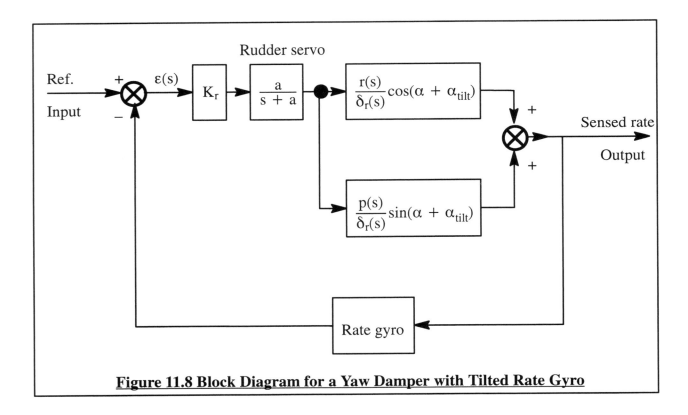

Figure 11.8 Block Diagram for a Yaw Damper with Tilted Rate Gyro

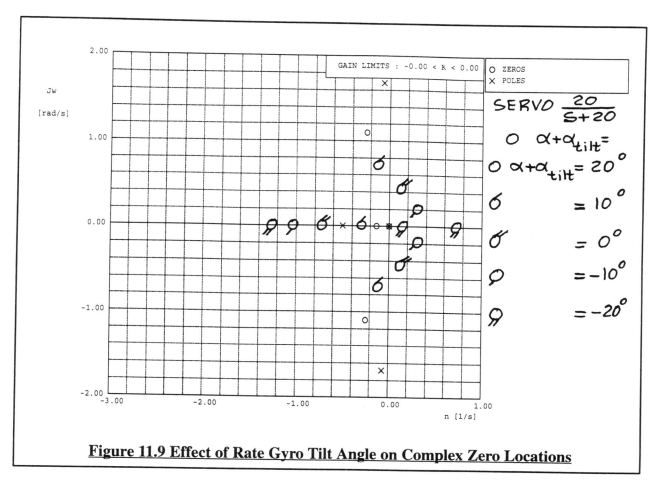

Figure 11.9 Effect of Rate Gyro Tilt Angle on Complex Zero Locations

can be caused by those zeros which migrate toward the unstable part of the s–plane. At high gain, that is where the closed loop poles of the system will move, thereby driving the system eventually unstable. Note that aft gyro tilt has a beneficial effect on the location of the complex zeros.

Figure 11.10 shows what happens to the root locus of the system for different gyro tilt angles. Observe that for forward (negative) tilt a low damped component at low frequency shows up in the closed loop response. For large negative gyro tilt angles this component is seen to become unstable. For aft (positive) tilt, the complex zeros move to the left in the s–plane and the system has very good closed loop damping.

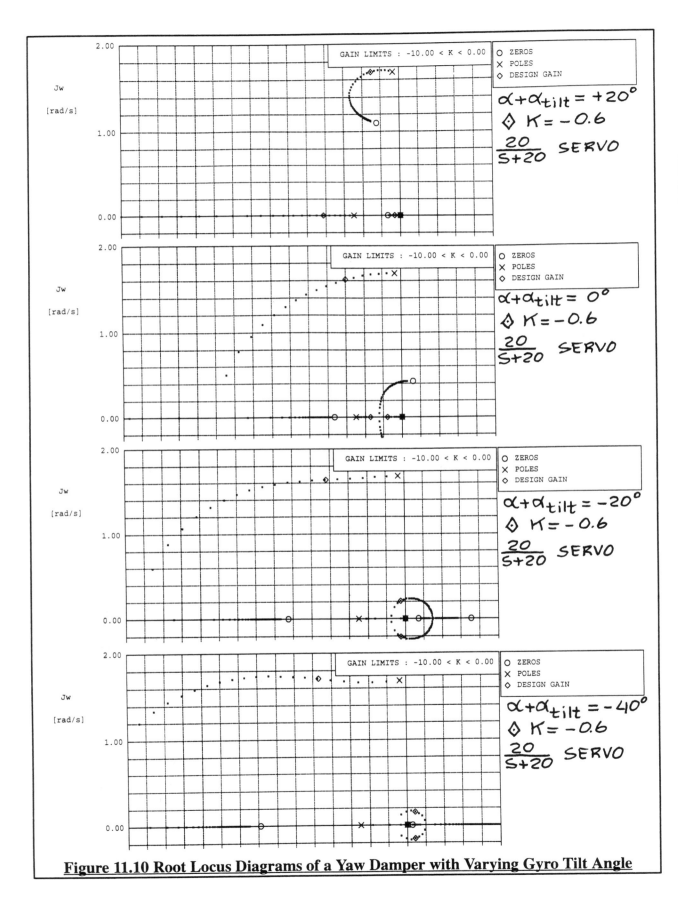

Figure 11.10 Root Locus Diagrams of a Yaw Damper with Varying Gyro Tilt Angle

11.2 PITCH DAMPERS

Most high performance airplanes also suffer from low short period damping at high altitude and/or low speed flight conditions. This effect can be illustrated by considering the open loop pitch–rate–to–elevator transfer function of the Douglas D–558–II: see Figure 3.5 in Part I for a three–view. The effect of altitude on the longitudinal dynamics of the open loop airplane may be determined with the data shown in Table 11.1. The resulting numerical open loop pitch–rate–to–elevator transfer functions are shown in Table 11.2.

It is clear from Table 11.2 that the open loop short period damping ratio and frequency both deteriorate rapidly with altitude. To maintain acceptable handling qualities the airplane must have much higher damping ratios. This can be achieved with a pitch damper. Figure 11.11 shows a block diagram for an airplane with a pitch damper. It is seen that pitch rate is fed back to the elevator. Figure 11.12 shows five root loci for this pitch damper, one for each altitude ranging from sealevel to 60,000 ft. The elevator servo is assumed to have a transfer function of $20/(s+20)$.

If the pitch damper gain, $K_{\dot{\theta}}$, is selected for the best possible closed loop damping ratio at sealevel it is seen that the performance of such a damper rapidly deteriorates with altitude. To solve this problem, the idea of gain scheduling is used. The pitch rate feedback gain, $K_{\dot{\theta}}$, is scheduled with altitude (and, as required, with Mach number) to achieve the desired closed loop performance for each flight condition. To achieve a damping ratio of 0.61 at 60,000 ft require 4–5 times the sealevel gain. Of course, there is another even worse problem at altitude: the undamped natural frequency deteriorates to the point where the airplane becomes too sluggish. To get faster (higher undamped natural frequency) response requires some form of angle–of–attack feedback. That type of feedback is discussed in Section 11.3.

Pitch dampers will tend to oppose any pitch rate away from the reference input depicted in Figure 11.11. In level flight the reference pitch rate input will normally be zero. However, if a pilot wants to maneuver an airplane in the vertical plane (pull–up or push–over) a non–zero pitch rate is desired. Just as was the case with the yaw damper of Section 11.1 there are two solutions to that problem:

a) use a washout in the feedback path
b) use computed pitch rate for the reference input: $\dot{\theta}_{ref.input} = \dfrac{g}{U_1}(n - 1)$

The latter equation follows from Eqn (4.116). The reader is asked to determine the effect of a washout circuit on the pitch damper performance for the D–558–II airplane using the data of Table 11.2.

Table 11.1   Aerodynamic and Inertial Characteristics for Determining the Longitudinal Characteristics of the Douglas D–558–II

$M = 0.8$ $I_{yy} = 1.7 \times 10^4 \text{ slug} - \text{ft}^2$ $W = 10,000 \text{ lbs}$

$S = 175 \text{ ft}^2$ $\bar{c} = 7.27 \text{ ft}$

Data \ Altitude	Sealevel	15,000 ft	30,000 ft	45,000 ft	60,000 ft
U_1 (kts)	529	501	471.4	458.6	458.6
$\bar{q}_1$ (lbs/ft^2)	947.4	534.9	281.9	138.5	67.6
C_{L_1}	0.0603	0.107	0.203	0.413	0.845
C_{L_α} (rad^{-1})	4.57	4.57	4.57	4.57	4.57
C_{D_1}	0.0210	0.0230	0.0280	0.0390	0.0550
α_1 (deg)	0.76	1.34	2.54	5.16	10.57
C_{L_u}	0.044	0.087	0.164	0.334	0.681
C_{D_u}	0	0	0	0	0
C_{m_u}	0	0	0	0	0
C_{L_q} (rad^{-1})	2.4	2.4	2.4	2.4	2.4
C_{m_q} (rad^{-1})	–6.6	–6.6	–6.6	–6.6	–6.6
C_{D_α} (rad^{-1})	0.045	0.115	0.277	0.620	1.32
C_{m_α} (rad^{-1})	–0.71	–0.71	–0.71	–0.71	–0.71
$C_{m_{T_\alpha}}$ (rad^{-1})	0	0	0	0	0

$C_{L_{\dot\alpha}} = 1.8 \text{ rad}^{-1}$ $C_{m_{\delta_e}} = -1.03 \text{ rad}^{-1}$

$C_{m_{\dot\alpha}} = -5.0 \text{ rad}^{-1}$ $C_{D_{\delta_e}} = 0 \text{ rad}^{-1}$

$C_{L_{\delta_e}} = 0.38 \text{ rad}^{-1}$

Valid for all altitudes

Table 11.2   Open Loop Pitch Rate To Elevator Transfer Functions of the Douglas D–558–II

Sealevel:

$$\frac{q(s)}{\delta_e(s)} = -72.7\frac{s(s + 2.59)(s + 0.0003)}{(s^2 + 6.07s + 55.03)(s^2 - 0.0007s + 0.0032)}$$

15,000 ft:

$$\frac{q(s)}{\delta_e(s)} = -41.1\frac{s(s + 1.54)(s - 0.0002)}{(s^2 + 3.62s + 30.08)(s^2 - 0.0012s + 0.0038)}$$

30,000 ft:

$$\frac{q(s)}{\delta_e(s)} = -21.7\frac{s(s + 0.86)(s - 0.0019)}{(s^2 + 2.03s + 15.50)(s^2 - 0.0022s + 0.0044)}$$

45,000 ft:

$$\frac{q(s)}{\delta_e(s)} = -10.7\frac{s(s + 0.44)(s - 0.0054)}{(s^2 + 1.03s + 7.49)(s^2 - 0.0042s + 0.0046)}$$

60,000 ft:

$$\frac{q(s)}{\delta_e(s)} = -5.21\frac{s(s + 0.22)(s - 0.0118)}{(s^2 + 0.507s + 3.62)(s^2 - 0.0080s + 0.0046)}$$

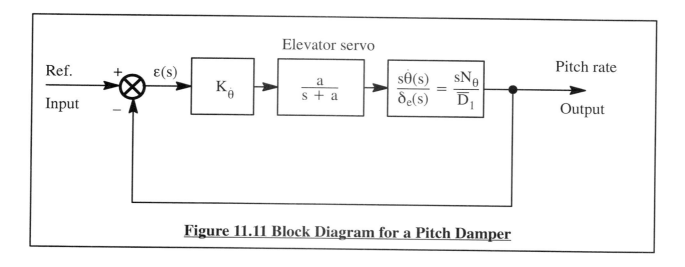

Figure 11.11 Block Diagram for a Pitch Damper

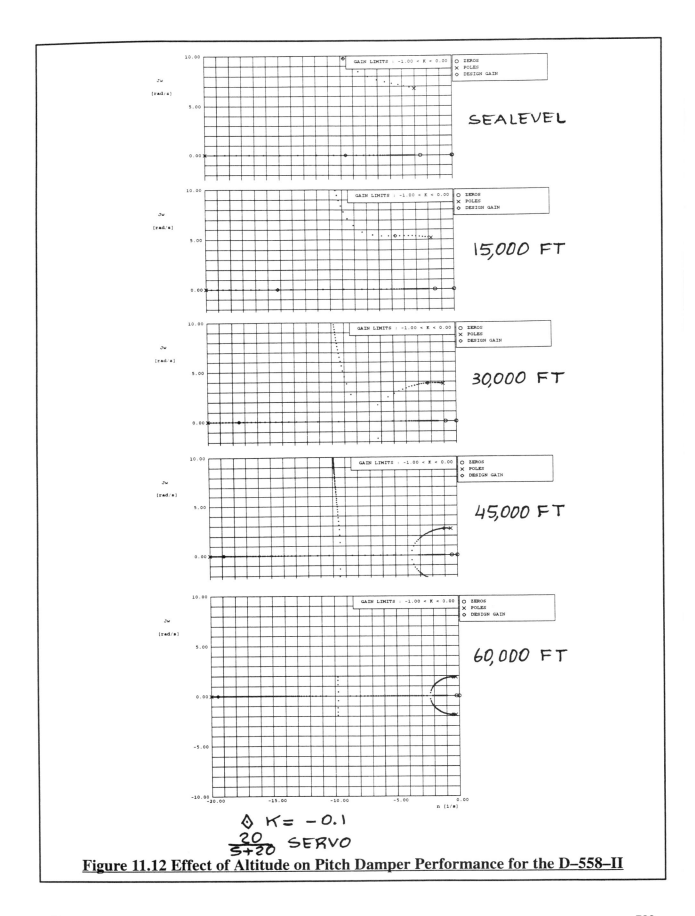

Figure 11.12 Effect of Altitude on Pitch Damper Performance for the D-558-II

11.3 STATIC STABILITY AUGMENTATION SYSTEMS

To enhance the maneuverability of modern fighter airplanes many are designed with inherent static longitudinal instability. A beneficial fallout is reduced horizontal tail size. This in turn reduces weight and drag. A problem is that the airplane still has to behave like a stable airplane as far as the pilot is concerned. The stability augmentation system which enables this must now be designed to have acceptably low failure rates (i.e. relative safety).

In principle the same ideas can be applied to reduced directional stability (and therefore reduced vertical tail size). A problem here is the structural strength of the fuselage. If an airplane is directionally unstable in a high dynamic pressure flight condition and the directional stability augmentation system were to fail, the airplane would have a tendency to "swap ends". Before it would actually do that the fuselage would probably break under the large imposed aerodynamic loading. Therefore, most modern high performance fighters still have some degree of inherent directional stability.

In this section three types of feedback used to alleviate inherent static stability problems will be discussed:

1) angle–of–attack feedback to the longitudinal controls
2) load factor feedback to the longitudinal controls
3) angle–of–sideslip feedback to the directional controls

These will be discussed in sub–sections 11.3.1 through 11.3.3 respectively.

11.3.1 ANGLE–OF–ATTACK FEEDBACK TO THE LONGITUDINAL CONTROLS

Figure 11.13 shows a block diagram of an angle of attack feedback system to the canard of an inherently unstable fighter airplane. The angle–of–attack–to–canard transfer function is that of Table 5.5 of Part I. Note that in Table 5.5 the longitudinal controller is identified as the elevator. That is incorrect and should be the canard.

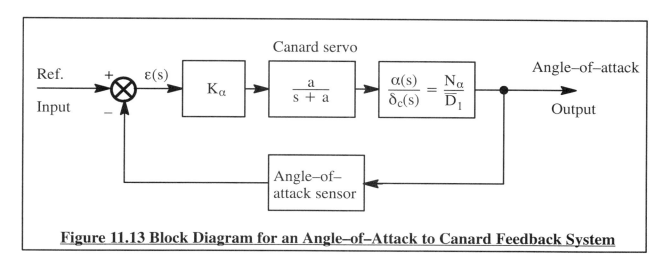

Figure 11.13 Block Diagram for an Angle–of–Attack to Canard Feedback System

For this example it will be assumed that the servo has a break frequency of a = 40 rad/sec and that the angle–of–attack sensor dynamics can be neglected. The angle–of–attack–to–canard transfer function from Table 5.5 of Part I is as follows:

$$\frac{\alpha(s)}{\delta_c(s)} = \frac{\left(-35.4s^3 + 5786s^2 + 11.5s + 22.5\right)}{\left(871s^4 + 608s^3 - 9065s^2 - 43.1s - 43.34\right)} \tag{11.6}$$

Figure 11.14 shows a root locus diagram for the system of Figure 11.13. It is seen that at the design gain of $K_\alpha = 2.5$ deg/deg the unstable real root has disappeared and that a "normal appearing" short period branch shows up. From a flying qualities viewpoint, the airplane in this flight condition should have a minimum equivalent short period frequency of about 2–3 rad/sec according to the Flight Phase Category B requirements of page 429 in Part I. The value of $n_\alpha = \dfrac{C_{L_\alpha}\overline{q}}{W/S}$ is computed to be about 11.8 g's/rad for this airplane in this flight condition. From the root locus diagram it follows that this requires an angle–of–attack to canard feedback gain of roughly 2.5 deg/deg. This level of feedback gain is acceptable because of the following consideration. At 45,000 ft altitude, the design vertical gust amounts to 15 ft/sec (severe gust according to MIL–F–8785C). With a true airspeed of 516 kts = 872 ft/sec this amounts to a gust induced angle of attack of about 1 degree. Therefore, in such a severe gust case the canard would be deflected by about K_αx1 = 2.5 deg. That is a reasonable canard deflection.

A problem with angle–of–attack feedback is the sensor and the sensor location. Figure 11.15 shows a typical vane type angle–of–attack sensor. The vane dynamics in local flow is always a concern. In practice such sensors require a significant amount of output filtering to prevent the sensor from feeding back local flow perturbations. For that reason load factor feedback is also used. That type of feedback is discussed in Sub–section 11.3.2.

11.3.2 LOAD FACTOR FEEDBACK TO THE LONGITUDINAL CONTROLS

Figure 11.16 shows a block diagram for load factor feedback to the longitudinal controls. The load–factor–to–canard transfer function in the forward path is found by the following reasoning. The perturbed load factor can be written in terms of the rate of change of flight path angle as:

$$n = \frac{U_1\dot{\gamma}}{32.2} \tag{11.7}$$

The corresponding load–factor–to–canard transfer function is therefore:

$$\frac{n(s)}{\delta_c(s)} = \frac{U_1}{32.2}\frac{\dot{\gamma}(s)}{\delta_c(s)} \tag{11.8}$$

Since: $\gamma = \theta - \alpha$ it is seen that:

$$\frac{n(s)}{\delta_c(s)} = \frac{U_1 s}{32.2}\left\{\frac{(N_\theta - N_\alpha)}{\overline{D}_1}\right\} \tag{11.9}$$

For the example fighter of Table 5.5 in Part 1 the reader is asked to show that this yields:

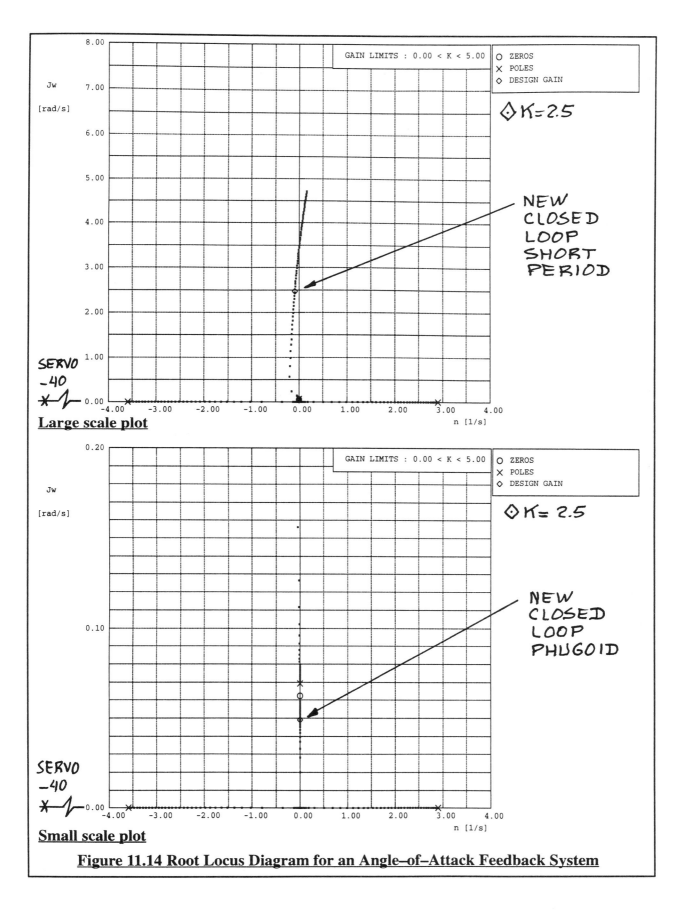

Figure 11.14 Root Locus Diagram for an Angle–of–Attack Feedback System

DESCRIPTION:

Model 2552 is a small, vane-type angle of attack transducer designed for application on small commercial aircraft where economics are stressed.

The Model 2552 is designed to provide two independent frictionless switch closures and an analogue signal from a potentiometric output. Provision for field adjustment of switch actuation point has been made. The vane is heated and provided with a spoiler bead. The transducer is not damped and uses Teflon coated surfaces for bearings; the case, cover and most of the small components are molded poly-carbonate. The extensive use of higher strength poly-carbonate is consistent with weight and cost requirements. The Model 2552 angle of attack transducer has been certi-fied for F.A.A. compliance.

PERFORMANCE AND ENVIRONMENTS:

Input Range, Vane Rotation: 0 to 25°* Switch #1 Closure
@ 12° ±½°; switch #2 closure @ 15.5° ±½°
Non-adjustable resident stops limit rotation to
approximately ±150° about aero. zero

*Input Range, Velocity: Angle of Attack Performance
applicable from 90 knots to Mach 1.5
Potentiometer Output: 5000 ohms ± 10% through 50°
Excitation: 28 VDC
Scale Factor: 1:1
Weight: 0.6 lbs. maximum
Accuracy: Switches ± 0.5° @ Room temperature (+25°C)
Potentiometer Linearity ± 2% F.S. (Independent)
Operating Temperature: −54°C to +71°C
Steady State Acceleration: 10 g
De-Icing: TSO-C54
Altitude: Sea Level to 50,000 ft.
Vibration: TSO-C54
Humidity: TSO-C54

Courtesy: Conrac Corporation, El Monte, California

Figure 11.15 Example of a Vane Type Angle–of–Attack Sensor

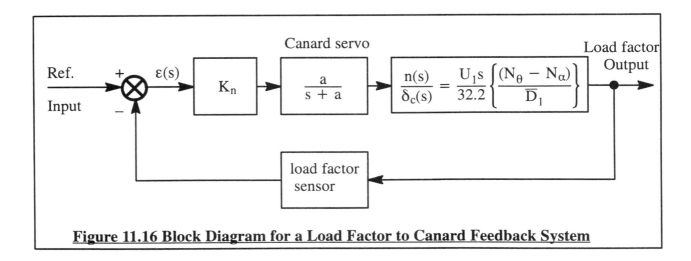

Figure 11.16 Block Diagram for a Load Factor to Canard Feedback System

$$\frac{n(s)}{\delta_c(s)} = (27.07s)\left\{\frac{\left(35.4s^3 + 25s^2 + 2145.5s - 22.4\right)}{\left(871s^4 + 608s^3 - 9065s^2 - 43.1s - 43.34\right)}\right\} \qquad (11.10)$$

The upper root locus diagram of Figure 11.17 shows that with load factor feedback a reasonable short period root pair can be obtained. The feedback gain required to attain the same level of short period undamped natural frequency of 2–3 rad/sec is about 0.3 deg/g. This appears to be a very reasonable feedback gain. Even for a 5–g perturbation the amount of canard activity required is a modest 0.3x5=1.5 deg.

One problem with this system is the fact that the phugoid remains as two real roots, one of which is unstable. This can be seen from the small–scale (lower) plot in Figure 11.17.

Another problem with load factor feedback is the sensitivity of the sensor. For accurate flight path control in turbulent air, a relatively low threshold is required for the acceleration sensor. However, that implies that any structurally induced vibrations (such as those caused by gun firing) can cause the system to feed back signals to the canard which are not really there. A certain amount of filtering and/or some type of firing interrupt feature would have to be added to make this work.

In the next sub–section an application of sideslip feedback to the directional controls (normally the rudder) will be discussed.

11.3.3 SIDESLIP FEEDBACK TO THE DIRECTIONAL CONTROLS

When an airplane is designed without inherent static directional stability a sideslip angle feedback system to the rudder can provide the required "SAS–on" stability referred to in Chapter 5 of Part I. Figure 11.18 shows a block diagram of a sideslip–angle–to–rudder feedback system.

Because there exist, at the time of this writing, no certified airplanes without inherent directional stability, the example given here is artificial. The example is obtained by examining the consequence of reducing the size of the vertical tail of the Douglas D–558–II airplane. The lateral–directional derivative (including reduced static directional stability) data for this airplane are summarized in Table 11.3.

Figure 11.19 presents root locus diagrams (large scale and small scale) for the sideslip feedback system shown in Figure 11.18. Note that the effect of sideslip is to reconstitute a dutch roll root pair. According to Table 6.12 in Part I, the minimum acceptable dutch roll undamped natural frequency is 0.4 rad/sec. It is seen from Figure 11.19 that to attain this required a feedback gain of 0.3 deg/deg. With an assumed sideslip disturbance of 1 degree in this flight condition, the required rudder deflection would be 0.3 deg. which is quite reasonable.

Observe, that sideslip feedback does generate a lateral phugoid mode. This is probably objectionable and should be compensated for by feedback of roll–rate to the ailerons. It is left as an exercise to the reader to show how this would decouple the lateral phugoid.

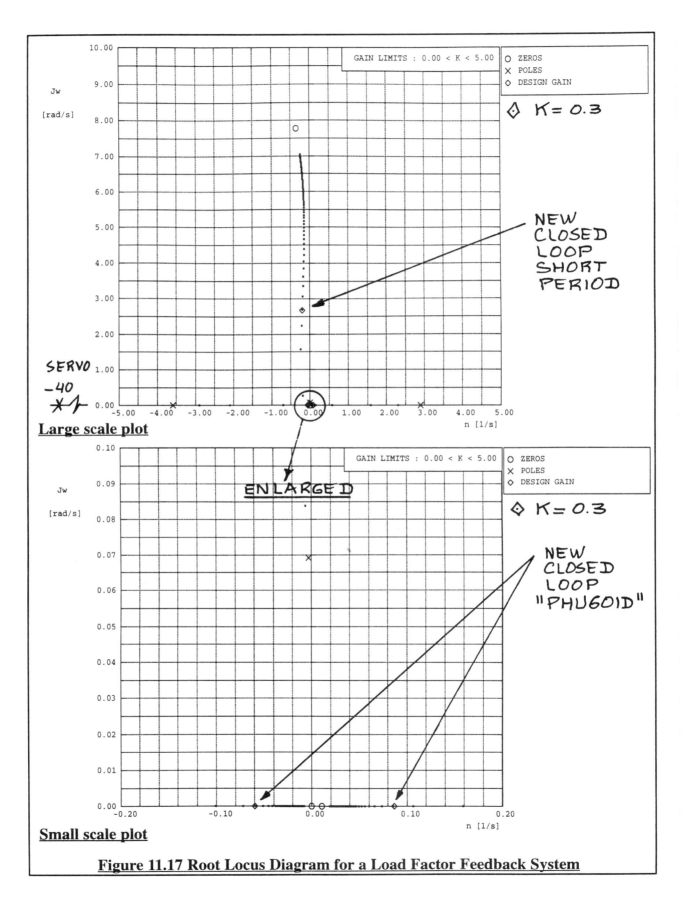

Figure 11.17 Root Locus Diagram for a Load Factor Feedback System

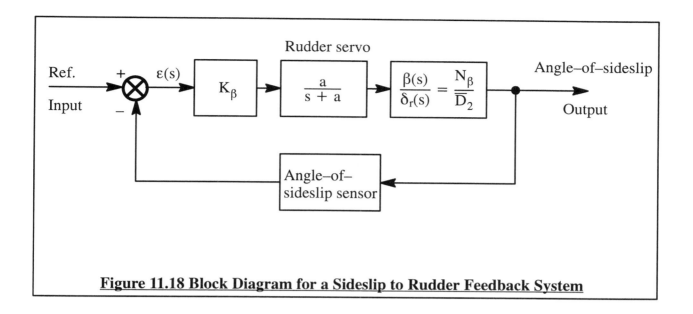

Figure 11.18 Block Diagram for a Sideslip to Rudder Feedback System

Table 11.3	Aerodynamic and Inertial Characteristics for Determining the Lateral–Directional Characteristics of the Douglas D–558–II		

M = 1.4 at 75,000 ft	S = 175 ft^2	b = 25.0 ft	W = 10,000 lbs
U_1 = 1,364 ft/sec = 808 kts		$\overline{q}_1$ = 101 lbs/ft^2	C_{L_1} = 0.56
α_1 = 9.25 deg	$I_{zz} = I_{xx}$ = 40,000 slugft^2		I_{xz} = 0 slugft^2

All derivatives in 1/rad

$C_{y_\beta} = -7.0$	$C_{l_\beta} = -0.018$	$C_{n_\beta} = 0$
$C_{y_p} = 0.19$	$C_{l_p} = -0.37$	$C_{n_p} = -0.057$
$C_{y_r} = 0.84$	$C_{l_r} = 0.041$	$C_{n_r} = -0.57$
$C_{y_{\delta_r}} = 0.075$	$C_{l_{\delta_r}} = -0.001$	$C_{n_{\delta_r}} = -0.061$

Sideslip–to–rudder transfer function:

$$\frac{\beta(s)}{\delta_r(s)} = (0.00307)\frac{(s - 0.0029)(s + 0.0401)(s + 220.6)}{(s + 0.0464)(s + 0.3432)(s^2 - 0.0073s + 0.0166)} \quad \text{or:}$$

$$\frac{\beta(s)}{\delta_r(s)} = \frac{4.19s^3 + 924.3s^2 + 34.36s - 0.108}{1364.1s^4 + 521.5s^3 + 40.43s^2 + 8.648s + 0.36}$$

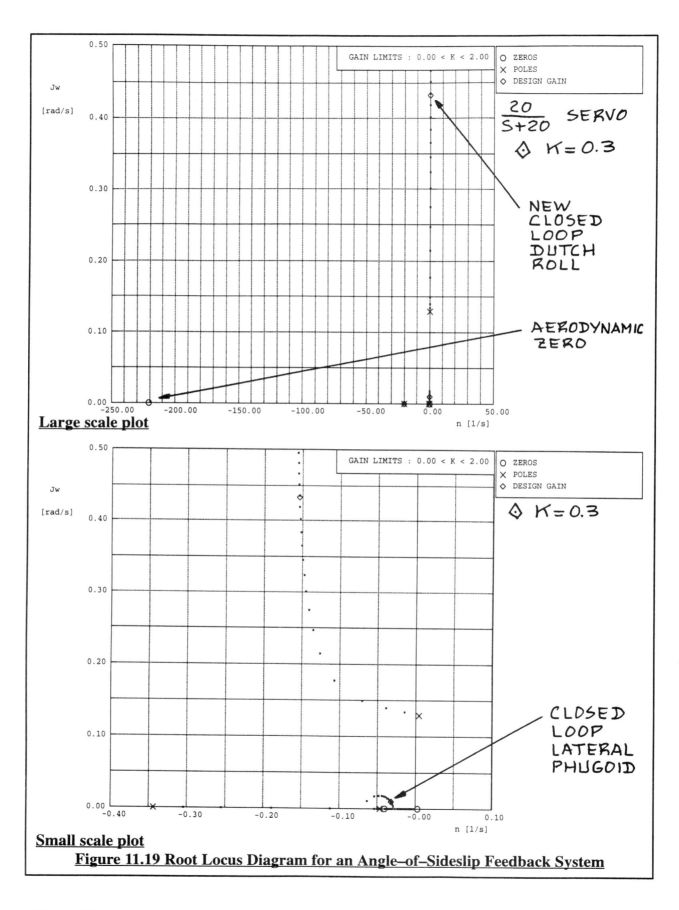

Large scale plot

Small scale plot
Figure 11.19 Root Locus Diagram for an Angle–of–Sideslip Feedback System

11.4 BASIC AUTOPILOT SYSTEMS

To lower the workload of pilots, particularly on long flights, most airplanes are equipped with some from of automatic flight control system (AFCS) or autopilot system. The capability of such systems to control the airplane depends on customer requirements and on the amount of investment the customer is willing to make. Therefore, autopilot systems are available from very basic to very sophisticated. The reader is referred to the annual issue of Business and Commercial Aviation magazine, called the Planning and Purchasing Handbook (Reference 11.4) for detailed information, including weight, power and pricing data on these systems.

Most autopilot systems have as a minimum the capability to control or hold certain flight parameters. In high performance airplanes and in airplanes used for medium to long range transportation, the autopilot system also has the ability to perform navigational tasks.

In a flight parameter control or hold mode, an autopilot can be designed to control and/or hold any one or more of the following parameters:

Longitudinal Control/Hold Functions

- Pitch attitude
- Altitude
- Airspeed or Mach number
- Climb or descent rate

Lateral–Directional Control/Hold Functions

- Bank angle
- Heading angle
- Turn rate at constant altitude and speed
- Zero lateral acceleration

In a navigational mode an autopilot can be designed to carry out any one or more of the following navigational functions:

Longitudinal Navigational Functions

- Glideslope intercept and hold
- Flare before landing
- Automatic landing

Lateral–Directional Navigation Functions

- Localizer intercept and hold
- Fly toward a radio beacon
- Fly toward an arbitrary way point

Obviously, the autopilot must be designed so that conflicting modes cannot be selected by the pilot. Pilots must have a way of communicating with the AFCS to command it to perform certain tasks. That communication is normally accomplished with a so–called interface panel. Examples of recent autopilot interface panels are given in Figures 11.20a and 11.20b.

Because of the natural split of the airplane equations of motion into longitudinal and lateral–directional equations, the discussion of autopilot system also follows this split. The material is therefore organized in the following manner:

11.5 Basic Longitudinal Autopilot Modes
11.6 Basic Lateral–Directional Autopilot Modes
11.7 Longitudinal Navigation Modes
11.8 Lateral–Directional Navigation Modes

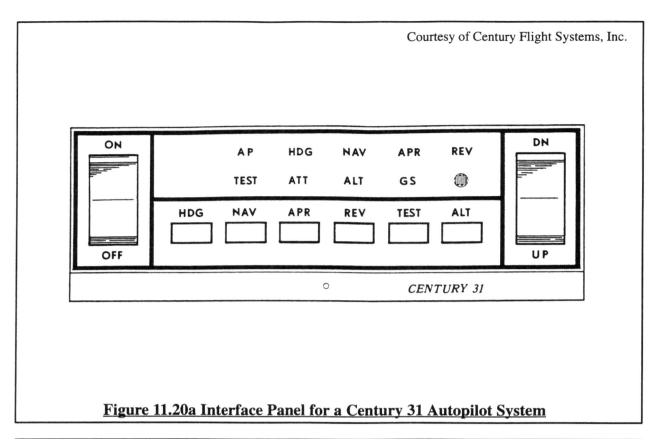

Figure 11.20a Interface Panel for a Century 31 Autopilot System

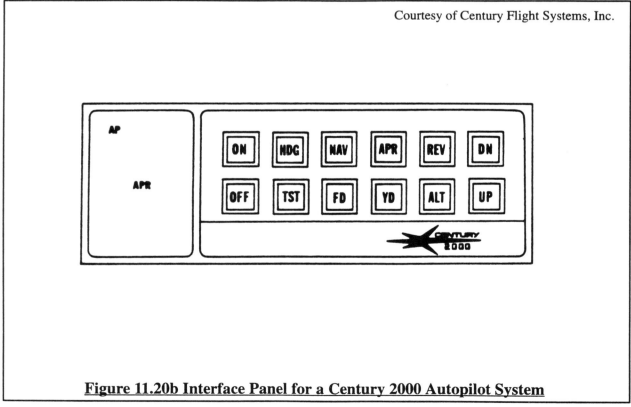

Figure 11.20b Interface Panel for a Century 2000 Autopilot System

Like airplanes, autopilot systems must meet minimum certification standards. Unlike airplanes, autopilot systems themselves are not certified. Instead, the specific installation of a given autopilot in a specific airplane type is certified. This means that autopilot systems manufacturers must seek individual certification of their systems in each airplane type.

To give the reader some idea of how autopilot systems can be installed in an airplane, a perspective of the installation of a Century 41 autopilot in a typical twin engine airplane is shown in Figure 11.21 The reader is referred to Appendix E (Appendices A through D are in Part I) for a more detailed presentation of autopilot systems. The author is grateful to Century Flight Systems for permission to use some of their material.

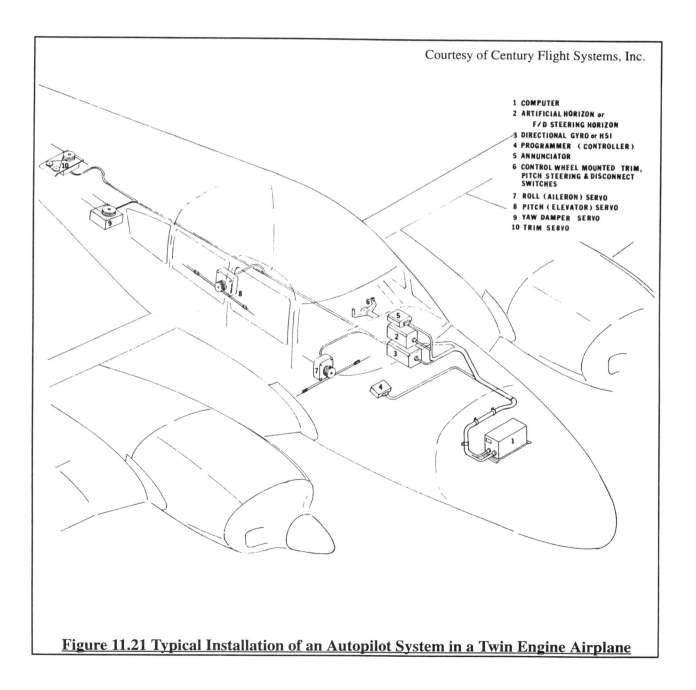

Courtesy of Century Flight Systems, Inc.

1 COMPUTER
2 ARTIFICIAL HORIZON or
   F/D STEERING HORIZON
3 DIRECTIONAL GYRO or HSI
4 PROGRAMMER (CONTROLLER)
5 ANNUNCIATOR
6 CONTROL WHEEL MOUNTED TRIM,
   PITCH STEERING & DISCONNECT
   SWITCHES
7 ROLL (AILERON) SERVO
8 PITCH (ELEVATOR) SERVO
9 YAW DAMPER SERVO
10 TRIM SERVO

Figure 11.21 Typical Installation of an Autopilot System in a Twin Engine Airplane

11.5 BASIC LONGITUDINAL AUTOPILOT MODES

In this Section the following basic longitudinal control or hold functions will be discussed:

11.5.1 Pitch Attitude Hold Mode
11.5.2 Altitude Hold Mode
11.5.3 Airspeed or Mach number Hold Mode
11.5.4 Control–wheel Steering Mode

The effect of airplane type, airplane performance, servo (or actuator) performance and flight condition on the closed loop behavior of these autopilot modes will be delineated.

11.5.1 PITCH ATTITUDE HOLD MODE

Pitch attitude control or hold modes were among the first autopilot modes used. One reason is to prevent the pilot from having to constantly control pitch attitude in turbulent air.

In analyzing and/or synthesizing any autopilot mode, two questions must be answered first:

1) Which type of controller is to be used to control or hold the parameter selected?

2) What type of feedback loop structure is needed?

In the case of pitch attitude hold, the answer to the first question may be obvious: a human pilot controls pitch attitude through the elevator. Therefore an autopilot would probably employ the same method. The answer to the second question is fairly obvious also. A human pilot, in instrument conditions will use a vertical (pitch attitude) gyro as a reference to control the pitch attitude of an airplane. Therefore a feedback loop of pitch attitude angle to the elevator is probably the simplest way to achieve the pitch attitude hold objective.

Consider the case of controlling the pitch attitude angle of a four–engine, propeller driven airplane (Airplane F of page 515 in Part I). Figure 11.22 shows the functional block diagram of the corresponding pitch attitude hold mode. In the approach flight condition selected for this example, the desired (reference) pitch attitude is taken to be zero degrees. The elevator servo is assumed to be a first order servo with as transfer function 10/(s+10). Break frequencies of 10 rad/sec were typical of servos of the era in which Airplane F was designed.

The lowest break frequency in the transfer function of a pitch attitude gyro is typically much higher than the highest break frequency in an airplane pitch–attitude–to–elevator transfer function. The gyro can thus be viewed as a pure gain and its transfer function eliminated from consideration.

Figure 11.23 shows an analytical block diagram of a pitch attitude hold mode system for Airplane F in its approach flight condition (sealevel and 189 ft/sec or M=0.17). The transfer function of the airplane is the short period approximation of the pitch–attitude–to–elevator transfer function, according to Eqn (5.60). The required derivative data were taken from page 518 of Part I.

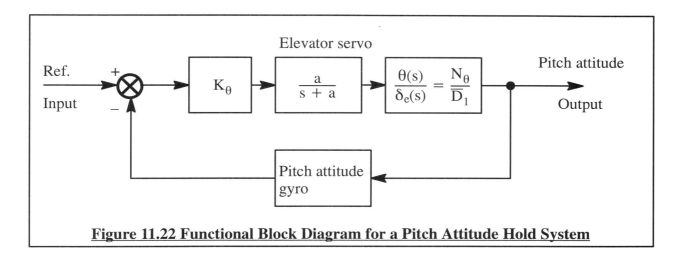

Figure 11.22 Functional Block Diagram for a Pitch Attitude Hold System

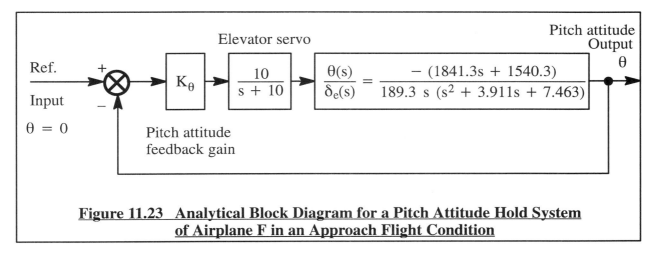

Figure 11.23   Analytical Block Diagram for a Pitch Attitude Hold System of Airplane F in an Approach Flight Condition

Figure 11.24 shows the corresponding root locus diagram. The following observations are in order. Note that the open loop system damping ratio is 0.72. The corresponding short period frequency is 2.7 rad/sec. The reader is asked to verify that the airplane easily meets the frequency/damping requirements of Sub–section 6.3.4 in Part I. The effect of the pitch attitude hold mode is to drive the short period root toward the imaginary axis. Figure 11.25 shows a Bode plot of the open loop transfer function of the system. It is seen that the gain margin is about 13.1 db which corresponds to a gain at which the autopilot becomes unstable of –4.5 deg/deg. A reasonable operating gain for pitch attitude hold modes is around –0.5 deg/deg. Figure 11.24 shows that the corresponding closed loop damping ratio is still a respectable 0.43. The minimum allowable according to Sub–section 6.3.4 is 0.35. The simple pitch attitude hold autopilot therefore works well.

Now consider a pitch attitude hold mode for a large jet transport in a high altitude cruise flight condition. For this example, Airplane J will be used. Figure 11.26 shows the analytical block diagram for this case. The servo transfer function for that airplane is assumed to be 20/s+20, which is representative for this type of airplane.

Figure 11.27 shows the corresponding root locus diagram. The following observations are in order. Note that the open loop system damping ratio is 0.35. This is the minimum acceptable

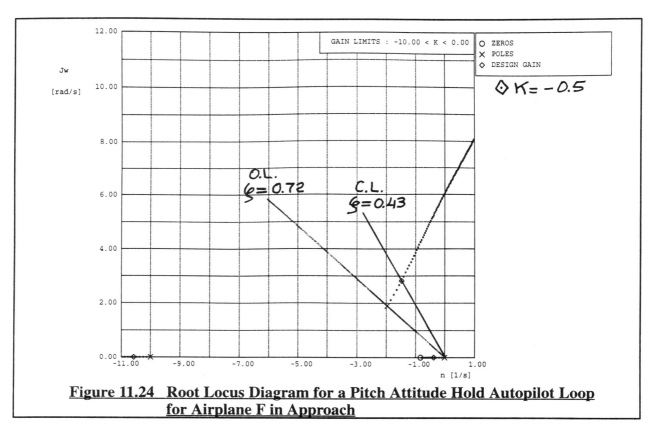

Figure 11.24   Root Locus Diagram for a Pitch Attitude Hold Autopilot Loop for Airplane F in Approach

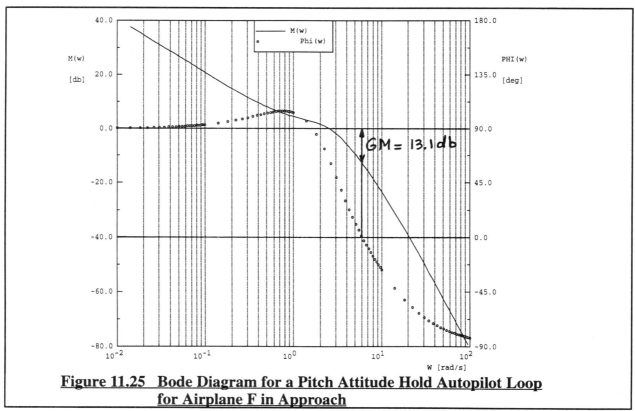

Figure 11.25   Bode Diagram for a Pitch Attitude Hold Autopilot Loop for Airplane F in Approach

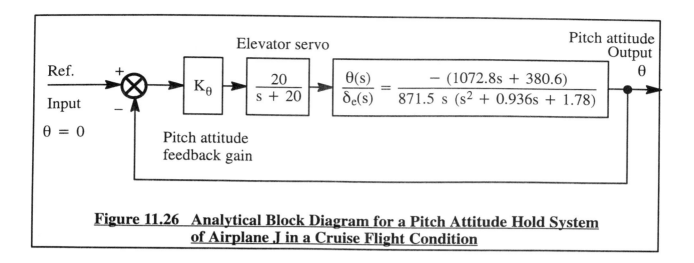

Figure 11.26 Analytical Block Diagram for a Pitch Attitude Hold System of Airplane J in a Cruise Flight Condition

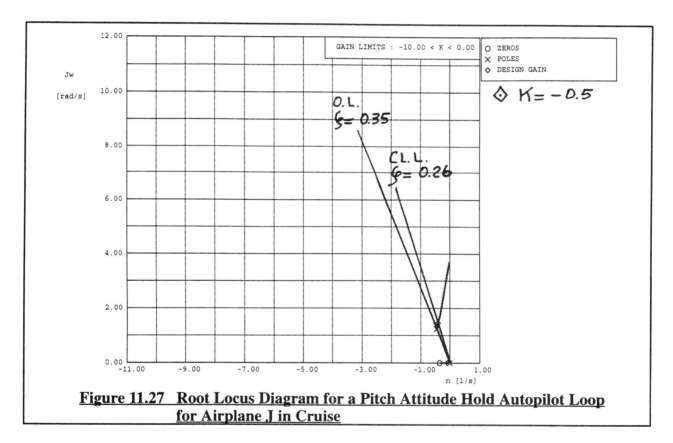

Figure 11.27 Root Locus Diagram for a Pitch Attitude Hold Autopilot Loop for Airplane J in Cruise

damping ratio according to the requirements of Sub–section 6.3.4. of Part I.   The effect of the pitch attitude hold mode is to drive the short period root toward the imaginary axis. Figure 11.28 shows a Bode plot of the open loop transfer function of the system. It is seen that the gain margin is about 21 db which corresponds to a gain at which the autopilot becomes unstable of –11.2 deg/deg. A reasonable operating gain for pitch attitude hold modes is around –0.5 deg/deg. Figure 11.27 shows that the corresponding closed loop damping ratio is an unacceptable 0.26. Clearly, a simple pitch attitude hold loop does not work for this type of airplane.

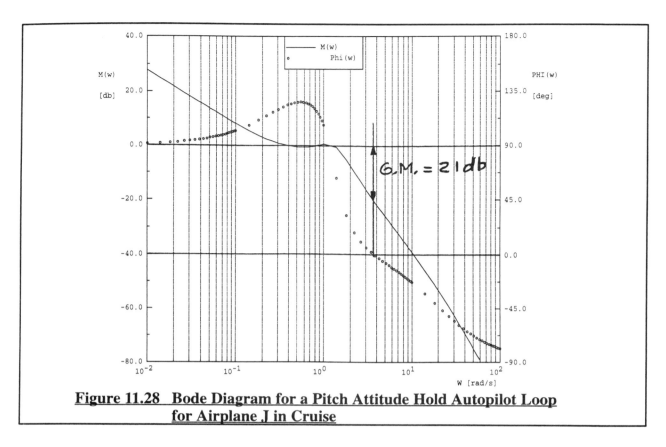

Figure 11.28 Bode Diagram for a Pitch Attitude Hold Autopilot Loop for Airplane J in Cruise

The reader is asked to remember the discussion of pitch dampers in Section 11.2. It was seen that a pitch damper drives the short period roots toward a region of higher damping ratio (i.e. away from the imaginary axis). One solution to the pitch attitude hold problem for this airplane is therefore to add an inner loop pitch damper. A block diagram showing the double loop configuration of a pitch attitude hold system with inner loop pitch rate damping is shown in Figure 11.29.

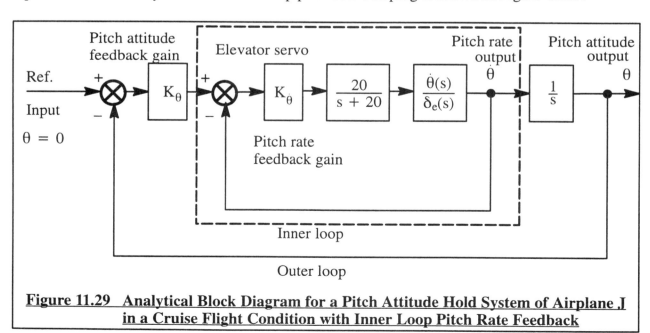

Figure 11.29 Analytical Block Diagram for a Pitch Attitude Hold System of Airplane J in a Cruise Flight Condition with Inner Loop Pitch Rate Feedback

The inner loop should be analyzed first. Figure 11.30 shows a root locus diagram of this inner (pitch rate feedback) loop. It is seen that as the pitch rate feedback gain, $K_{\dot{\theta}}$, is increased the short period poles are moved toward much higher damping ratios. Two different inner loop gains are being considered: $K_{\dot{\theta}} = -1.0$ and $K_{\dot{\theta}} = -1.5$ deg/deg/sec. The corresponding closed loop pole locations are indicated in Figure 11.30.

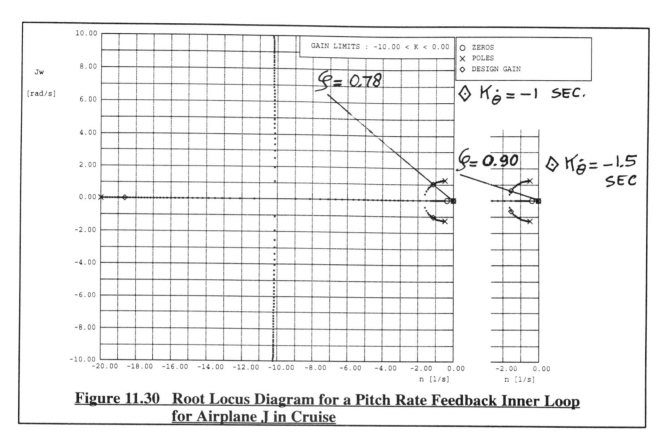

Figure 11.30   Root Locus Diagram for a Pitch Rate Feedback Inner Loop for Airplane J in Cruise

The outer loop (pitch attitude hold loop) will now be considered at the two inner loop gain levels. The closed inner loop pole locations of Figure 11.30 now form the so–called outer loop departure poles. In addition there is the integrator pole caused by changing pitch rate to pitch attitude in the outer loop. Figure 11.31 shows a root locus diagram with the critical pitch attitude loci for each inner loop gain. It is seen that the pitch attitude hold loop corresponding to the higher inner loop gain has somewhat better frequency and damping behavior.

In a real case, the behavior of the outer loop should be simulated in the presence of turbulence and also for different flight conditions, weight and mass distributions before a final gain combination is decided upon.

Several questions should now be asked:

1) What is the effect of the servo break frequency on closed loop performance?

2) What is the effect of the flight condition on closed loop performance?

3) What is the effect of using the complete instead of the approximate pitch–attitude–to–elevator transfer function?

These questions are answered in the following.

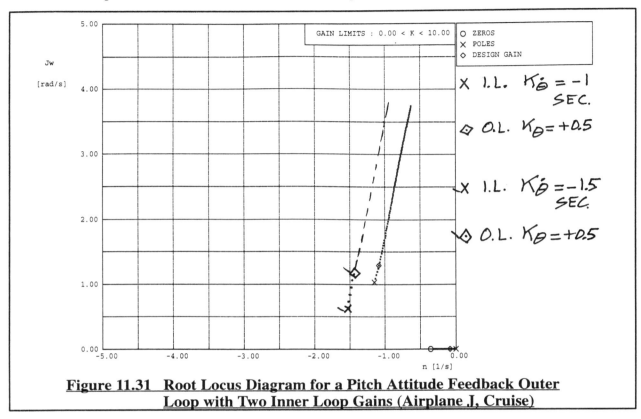

Figure 11.31 Root Locus Diagram for a Pitch Attitude Feedback Outer Loop with Two Inner Loop Gains (Airplane J, Cruise)

1) Effect of the servo break frequency on closed loop performance.

Many servos (actuators) can be modelled as first order lags, a/s+a being a typical form. The magnitude of the break frequency "a" is an indication of how fast a servo reacts to an input command. Clearly, the faster an actuator moves a control surface, the faster the airplane can react. It turns out that the cost and complexity of an actuator are related to the magnitude of "a". The higher the break frequency, the greater the cost of the actuator. To illustrate the effect of actuator break frequency on closed loop performance, consider the case of the pitch attitude hold autopilot of Figure 11.23.

Figure 11.32 shows a composite root locus for four values of servo break frequency: a= 20, a=10, a=5 and a=2.5 rad/sec. It is clear from these root loci that as the break frequency of the actuator is lowered, the undamped natural frequency at the constant gain point of $K_\theta = -0.5$ deg/deg is lowered. The damping ratio is not significantly affected: this may not be true in other examples.

2) Effect of the flight condition on closed loop performance.

The effect of flight condition on the closed loop performance of a pitch damper was already illustrated in Section 11.2 where it was shown that gain scheduling with altitude is required. This

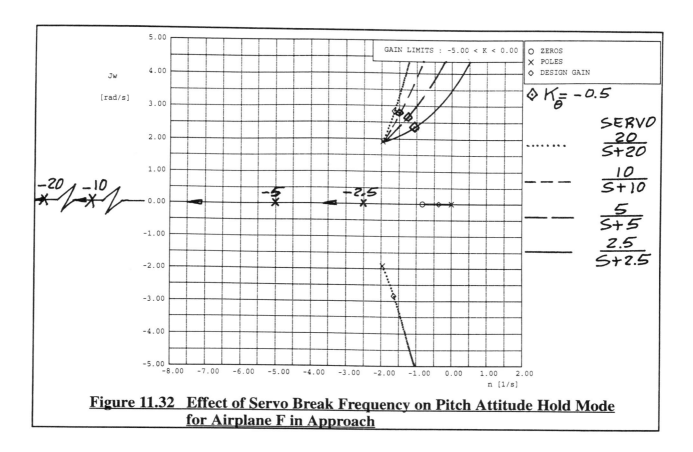

Figure 11.32   Effect of Servo Break Frequency on Pitch Attitude Hold Mode for Airplane F in Approach

tends to be generally true, particularly for high performance airplanes. The effect of flight condition on the closed loop performance of a pitch attitude hold system will be considered for Airplane J for the three flight conditions defined in Table B10 of Part I.

Figure 11.33 shows a composite root locus diagram for a pitch attitude hold system in approach, low altitude (20,000 ft) cruise and high altitude (40,000 ft) cruise. The diamond symbols indicate the operating points at the same feedback gain as used in the example of Figure 11.31.

3) Effect of using the complete instead of the approximate pitch–attitude–to–elevator transfer function?

The effect of using the complete instead of the approximate pitch–attitude–to–elevator transfer function in a pitch attitude hold autopilot is shown in Figure 11.34 for Airplane F in an approach flight condition.

Observe that the effect on the "short period" pitch attitude branch of the root locus is negligible. The approximate root locus does not have (of course) a phugoid branch. The complete root locus does. It is of interest to observe that pitch attitude feedback improves the phugoid damping very significantly. In other words, pitch attitude feedback serves to "augment" the stability of the phugoid mode!

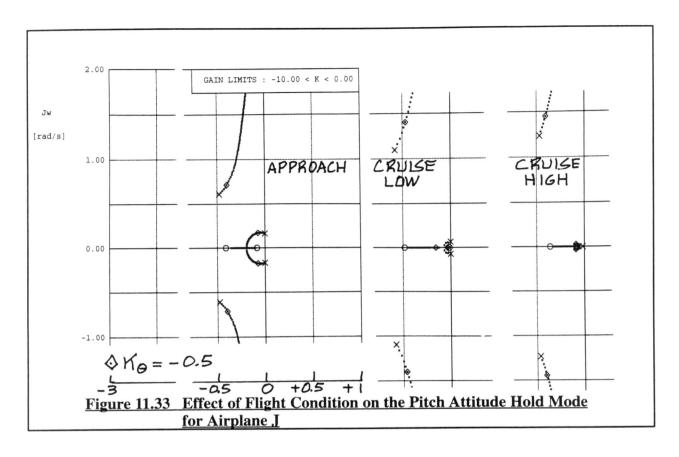

Figure 11.33 Effect of Flight Condition on the Pitch Attitude Hold Mode for Airplane J

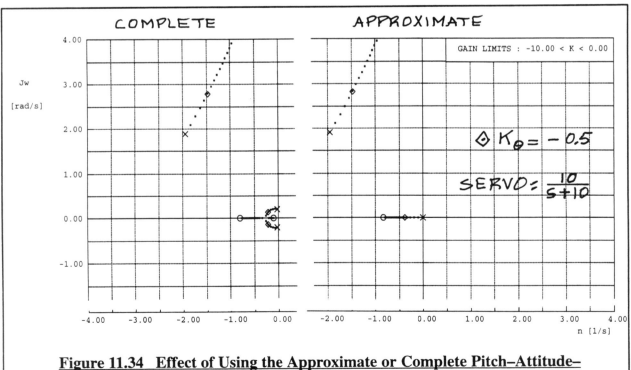

Figure 11.34 Effect of Using the Approximate or Complete Pitch–Attitude–to–Elevator Transfer Function on the Pitch Attitude Hold Mode for Airplane F

11.5.2 ALTITUDE HOLD MODE

Altitude hold is an important mode in many autopilot systems. To control altitude is the same as controlling rate of climb (or rate of descent). By commanding zero climb rate, altitude will be kept constant. In most airplanes altitude is controlled with the elevator. The reader may have observed from Chapter 5 in Part I that no expression was derived for the altitude–to–elevator transfer function of an airplane. To derive such a transfer function first consider Figure 11.35.

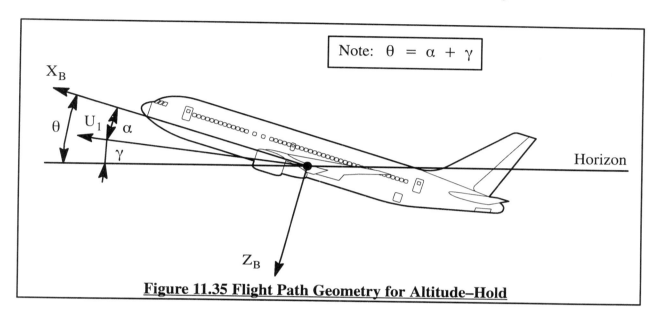

Figure 11.35 Flight Path Geometry for Altitude–Hold

The rate of climb, h , can be written as:

$$\dot{h} = U_1 \sin \gamma \approx U_1 \gamma \qquad (11.11)$$

Upon applying the Laplace transform:

$$sh(s) = U_1 \gamma(s) \qquad (11.12)$$

If the elevator is used as the controller it follows that:

$$\frac{h(s)}{\delta_e(s)} = \frac{U_1}{s} \left\{ \frac{\gamma(s)}{\delta_e(s)} \right\} \qquad (11.13)$$

Note from the insert in Figure 11.35:

$$\theta = \alpha + \gamma \quad \text{and therefore}: \quad \theta(s) = \alpha(s) + \gamma(s) \qquad (11.14)$$

The altitude–to–elevator transfer function can thus be written as follows:

$$\frac{h(s)}{\delta_e(s)} = \frac{U_1}{s}\left\{\frac{\theta(s) - \alpha(s)}{\delta_e(s)}\right\} \tag{11.15}$$

A block diagram for the altitude control system is sketched in Figure 11.36.

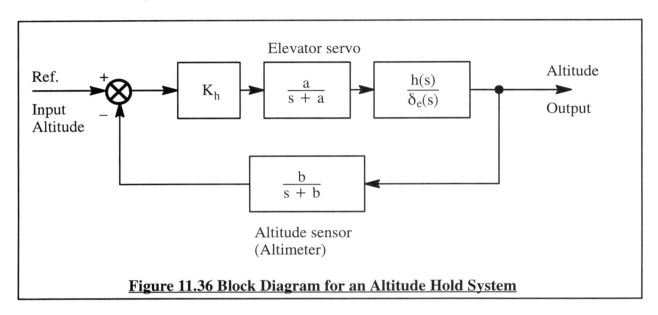

Figure 11.36 Block Diagram for an Altitude Hold System

The altitude–to–elevator transfer function is that of Eqn (11.15). Note the additional lag in the feedback path. Barometric altimeters tend to have a built–in lag, the magnitude of which depends on the detail design of the aneroid bellows and the line lengths in the system.

In the following example, the data for Airplane E of page 508 in Part I are used to find the altitude–to–elevator transfer function in a 20,000 ft cruise condition. Note that Eqn (11.15) can also be written as follows:

$$\frac{h(s)}{\delta_e(s)} = \frac{U_1}{s}\left(\frac{N_\theta - N_\alpha}{\overline{D}_1}\right) \tag{11.16}$$

From pages 511 and 512:

$$N_\theta = -10,371s^2 - 12,043s - 226.3 \tag{11.17}$$

$$N_\alpha = -62.64s^3 - 10,413s^2 - 129.8s - 107.9 \tag{11.18}$$

$$\overline{D}_1 = 451.8s^4 + 2,197.2s^3 + 11,333s^2 + 154s + 102 \tag{11.19}$$

With a steady state speed of 450 ft/sec this yields for Eqn (11.16):

$$\frac{h(s)}{\delta_e(s)} = \frac{450}{s}\left(\frac{62.64s^3 + 42s^2 - 11,913s - 118.4}{451.8s^4 + 2,197.2s^3 + 11,333s^2 + 154s + 102}\right) \tag{11.20}$$

The servo break frequency is assumed to be a=10 rad/sec. Three altimeter break frequencies will be considered: b=0 rad/sec (no lag), b=0.2 rad/sec and b=1 rad/sec. A root locus diagram of the altitude hold system of Figure 11.36 is presented in Figure 11.37.

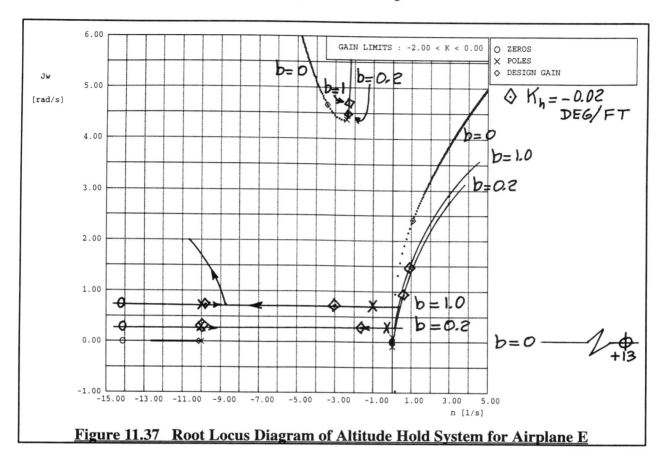

Figure 11.37 Root Locus Diagram of Altitude Hold System for Airplane E

It is seen that the phugoid mode is driven unstable at very low feedback gain. This problem is fairly typical for altitude hold control in airplanes with low phugoid damping. Note that the problem does not disappear even if the altimeter lag is negligible. To solve this problem several options are available:

1) Pitch attitude feedback to stabilize the phugoid mode. The effect of pitch attitude feedback on the phugoid was already discussed in Sub–section 11.5.1, item 3.

2) Vertical acceleration feedback. The effect of vertical acceleration feedback was already discussed in Sub–section 11.3.2.

3) Lead–lag compensation. A lead–lag compensator, designed to provide two zeros into which to draw the phugoid poles can stabilize the overall system. The effect of this lead–lag compensator is illustrated in Figure 11.38. The lead–lag network used is: $\dfrac{(s + 0.1)(s + 0.4)}{(s + 2)(s + 3)}$.

It is seen that such a lead–lag can indeed stabilize the system. Before accepting this as a solution other flight conditions would have to be investigated as well.

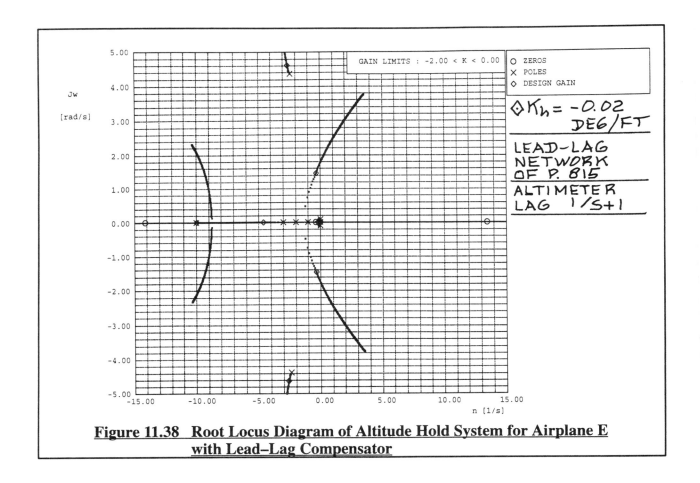

Figure 11.38 Root Locus Diagram of Altitude Hold System for Airplane E with Lead–Lag Compensator

11.5.3 AIRSPEED OR MACH NUMBER HOLD MODE

Automatic control of airspeed and/or Mach number is a feature required in nearly all high performance airplanes. Such a feature prevents pilots from having to "chase" Mach number during long cruising flights. It also makes carrying out automatic approaches much easier.

In several high subsonic airplanes the possibility of Mach tuck exists. Mach tuck was discussed in Part I (see Index). To prevent the tuck phenomenon from becoming a flight safety problem so–called Mach trim systems are installed in some airplanes.

There are two methods in use for controlling airspeed, depending on the flight condition. In up–and–away flight conditions, airspeed is normally controlled by using the engine throttles. Such systems are referred to as autothrottle systems. On final approach airspeed can also be controlled with autothrottles but there is another option available: speedbrakes. Airspeed hold using autothrottles is discussed in 11.5.3.1. Airspeed hold using speedbrakes is discussed in 11.5.3.2.

In earlier jets flight Mach numbers were controlled by feeding back Mach number to the elevator. Because this method is still used in some airplanes, an example is discussed in 11.5.3.3.

An approach to a Mach tuck control system is presented in 11.5.3.4.

11.5.3.1 Airspeed Hold Mode Using Autothrottles

Figure 11.39 shows a typical block diagram for an autothrottle system.

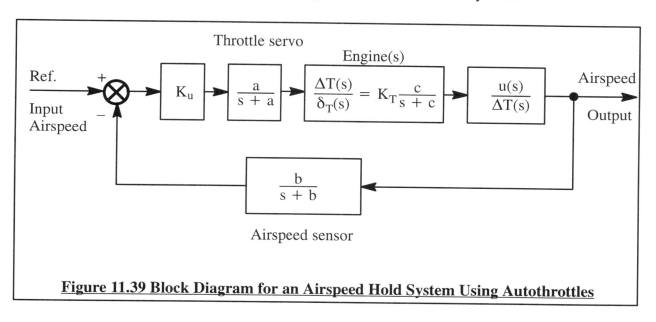

Figure 11.39 Block Diagram for an Airspeed Hold System Using Autothrottles

In the autothrottle system of Figure 11.39 the actuator moves the engine throttles. These in turn adjust the fuel supply to the engines. The engines respond with an increase in thrust. The engine –to–throttle gain, K_T, can be expressed in lbs/in of throttle movement or lbs/rad (or lbs/deg) of throttle movement. In this chapter the latter units will be used. Engine thrust response to throttle motion can be represented by a first order lag with break frequency of "c" rad/sec. The airplane responds to this with a change in speed according to the speed–to–thrust transfer function.

In the feedback path of Figure 11.39 there appears yet another first order lag, this one due to the speed sensing system. Because such systems are normally dependent on pressure differences in static ports and lines a certain amount of lag is inevitable.

The gain, K_u, in the forward path is the throttle movement in radians per ft/sec change in airspeed. This gain needs to be determined consistent with closed loop system stability.

The reader should observe that autothrottle systems such as the one in Figure 11.39 have a built–in 270 phase lag due to the three first orders. The relative stability of these systems is therefore always a concern. Consider as an example Airplane J in the approach flight condition.

First, the various transfer functions in Figure 11.39 will be defined for Airplane J in an approach flight condition.

Throttle servo transfer function: $\dfrac{a}{(s + a)} = \dfrac{20}{(s + 20)}$ is typical for this type of airplane.

Engine transfer function: for Airplane J, the lift–to–drag ratio on final approach is about 7.0 according to page 544 in Part I. The thrust required is therefore 564,000/7.0 = 80,571 lbs. The maximum available thrust in this airplane is about 198,000 lbs. Assuming a 0.5 radian throttle movement from the approach thrust setting, the engine–to–throttle gain is $(198,000 - 80,571)/0.5 = 234,858$ lbs/rad.

It will be assumed that the engines have a spool–up time constant of 5 seconds. This gives the first order lag model for the engine a break frequency of 0.2 rad/sec. The engine model therefore

is: $K_T \dfrac{c}{(s + c)} = 234,858 \dfrac{0.2}{(s + 0.2)}$

Airplane speed–to–thrust transfer function: This transfer function can be determined from Eqn (5.33) in Part I by substituting:

$X_{\Delta T}$ **for** X_{δ_e} : where $X_{\Delta T}$ is the forward acceleration imparted to the airplane per unit

thrust. It is assumed that the available thrust is aligned with the X–stability–axis.

For the approach flight condition this means: $\dfrac{1}{m} = 1 \times 32.2/564,000 = 0.000057$ ft/sec^2/lbs.

$Z_{\Delta T} = 0$ **for** Z_{δ_e} : where $Z_{\Delta T}$ is the upward acceleration imparted to the airplane per unit

thrust. It is assumed that the available thrust is aligned with the X–stability–axis so that there is no Z–component.

$M_{\Delta T} = \dfrac{z_T}{I_{yy}}$ **for** M_{δ_e} : where $M_{\Delta T}$ is the pitch angular acceleration imparted to the

airplane per unit thrust. This assumes that the net thrust line is a distance z_T below the center of gravity. For Airplane J: $z_T = 6.4$ ft. For the approach flight condition this means:

$\dfrac{z_T}{I_{yy}} = 6.4/30,500,000 = 0.0000002$ rad/sec^2/lbs.

These substitution and the other data from Table B10 (Part I) were entered into the AAA program to produce the following speed–to–thrust transfer function:

$$\frac{u(s)}{\Delta T(s)} = \frac{0.0033}{228.5} \left\{ \frac{(s - 0.11)(s^2 + 1.015s + 0.599)}{(s^2 + 0.951s + 0.594)(s^2 - 0.0005s + 0.0281)} \right\} \qquad (11.21)$$

$$= \left\{ \frac{(0.0033s^3 + 0.0030s^2 + 0.0016s - 0.0002)}{(228.5s^4 + 217.2s^3 + 141.96s^2 + 6.043s + 3.815)} \right\}$$

Airspeed sensor transfer function: For this transfer function the assumption will be made that a time constant of 1 second is achievable. Therefore: $\dfrac{b}{(s + b)} = \dfrac{1}{(s + 1)}$.

Figure 11.40 shows a root locus diagram for this system. A reasonable operating gain for this type of a system could be K_u = 0.02 rad/ft/sec. Figure 11.40 indicates that this system works well: the gain margin is certainly sufficient.

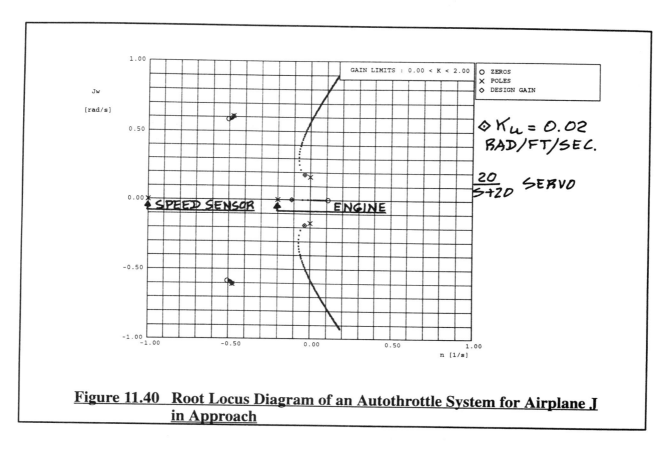

Figure 11.40   Root Locus Diagram of an Autothrottle System for Airplane J in Approach

Whether or not a system such as this is workable depends strongly on the engine spool–up time constant and on the speed sensor lag. If the engine spool–up time constant is 10 seconds and the speed sensor time constant is five seconds, the root locus diagram of Figure 11.41 shows that the system no longer has acceptable closed loop characteristics. The designer should therefore determine the actual time constant behaviors of engine and speed sensor before analyzing such a loop.

11.5.3.2 Airspeed Hold Mode Using Speedbrakes

Figure 11.42 shows a typical speedbrake installation for airplanes which use this system for speed control on final approach. Example airplanes are the Fokker F–28 and AVRO RJ series.

Figure 11.43 depicts a block diagram for a speedbrake speed control system. It is seen that in this case there are only two instead of three first order lags in the system. This should improve the relative stability of such speed control systems over that of the autothrottle system.

Although Airplane J has no such system, one will be "invented". In this case, the speed–to–speed–brake transfer function of the airplane will be needed.

To arrive at a reasonable estimate for the drag characteristics of this system some assumptions will have to be made. The first assumption is that the required fuselage mounted speedbrake area in the fully deployed position amounts to approximately 90 ft^2. In that position a drag coefficient of 0.8, based on the deployed area, is also assumed.

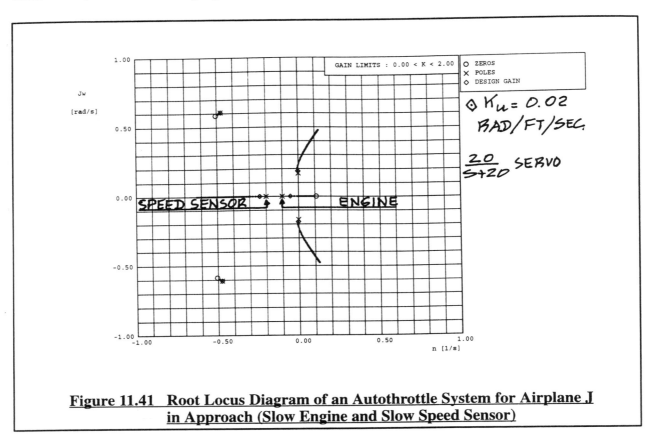

Figure 11.41   Root Locus Diagram of an Autothrottle System for Airplane J in Approach (Slow Engine and Slow Speed Sensor)

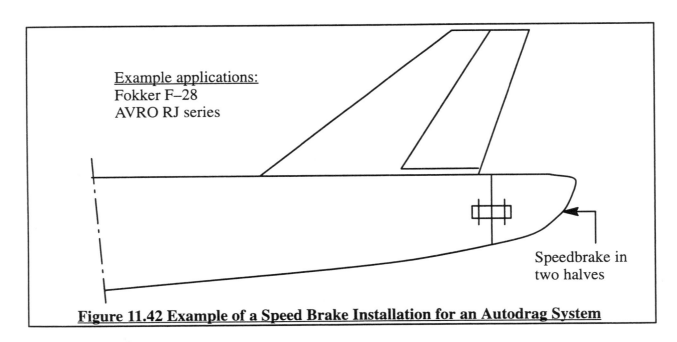

Figure 11.42 Example of a Speed Brake Installation for an Autodrag System

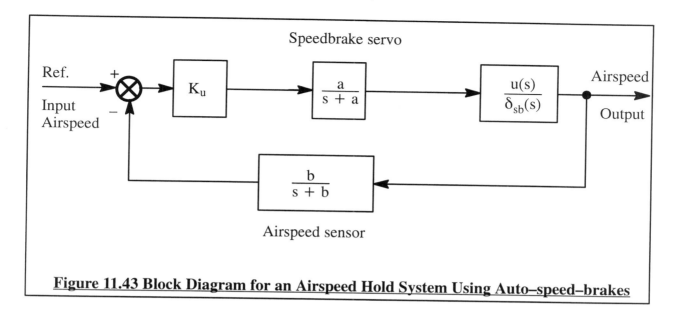

Figure 11.43 Block Diagram for an Airspeed Hold System Using Auto–speed–brakes

The total drag coefficient of the fully deployed speedbrake, based on wing reference area is therefore: $\Delta C_{D_{sb}} = 0.8 \times 90/5500 = 0.0131$. Assuming that, in the fully deployed position, the speedbrake has a deflection angle of 60 degrees, the speedbrake drag derivative is then: $C_{D_{\delta_{sb}}} = (0.0131/60) \times 57.3 = 0.0125 \ 1/rad$.

It will be assumed, that the speedbrake has no effect on lift, therefore: $C_{L_{\delta_{sb}}} = 0 \ 1/rad$.

The distance from the fuselage mounted speedbrake to the c.g. of the airplane is assumed to be 14 ft. The pitching moment derivative due to speedbrake deflection can therefore be found as: $C_{m_{\delta_{sb}}} = 0.0125 \times 14/27.3 = 0.0064 \ 1/rad$, where $\bar{c} = 27.3ft$. Note that this derivative is positive because an increase in drag due to speedbrake deflection would raise the nose of the airplane.

With this information the airplane speed–to–speedbrake transfer function was determined by entering the appropriate data into the AAA program. The resulting speed–to–speedbrake transfer function was found as:

$$\frac{u(s)}{\delta_{sb}(s)} = \frac{-52.0}{228.5}\left\{\frac{(s + 0.19)(s^2 + 0.715s + 0.60)}{(s^2 + 0.951s + 0.594)(s^2 - 0.0005s + 0.0281)}\right\} \qquad (11.22)$$

$$= \left\{\frac{(-52.0s^3 - 47.1s^2 - 38.25s - 5.936)}{(228.5s^4 + 217.2s^3 + 141.96s^2 + 6.043s + 3.815)}\right\}$$

Figure 11.44 shows a root locus diagram for this system. Note the rather high design gain. That gain is directly related to the size of the speedbrake. If a lower operating gain is desired, the speedbrake area should be enlarged. The assumed speed brake area of 90 ft2 is rather small for an airplane the size of Airplane J.

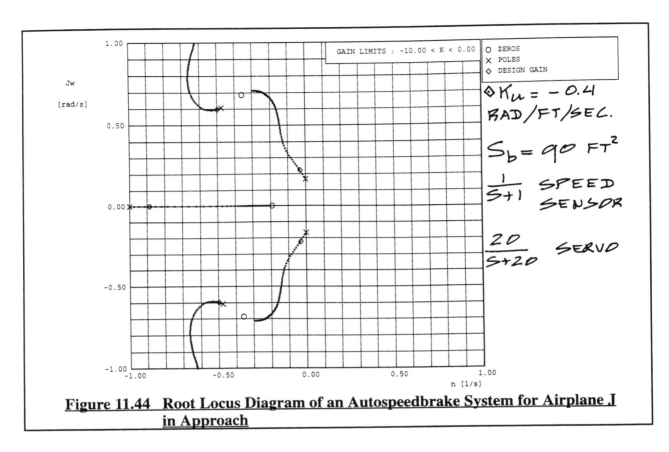

Figure 11.44 Root Locus Diagram of an Autospeedbrake System for Airplane J in Approach

At this point it is desirable to summarize some pros and cons of autothrottle and autospeed-brake systems. This summary will be given for two speed regimes: high speed (cruise) and low speed (approach).

At high speed (cruise): The autodrag system for speed control in cruise makes no sense due to the increase in cruise drag. In this speed range, only autothrottles (called full–time autothrottles in this case) are a viable option.

At low speed (final approach):

Potentially, autothrottles have the following problems:

● In turbulent air, due to the long spool–up time of the engines, there is considerable throttle activity. This results in the engines whining up and down which can be disturbing to passengers. Also, this results in more engine wear and tear.

● In the case of a go–around, because the engines are operating at a relatively low thrust level, the spool–up time can result in flight path response delays.

Potentially, autothrottles have the following advantages:

● The aft end of the fuselage is free for an A.P.U. installation.

● Because of the lower required thrust setting on final approach, there will be less fuel consumption and less noise.

At low speed (final approach):

Potentially, autospeedbrakes have the following problems:

● Because of the added drag, a higher engine thrust setting is required. This results in increased fuel consumption and increased noise.

● Because of the preferred installation of the speedbrake at the aft end of the fuselage, it is difficult to use that location for the A.P.U. (Auxiliary Power Unit). Aft fuselages are ideal locations for APU's because of the lower exposure to noise by ground personnel.

Potentially, autospeedbrakes have the following advantages:

● The thrust in turbulent air is kept constant. The speedbrake controls the speed. This creates less engine wear and tear and is also not disturbing to the passengers.

● Because the engines are operating at a relatively high thrust level, their response to a go–around command is faster. In addition, in the case of a go–around, the speedbrakes would be automatically closed which also results in an instantaneous forward acceleration.

11.5.3.3 Mach Hold Using the Elevator

Figure 11.45 shows a block diagram of a Mach hold system using the elevator as controller.

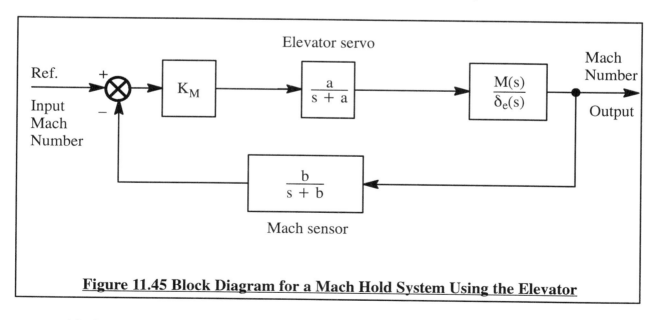

Figure 11.45 Block Diagram for a Mach Hold System Using the Elevator

Airplane J in a high altitude, high speed flight condition is used to illustrate what a root locus diagram for this type of system would be like. The corresponding root locus diagram is shown in Figure 11.46. The servo break frequency was assumed to be 20 rad/sec and the Mach sensor break frequency was assumed to be 0.2 rad/sec. The Mach–number–to–elevator transfer function is obtained from the speed–to–elevator transfer function in Table B10 (Part I) by dividing by the speed of sound at 40,000 ft: 968.1 ft/sec.

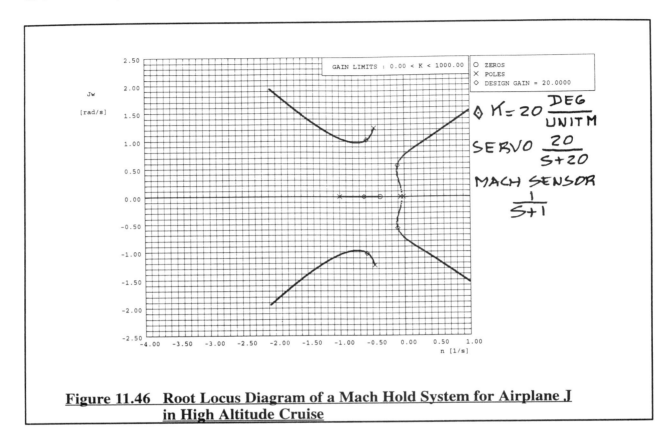

Figure 11.46   Root Locus Diagram of a Mach Hold System for Airplane J in High Altitude Cruise

It is seen from Figure 11.46 that the degenerate phugoid roots are driven unstable by the Mach hold system. By adding a compensator with the transfer function {(s+1.5)/1.5}{4/(s+4)} the problem can be solved as seen in Figure 11.47. The corresponding gain and phase margins are satisfactory as seen from the Bode plot in Figure 11.48.

11.5.3.4 Mach Tuck Control (Mach Trim)

In the high subsonic speed range changes can occur in the pressure distribution around an airfoil which can result in a nose down pitching moment of increasing magnitude as the flight Mach number increases. This can give the airplane a tendency to nose down (this is called: tuck). In turn this may result in flying quality problems such as reversals in stick–force–speed–gradients.

The following discussion of one solution (used on the Boeing 707) to this problem was adapted from Reference 11.5.

The Boeing 707 has both maneuvering and speed stability in the entire subsonic Mach range below M=0.81 within certain weight and c.g. limits. The airplane has maneuvering stability over the entire subsonic and transonic speed range. A mild speed instability becomes evident in the transonic range above M=0.84. It is emphasized that there are no changes in the fundamental flying

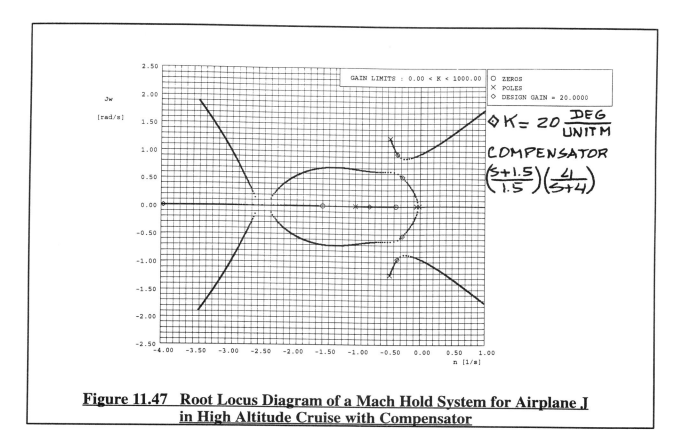

Figure 11.47   Root Locus Diagram of a Mach Hold System for Airplane J in High Altitude Cruise with Compensator

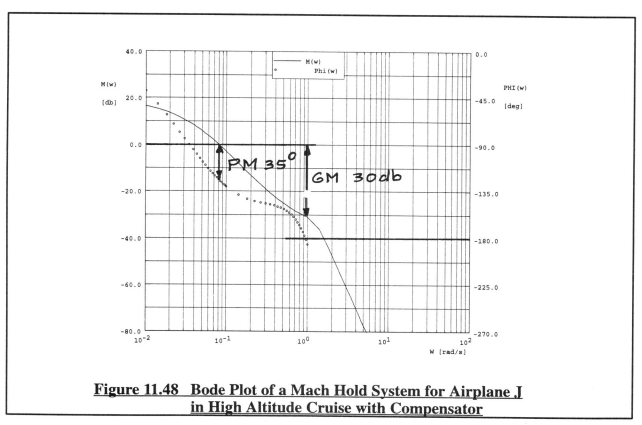

Figure 11.48   Bode Plot of a Mach Hold System for Airplane J in High Altitude Cruise with Compensator

characteristics of the airplane, either manually or on automatic, as long as normal control procedures are followed. The movable stabilizer is still used for trim and a pull on the control column will raise the nose while a push will lower the nose.

As speed is increased there is a change in the pressure distribution over a typical airfoil: as the Mach number increases the center of pressure does shift aft. Figures 11.49 and 11.50 illustrate this trend. If the c.p. location was the only factor which affects airplane pitch, the airplane would tend to nose down. However, in the 707 there is an offsetting pitching moment generated by the horizontal tail which actually keeps the nose up as Mach number increases. However, as the Mach number builds up the aft shift in the c.p. will overcome the offsetting trend of the tail and the airplane will nose down unless corrected by the pilot or by the autopilot.

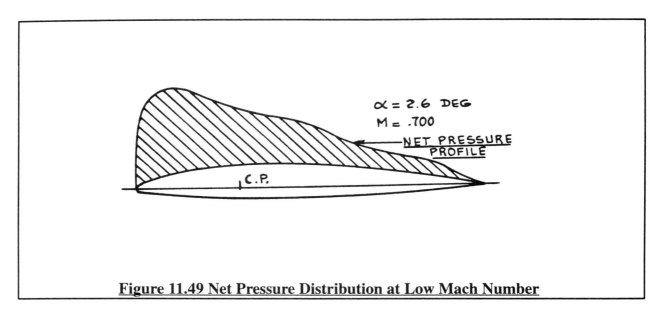

Figure 11.49 Net Pressure Distribution at Low Mach Number

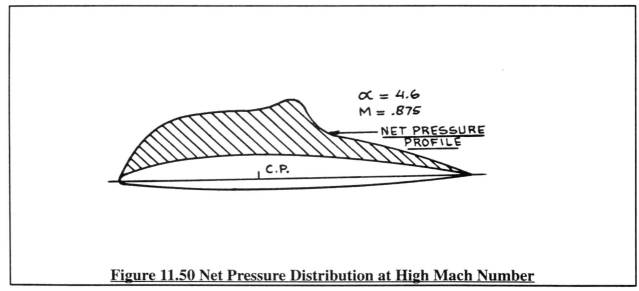

Figure 11.50 Net Pressure Distribution at High Mach Number

As the Mach number increases, the variation of elevator control force with Mach number does tend to reverse as indicated in Figure 11.51 with the Mach trim system inoperative. Note that the airplane is trimmed at M=0.82. If the pilot should decide to increase speed without changing trim, he must push on the column with increasing force as shown in Figure 11.51. Above M=0.85 the required column push force becomes less and less until above about M=0.87 a pull will be required to increase speed. However, a pull is still required to pull positive "g" and a push is still required to obtain negative "g".

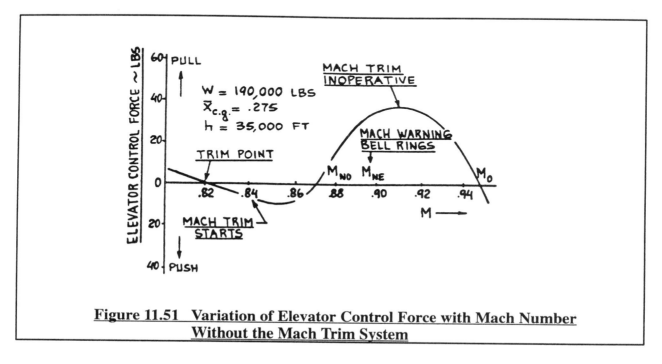

Figure 11.51   Variation of Elevator Control Force with Mach Number Without the Mach Trim System

To overcome the reversal in column force with speed a so–called Mach trim system was installed in the 707. Figure 11.52 shows the authority of the Mach trim system over the stabilizer. In turn, with the Mach trim system operating the elevator control force varies with Mach number as shown in Figure 11.53. Note that with the Mach trim system operative the control–wheel–force–versus–speed gradient is stable over the entire range of Mach numbers.

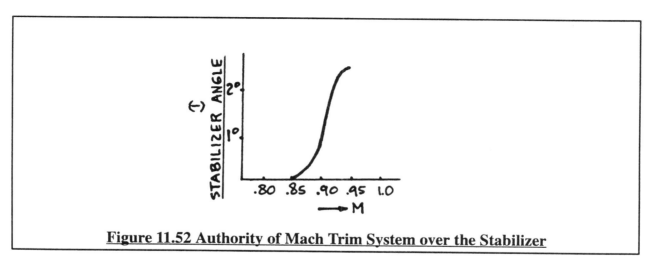

Figure 11.52 Authority of Mach Trim System over the Stabilizer

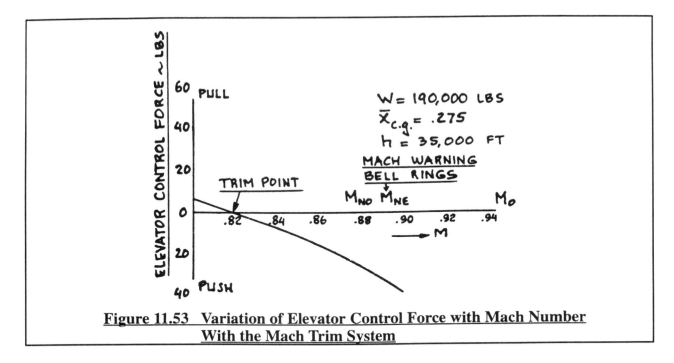

Figure 11.53 Variation of Elevator Control Force with Mach Number With the Mach Trim System

With modern airfoil shapes and computational design/analysis methods it has become possible to produce airfoils with significantly less "tuck" behavior. Most modern jets therefore do not require Mach trim systems in their normal speed range.

11.5.4 CONTROL WHEEL STEERING MODE

Airplanes can be controlled manually by means of the control stick (some light airplanes and fighters) or the control wheel (most light airplanes, transports and bombers). With the availability of an autopilot it is also possible to control an airplane with the control wheel but through the autopilot. This can be done in a variety of ways. One way is to add a force or position transducer to the control column and to consider the output of that transducer to be a pitch rate command signal. Such a system is called a control wheel steering system.

Consider the case of a force transducer mounted on the control column. Figure 11.54 shows a functional block diagram of such a control wheel steering system. When the pilot lets go of the control column he in fact commands zero pitch rate. Mathematics dictates that the first integral of $\dot{\theta} = 0$ is $\theta = $ constant it follows that such a system then will hold the last pitch attitude thereby acting like a pitch attitude hold mode.

It will be shown that such a system can in fact hide inherent instabilities of an airplane from the pilot. As an example the inherently unstable fighter of Table 5.5 will be considered. Before doing that, consider the block diagram of the control wheel steering system shown in Figure 11.55. In turn, this block diagram can be translated into the computational block diagram of Figure 11.56.

The pitch–rate–to–canard transfer function of the inherently unstable fighter airplane of Table 5.5 in Part I will be used. Note that because the example airplane is a fighter, the system of Figure 11.56 is now called a control stick steering system.

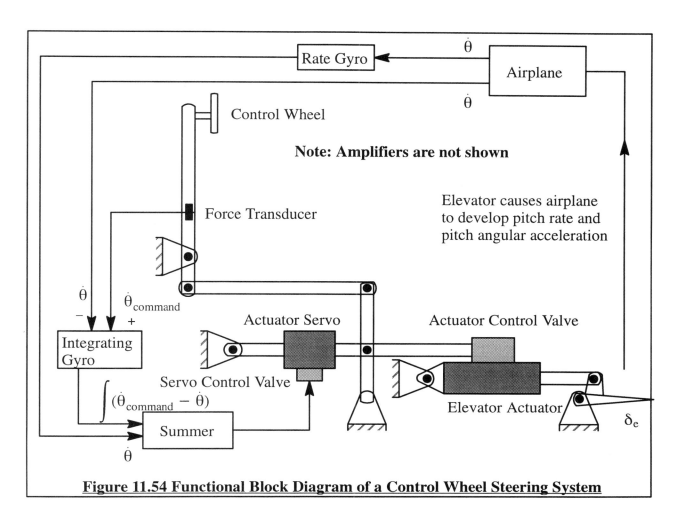

Figure 11.54 Functional Block Diagram of a Control Wheel Steering System

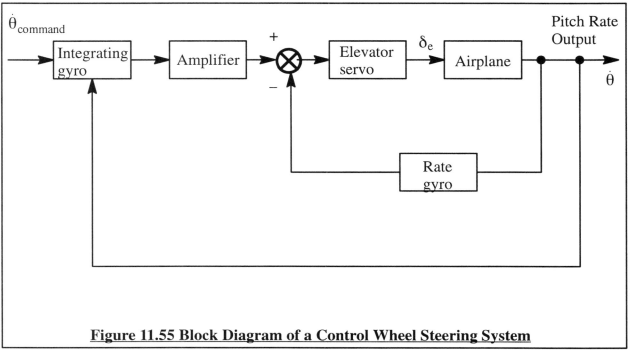

Figure 11.55 Block Diagram of a Control Wheel Steering System

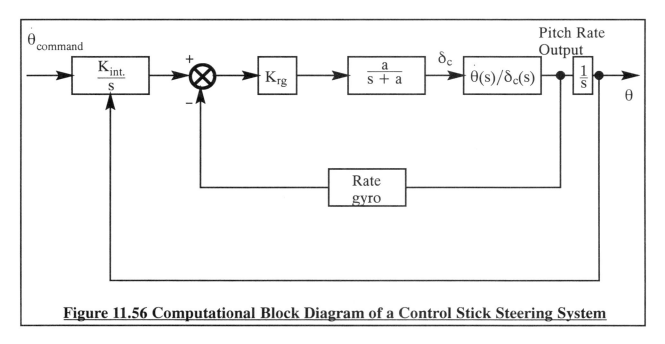

Figure 11.56 Computational Block Diagram of a Control Stick Steering System

Using a canard servo break frequency of 40 rad/sec, the root locus diagram for the system of Figure 11.56 is shown in Figure 11.57. Note that the system does indeed stabilize the airplane. As might be expected, the outer loop performance is very sensitive to the value selected for the inner loop gain. In Figure 11.57 the inner loop gain is $K_{rg} = 0.5$ deg/deg/sec . By doubling the inner loop gain to $K_{rg} = 1.0$ deg/deg/sec the root locus diagram of Figure 11.58 is obtained. Note that at the selected operating point the airplane frequency and damping are excellent.

The Bode plot of Figure 11.59 shows that this system is an example of a so–called conditionally stable system. At the selected operating point the system gain margin is seen to be GM=19 db, while the system phase margin is PM=45 deg which are both adequate.

Obviously, the gains used in this example will probably have to be scheduled with altitude, Mach number and also with center of gravity location. At forward c.g. this example fighter does become inherently stable which implies a major change in the open loop pitch–rate–to–canard transfer function of the airplane.

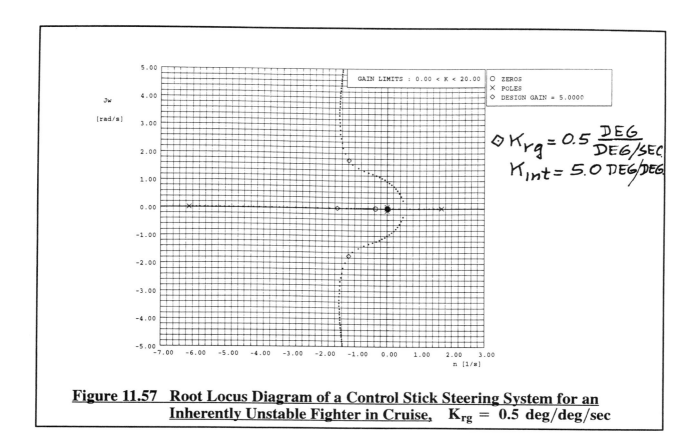

Figure 11.57   Root Locus Diagram of a Control Stick Steering System for an Inherently Unstable Fighter in Cruise, K_{rg} = 0.5 deg/deg/sec

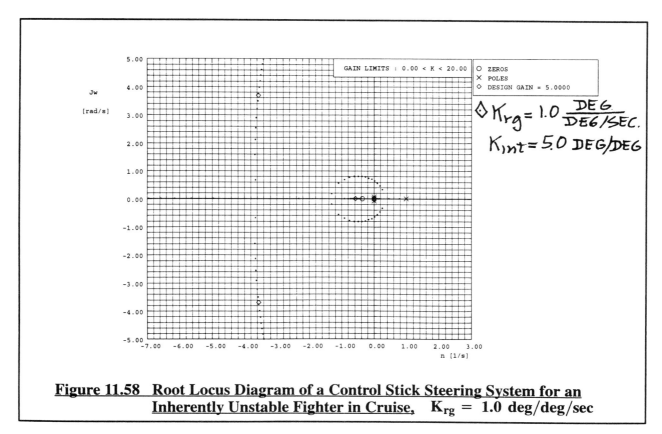

Figure 11.58   Root Locus Diagram of a Control Stick Steering System for an Inherently Unstable Fighter in Cruise, K_{rg} = 1.0 deg/deg/sec

K_rg = 1.0 deg/deg/sec   **K_int. = 5.0 deg/deg**

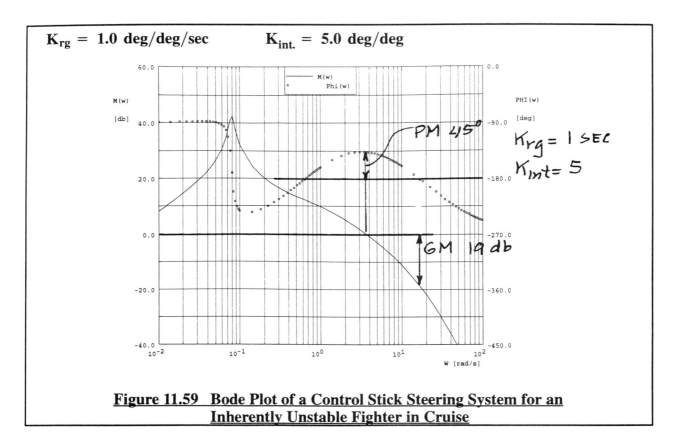

Figure 11.59   Bode Plot of a Control Stick Steering System for an Inherently Unstable Fighter in Cruise

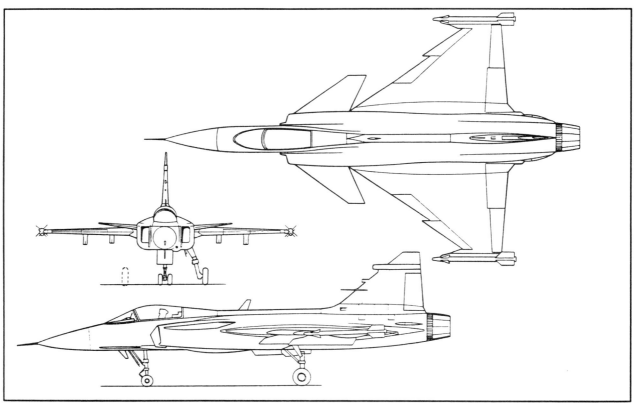

11.6 BASIC LATERAL–DIRECTIONAL AUTOPILOT MODES

In this Section the following basic lateral–directional autopilot modes will be discussed:

11.6.1 Bank Angle Hold Mode
11.6.2 Heading Angle Hold Mode
11.6.3 Turn Rate at Constant Altitude and Speed
11.6.4 Turn Coordination (Zero Lateral Acceleration)

11.6.1 BANK ANGLE HOLD MODE

The bank angle hold mode of an autopilot controls the airplane in a bank angle. If that bank angle is zero this is sometimes also referred to as a wing–levelling mode or wing–leveler.

Figure 11.60 shows a basic block diagram for a bank angle hold mode autopilot using a bank–angle gyro as the sensor.

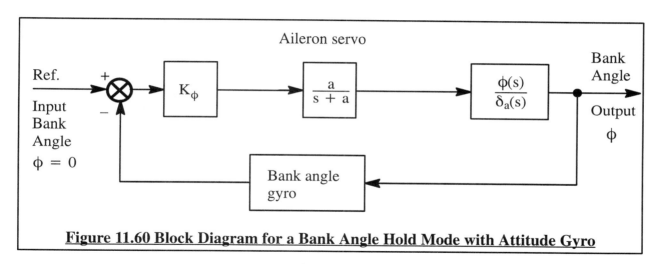

Figure 11.60 Block Diagram for a Bank Angle Hold Mode with Attitude Gyro

As was the case with sensing pitch attitude angle, the assumption will be made that the lowest break frequency of the gyro transfer function is considerably higher than the highest break frequency in the airplane bank–angle–to–aileron transfer function. Therefore, for all practical purposes it is acceptable to treat the gyro as a gain.

To illustrate the stability of a bank angle control system, the cruise flight condition of Airplane A of Table B1 (Part I) will be used. The aileron servo is modelled as a $10/(s+10)$ first order lag. The airplane bank–angle–to–aileron transfer function is taken directly from Table B1 (Cruise). Figure 11.61 shows the corresponding root locus diagram.

A reasonable operating gain in such a mode is 0.5 deg/deg (i.e. 0.5 deg of aileron deflection per degree of bank angle). At this gain the damping ratio of the bank angle mode is about 0.60. Note the dutch roll mode loop. Since the dutch roll pole and zero pair are very close together the participation of dutch roll in bank angle control can be expected to be minor.

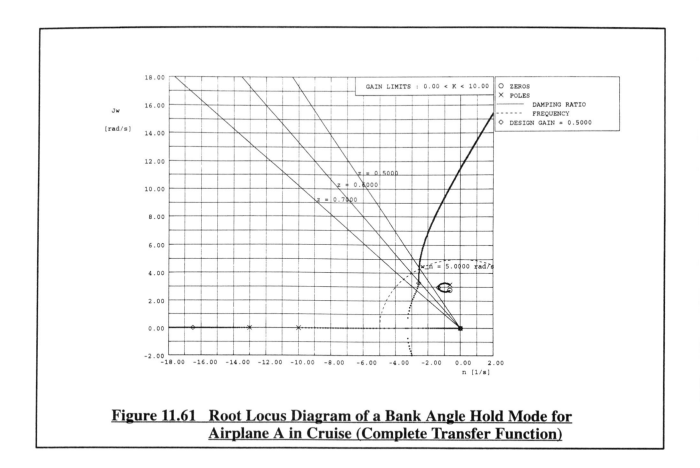

**Figure 11.61 Root Locus Diagram of a Bank Angle Hold Mode for
Airplane A in Cruise (Complete Transfer Function)**

This can be verified by replotting Figure 11.61 for the approximate bank–angle–to–aileron

transfer function: $\dfrac{\phi(s)}{\delta_a(s)} = \dfrac{L_{\delta_a}}{s(s - L_p)} = \dfrac{75.1}{s(s + 13)}$. The result is shown in Figure 11.62. Compar-

ing Figures 11.61 and 11.62 it is seen that the operating point is roughly the same in both.

The effect of servo performance on the bank angle hold mode can be seen in Figure 11.63. Servo break frequencies of 20 rad/sec, 10 rad/sec (as in Figure 11.61), 5 rad/sec and 2.5 rad/sec are shown. It is clear that as the servo performance deteriorates, the operating point (at the same gain) moves toward lower closed loop frequency and damping. For this airplane even a poorly performing servo still yields a credible combination of frequency and damping.

To see how a bank angle hold mode behaves for a jet transport, the example of Airplane J in a high altitude cruise condition will be used. Transfer function data are presented in Table B10 of Part I. The block diagram of Figure 11.60 still applies to this case. Figure 11.64 shows the corresponding root locus diagram. The diamond symbols represent the operating point at the design gain of 0.5 deg/deg. The point close to the dutch roll pole will have very little effect on the bank angle control of the airplane because in reality the airplane is always operated with a yaw damper turned on. For all practical purposes the airplane bank angle control loop behaves as if the dutch roll pole–zero pair cancel each other.

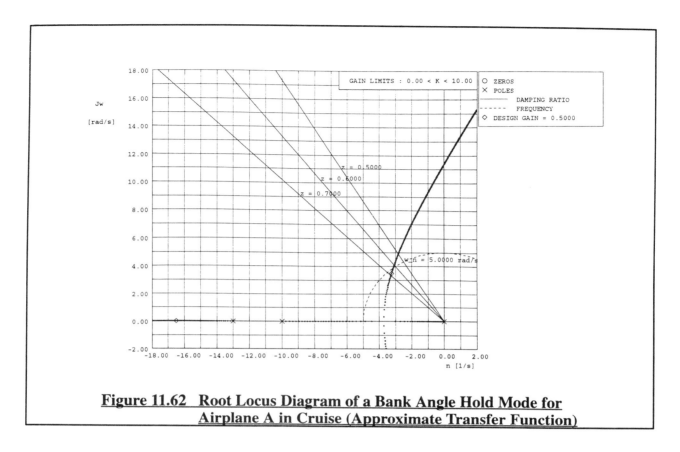

Figure 11.62 Root Locus Diagram of a Bank Angle Hold Mode for Airplane A in Cruise (Approximate Transfer Function)

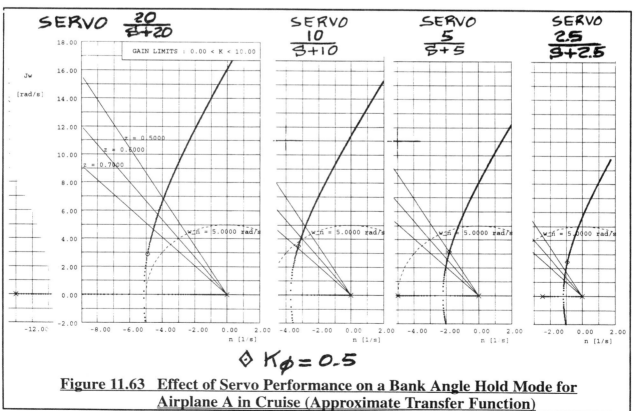

Figure 11.63 Effect of Servo Performance on a Bank Angle Hold Mode for Airplane A in Cruise (Approximate Transfer Function)

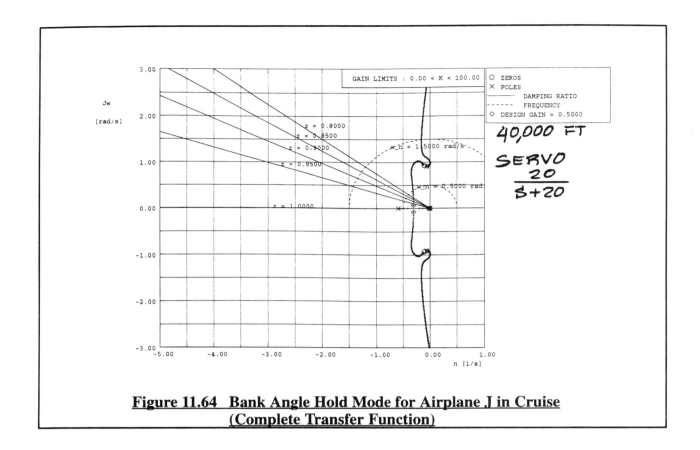

Figure 11.64 Bank Angle Hold Mode for Airplane J in Cruise (Complete Transfer Function)

11.6.2 HEADING ANGLE HOLD MODE

To control the heading angle of an airplane a directional gyro is used. Heading angle is normally controlled by establishing a certain bank angle and holding that angle until the desired heading change has been achieved. Therefore, the bank angle control loop of Sub–section 11.6.1 is often used as an inner loop in a heading angle control system. Figure 11.65 shows a block diagram of a heading angle control system. Observe the transfer function $\frac{\psi(s)}{\phi(s)} = \frac{g}{U_1 s}$ in the forward path of the outer loop. That transfer function is based on Eqn (4.90) in Part I.

The bank angle control loop of Figure 11.60 will be used as the inner loop for the heading control system of Figure 11.65. The airplane is Airplane A in a 5,000 ft cruise flight condition. Figure 11.66 shows the corresponding root locus diagram. The reader is asked to show that in the present case the gain margin is 17 db (relative to the outer loop gain of 5.0) which is adequate.

In the heading hold system discussed so far the bank angle control system was used as the controlling system for the (outer) heading loop. Another way to command a change in heading is to command turn rate ($= \dot{\psi}$) directly. How that can be done is discussed in Sub–section 11.6.3.

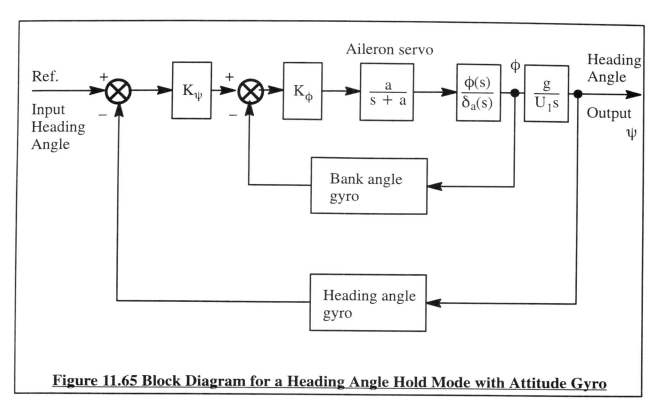

Figure 11.65 Block Diagram for a Heading Angle Hold Mode with Attitude Gyro

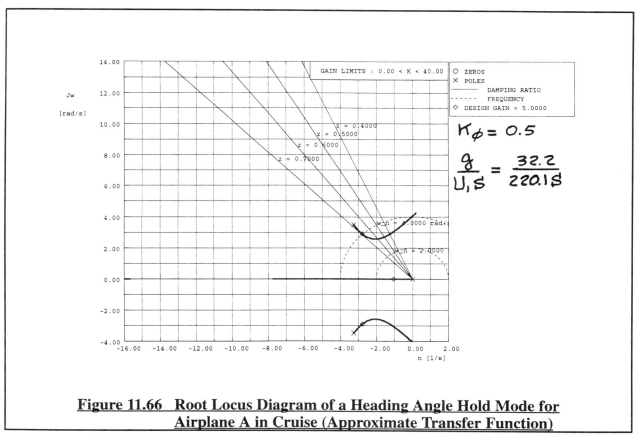

**Figure 11.66   Root Locus Diagram of a Heading Angle Hold Mode for
Airplane A in Cruise (Approximate Transfer Function)**

As any pilot knows, when a turn is commanded, the airplane (at constant speed and altitude) requires more lift (see Figure 4.17 in Part I). For an inherently stable airplane this increase in lift requires more negative elevator deflection (trim). Also, because more drag is produced the pilot will have to add thrust (or power). Modern autopilots do all this automatically.

There are other ways of controlling turns and heading. One such way is to use a turn rate command system. Such a system is discussed in Sub–section 11.6.3.

11.6.3 TURN RATE MODE AT CONSTANT SPEED AND ALTITUDE

Figure 11.67 shows a block diagram for a turn rate command system. Note the use of a tilted rate gyro. Because this is a double loop system, two gains have to be established: K_{rg} in the inner loop and $K_{\dot{\psi}}$ in the outer loop. Airplane A in a 5,000 ft cruise flight condition will be used as an example. A tilt angle of –45 degrees was selected. Figure 11.68 shows the root locus diagram for the inner loop. The aileron servo is modelled as a $10/(s+10)$ lag. In this loop $K_{rg} = -0.10 \deg/\deg/\sec$ was selected as a reasonable operating gain. Figure 11.69 shows the outer loop root locus. In the outer loop a gain of $K_{\dot{\psi}} = +1.0$ (deg/sec)/(deg/sec) was selected.

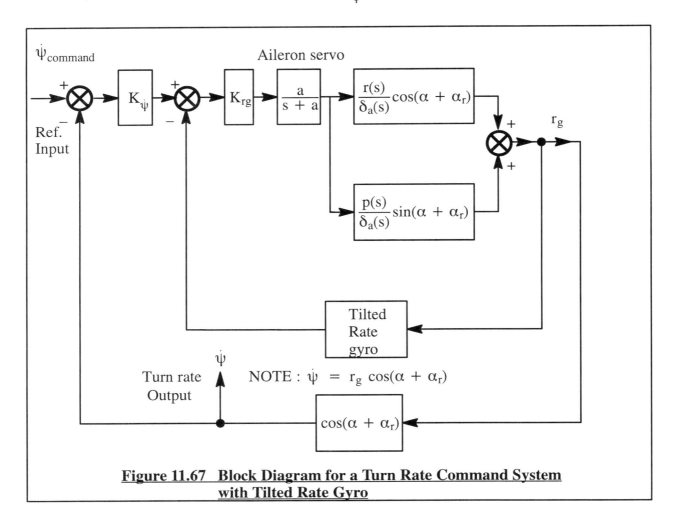

Figure 11.67   Block Diagram for a Turn Rate Command System with Tilted Rate Gyro

11.6.4 TURN COORDINATION (ZERO LATERAL ACCELERATION)

A coordinated turn is defined as a turn during which the net lateral acceleration at the airplane center of gravity is zero. From Eqn (5.2a) it follows that the net lateral acceleration (measured at the center of gravity) is:

$$a_{lat} = (\dot{v} + U_1 r) = g\phi\cos\theta_1 +$$

$$+ \frac{\bar{q}_1 S}{m}\left\{C_{y_\beta}\beta + C_{y_p}\frac{pb}{2U_1} + C_{y_r}\frac{rb}{2U_1} + C_{y_{\delta_a}}\delta_a + C_{y_{\delta_r}}\delta_r\right\} \qquad (11.23)$$

In a general turn, the airplane may experience nonzero values for any of the motion variables on the right hand side of Eqn (11.23). Coordinating a turn is therefore a complicated matter which involves striking a balance between a large number of small inputs. To function properly the lateral accelerometer which measures a_{lat} must have a relatively low threshold. This makes that accelerometer sensitive to local structural vibrations which requires some form of filtering. In many turn coordination systems the designer therefore seeks a compromise. A detailed discussion of turn coordination is beyond the scope of this text. Several options for turn coordination systems are discussed in Reference 11.5.

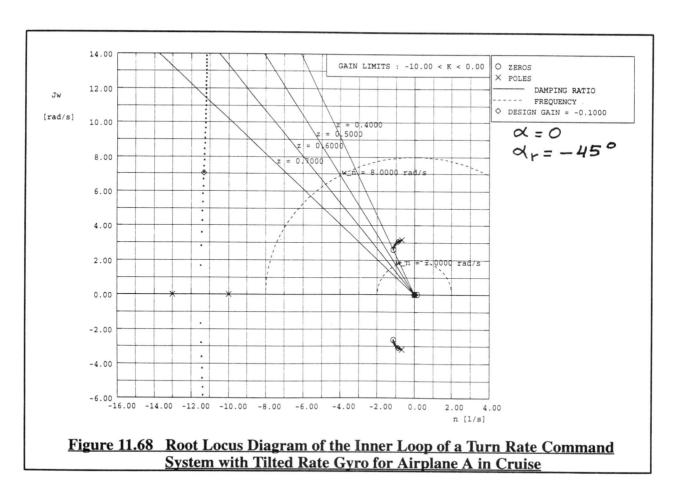

Figure 11.68   Root Locus Diagram of the Inner Loop of a Turn Rate Command System with Tilted Rate Gyro for Airplane A in Cruise

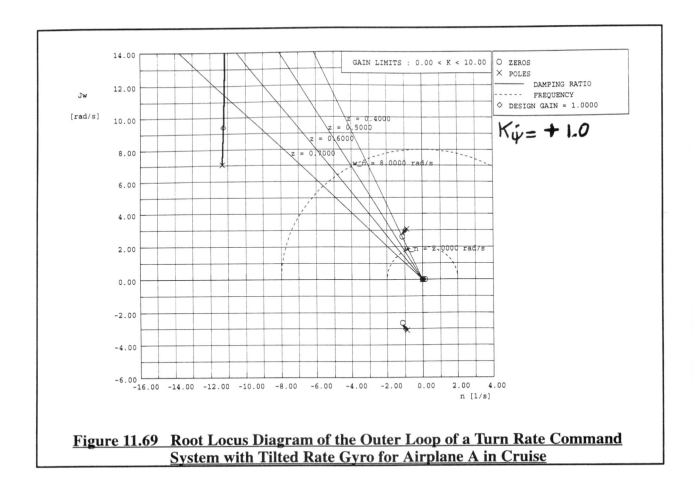

Figure 11.69 Root Locus Diagram of the Outer Loop of a Turn Rate Command System with Tilted Rate Gyro for Airplane A in Cruise

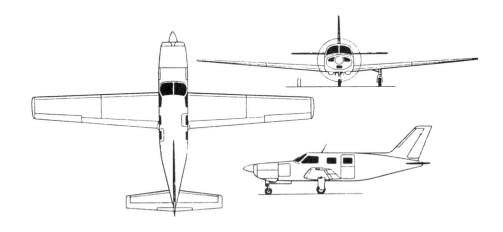

11.7 LONGITUDINAL NAVIGATION MODES

Longitudinal navigation modes are used to guide the airplane along pre–determined paths such as:

a) a glideslope intercept and hold mode as part of an automatic ILS (Instrument Landing System) approach

b) a predetermined climb–cruise–descent profile

c) an automatic flare path leading to an automatic landing

The types of guidance and control required to accomplish these tasks are similar in nature. For that reason only the ILS approach and the flare maneuver cases will be discussed.

11.7.1 APPROACH CATEGORIES AND GUIDANCE

The Instrument Landing System (ILS) is still the most frequently used system to guide airplanes toward a landing. Figure 11.70 shows the typical relation between the approach path, the glideslope transmitter, the localizer transmitter and the runway used with the ILS.

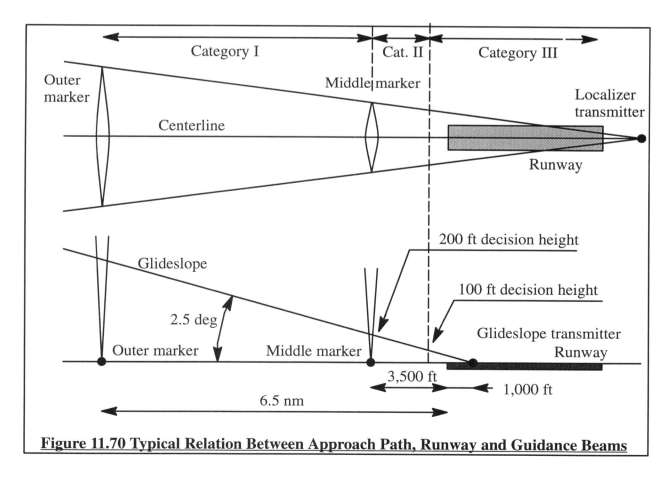

Figure 11.70 Typical Relation Between Approach Path, Runway and Guidance Beams

As seen from Figure 11.70 the pilot is made aware of his position relative to the runway touchdown point via signals emitted by the outer marker and inner marker transmitters. In addition, in most modern airplanes the actual distance to touchdown is also displayed to the pilot.

When a height of 200 ft above the ground is reached a decision must be made by the crew whether or not to proceed with the approach. That decision is subject to very strict rules with regard to prevailing visibility and the type of guidance equipment carried on board the airplane. Three operational approach categories are recognized:

Category I: Ceiling of 200 ft or more above the point of touchdown and runway visual range of 2600 ft (800 meters) or more.

Category II: Ceiling of 100 ft or more above the point of touchdown and runway visual range of 1200 ft (400 meters) or more.

Category IIIa: Zero ceiling and runway visual range of 700 ft (200 meters) or more.

Category IIIb: Zero ceiling and runway visual range of 150 ft (80 meters) or more.

Category IIIc: Zero ceiling and zero runway visual range (zero visibility).

Under Category I, a pilot must be able to fly on instruments and follow an approach aid (such as ILS) down to 200 ft height above ground with "due regard" for safety. For autopilots used in Category I approaches it must be demonstrated that a single failure occurring at 200 ft and followed by a manual takeover does not endanger the airplane.

Under Category I, if visual contact with the runway is not made at 200 ft a go–around maneuver must be initiated and completed.

Under Category II, the crew training is a regulatory issue. The same is true for maintenance of the equipment. The minimum equipment list on board the airplane includes:

- Dual localizer and glideslope receivers
- Either an AFCS with radio coupler and a flight director with dual displays or two independent flight directors
- Altitude measuring equipment of defined precision
- Go–around guidance
- Autothrottle unless it can be demonstrated that this is not required
- An instrument failure warning system
- Rain removal equipment

Under Category III even stricter rules apply for flight crew training and for minimum equipment. In Category III a triplicated automatic control system, including an automatic flare system is required as a minimum.

With Category IIIa automatic landings may be carried out with the pilot taking over manually during rollout on the runway.

With Category IIIb automatic landings followed by automatic rollout may be carried out. The pilot still takes over manually for taxi to the terminal.

With Category IIIc all is automatic, including taxi to the terminal.

In 1994 no Category IIIb operations have yet been certified. Several airports in Europe however have Category IIIb capability.

There are other means of generating approach paths to a landing site. A recently developed method is to employ the Global Positioning System (GPS) to guide an airplane along a geometrically defined line toward the runway. A major advantage of GPS will eventually be that no ground based equipment is needed. This avoids the costly maintenance and checkout procedures associated with the ILS systems still used at most airports.

11.7.2 GLIDESLOPE HOLD MODE

It will be assumed that the airplane already has a pitch attitude command control system as well as a speed control system. A discussion of pitch attitude command systems was presented in Sub–section 11.5.1. Speed control systems were discussed in Sub–section 11.5.3.

Figure 11.71 shows the pertinent flight path geometry for a glideslope hold mode.

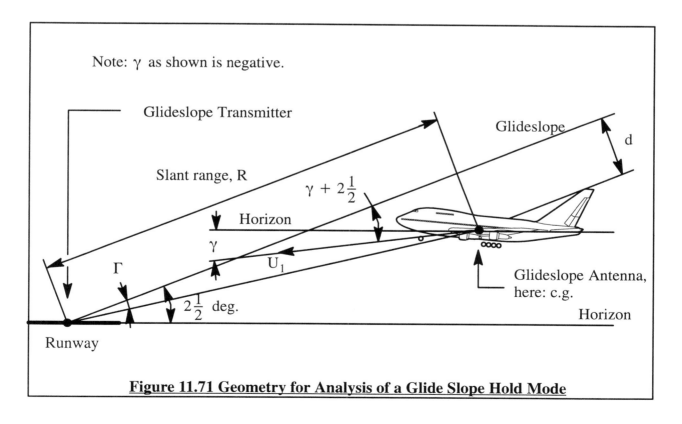

Figure 11.71 Geometry for Analysis of a Glide Slope Hold Mode

Several aspects of Figure 11.71 must be explained:

a) the airplane glide slope antenna location is assumed to be coincident with the c.g.
b) the c.g. is supposed to be driven along the glideslope.
c) the glideslope error angle, Γ, is sensed by a glideslope receiver mounted on board the airplane.
d) the airplane pitch attitude command system is used to keep the airplane on the glideslope.
e) some form of speed control (autothrottle or autodrag) is assumed to exist.

The velocity with which the airplane approaches the glideslope under the control of the pitch attitude command system is:

$$\dot{d} = U_1 \sin(\gamma + 2.5) \approx U_1 \frac{(\gamma + 2.5)}{57.3} \qquad (11.24)$$

The distance d from the c.g. (glideslope antenna!) to the glideslope is found by integration of Eqn (11.24):

$$d \approx \int U_1 \frac{(\gamma + 2.5)}{57.3} dt \qquad (11.25)$$

In the s–domain this yields:

$$d(s) \approx \frac{U_1}{(57.3)s} \quad \mathcal{L} (\gamma + 2.5) \qquad (11.26)$$

The glideslope error angle, Γ, is related to d and to the slant range, R, by:

$$\Gamma \approx \frac{d}{R} \qquad (11.27)$$

With the flight path geometry established it is now possible to construct a functional block diagram for the glideslope hold system. That is done in Figure 11.72. Note the glideslope coupler. The function of the coupler network is to "couple" the error signal, formed by subtracting the glideslope receiver signal from the reference input signal, to the autopilot.

The autopilot+airplane combination acts like a pitch attitude command system. The block diagram of Figure 11.73 represents this pitch attitude command system. The reader will recognize this as similar to the system of Figure 11.29 which includes a pitch damper in the inner loop. The system of Figure 11.72 is therefore a triple loop system.

Continuing around the loop in Figure 11.72, the output of the pitch attitude command system changes the airplane flight path angle, γ. The $\gamma(s)/\theta(s)$ transfer function is obtained by considering that the flight path angle, γ, the pitch attitude angle, θ, and the angle of attack, α, are related by:

$$\gamma = \theta - \alpha \qquad (11.28)$$

After taking the Laplace transform and dividing by $\theta(s)$:

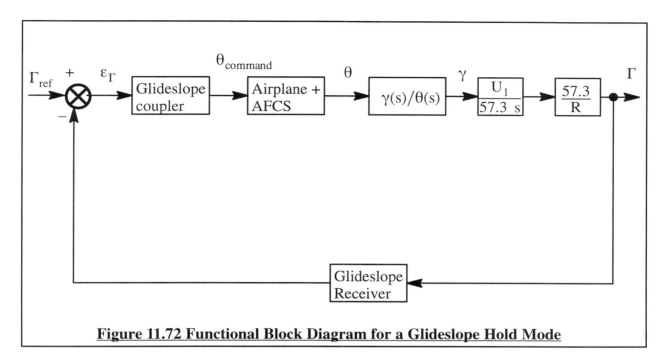

Figure 11.72 Functional Block Diagram for a Glideslope Hold Mode

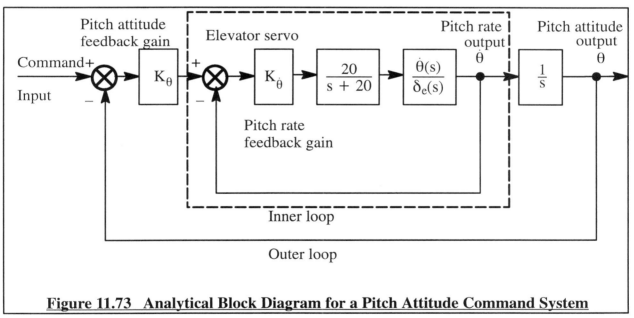

Figure 11.73 Analytical Block Diagram for a Pitch Attitude Command System

$$\frac{\gamma(s)}{\theta(s)} = 1 - \frac{\alpha(s)}{\theta(s)} = 1 - \frac{\alpha(s)/\delta_e(s)}{\theta(s)/\delta_e(s)} = 1 - \frac{N_\alpha(s)}{N_\theta(s)} \qquad (11.29)$$

The change in flight path angle, γ, causes a change in the glideslope error angle, Γ, which is sensed by the glideslope receiver and fed back to the coupler. The bandwidth of the glideslope receiver is considered very large relative to that of the other blocks in the system. The glideslope receiver will therefore be considered as a pure gain.

The coupler transfer function usually takes the form of a so–called "proportional plus" network with the following transfer function:

$$\text{TFF}_{\text{coupler}} = K_c\left(1 + \frac{0.1}{s}\right) \tag{11.30}$$

where: K_c is the so–called coupler gain which must be set to achieve acceptable closed loop behavior.

           0.1   is a "weighting" constant. The purpose of the weighted integrator in the coupler transfer function is to allow the system to cope with turbulence while on the glideslope.

As an example, Airplane J of Table B10 in Part I will be considered in an approach flight condition. The corresponding transfer function data are given in Table 11.4.

The data in Table 11.4 were determined with the AAA program (see Appendix A, Part I).

Figure 11.74 shows the inner loop root locus of the pitch attitude command system. The design gain was selected as $K_{\dot{\theta}} = -1$ deg/deg/sec. Figure 11.75 shows the outer loop for which a design gain of $K_\theta = +0.5$ deg/deg was chosen. The following closed loop transfer function of the pitch attitude command system with an inner loop gain, $K_{\dot{\theta}} = -1$ deg/deg/sec, and an outer loop gain of $K_\theta = +0.5$ deg/deg was calculated with the AAA program:

$$\frac{\theta(s)}{\theta_{\text{command}}(s)} = \frac{(910.2s^2 + 446.4s + 30.97)}{(228.5s^5 + 4,787s^4 + 6,307s^3 + 4,648s^2 + 633.0s + 107.3)} \tag{11.31}$$

The numerators N_α and N_θ needed for the flight–path–angle–to–pitch–attitude–angle transfer function in Eqn (11.29) are indicated in Table 11.4. With these numerators Eqn (11.29) for the example airplane becomes:

$$\frac{\gamma(s)}{\theta(s)} = \frac{(6.555s^3 - 2.4s^2 - 42.5s + 0.296)}{(-91.01s^2 - 44.6s - 3.097)} \tag{11.32}$$

There are two potential problems with glideslope hold loops as shown in Figure 11.72: the first one is the appearance of the two s=0 poles and the second one is the fact that the slant range, R, becomes smaller as the airplane approaches the runway. As the slant range decreases the effective loop gain will become very large. To guard against the two poles at the origin going unstable too soon, some form of distance measuring equipment (DME) is often required to adjust the coupler gain as the airplane gets closer to the runway.

Figure 11.76 shows the glideslope hold root locus for the case of R= 5 nm = 30,380 ft. This figure shows all open loop system poles and zeros. To better judge the relative stability of the system the root locus diagram of Figure 11.76 was rescaled in Figure 11.77. At 5 nm slant range the system stability is acceptable at the chosen coupler gain of $K_c = 10$ deg/deg.

Table 11.4 Transfer Function Data for Airplane J in Approach

Altitude	=	0 ft		M_1	=	0.198	
U_1	=	130.92 kts		n	=	1.00 g	
W_current	=	564000.0 lb					
S_w	=	5500.00 ft^2		q_bar_1	=	58.03 psf	
Theta_1	=	8.50 deg		(W/S)_TO	=	102.55 psf	
MGC_w	=	27.30 ft		X_u	=	-0.0433 1/s	
I_yy_B	=	30500000 slgft2		X_T_u	=	-0.0022 1/s	
C_m_1	=	0.0000		X_a	=	11.4708 ft/s^2	
C_m_u	=	0.0710		Z_u	=	-0.2719 1/s	
C_m_a	=	-1.4500 1/rad		Z_a	=	-108.0258 ft/s^2	
C_m_a.dot	=	-3.3000 1/rad		Z_a_dot	=	-7.5356 ft/s	
C_m_q	=	-21.4000 1/rad		Z_q	=	-6.3546 ft/s	
C_m_T_1	=	0.0000		M_u	=	0.0001 1/ft/s	
C_m_T_u	=	0.0000		M_T_u	=	0.0000 1/ft/s	
C_m_T_a	=	0.0000		M_a	=	-0.4142 1/s^2	
C_L_1	=	1.7600		M_T_a	=	0.0000 1/s^2	
C_L_u	=	-0.2200		M_a_dot	=	-0.0582 1/s	
C_L_a	=	5.6700 1/rad		M_q	=	-0.3777 1/s	
C_L_a.dot	=	6.7000 1/rad					
C_L_q	=	5.6500 1/rad		w_n_SP	=	0.7704 rad/s	
C_D_1	=	0.2630		z_SP	=	0.6172	
C_D_a	=	1.1300 1/rad		w_n_P	=	0.1677 rad/s	
C_D_u	=	0.0000		z_P	=	-0.0015	
C_T_X_1	=	0.2630		X_del_e	=	0.0000 ft/s^2	
C_T_X_u	=	-0.5523		Z_del_e	=	-6.5547 ft/s^2	
C_L_d_e	=	0.3600 1/rad		M_del_e	=	-0.4000 1/s^2	
C_D_d_e	=	0.0000 1/rad					
C_m_d_e	=	-1.4000 1/rad					

POLYNOMIAL ANGLE OF ATTACK TO ELEVATOR TRANSFER FUNCTION

```
 - 6.5547 S^3 - 88.6136 S^2 - 2.1170 S - 3.3932
--------------------------------------------------------------
 + 228.5107 S^4 + 217.2212 S^3 + 141.9559 S^2 + 6.0431 S + 3.8151
```
FACTORED ANGLE OF ATTACK TO ELEVATOR TRANSFER FUNCTION

```
-6.5547  (S + 13.4979)(S^2 + 0.0211 S + 0.0384)
--------------------------------------------------------------
228.5107  (S^2 + 0.9511 S + 0.5936)(S^2 + -0.0005 S + 0.0281)
```
ANGLE OF ATTACK TO ELEVATOR TRANSFER FUNCTION K_gain =   -0.889414

POLYNOMIAL PITCH ATTITUDE TO ELEVATOR TRANSFER FUNCTION

```
 - 91.0137 S^2 - 44.6327 S - 3.0970
--------------------------------------------------------------
 + 228.5107 S^4 + 217.2212 S^3 + 141.9559 S^2 + 6.0431 S + 3.8151
```

FACTORED PITCH ATTITUDE TO ELEVATOR TRANSFER FUNCTION

```
-91.0137  (S + 0.4067)(S + 0.0837)
--------------------------------------------------------------
228.5107  (S^2 + 0.9511 S + 0.5936)(S^2 + -0.0005 S + 0.0281)
```

PITCH ATTITUDE TO ELEVATOR TRANSFER FUNCTION K_gain =   -0.811789

Figure 11.78 shows the root locus for R=1 nm = 6,076 ft. Note the shift of the operating point to the right. Note that the system is now neutrally stable at the same coupler gain.

Figure 11.79 shows the root locus for R= 0.1 nm = 608 ft. Because the glideslope transmitting antenna is located at a relatively short distance from the runway threshold the latter case represents a situation where the airplane should be starting its flare maneuver. Clearly the system is unstable at this point.

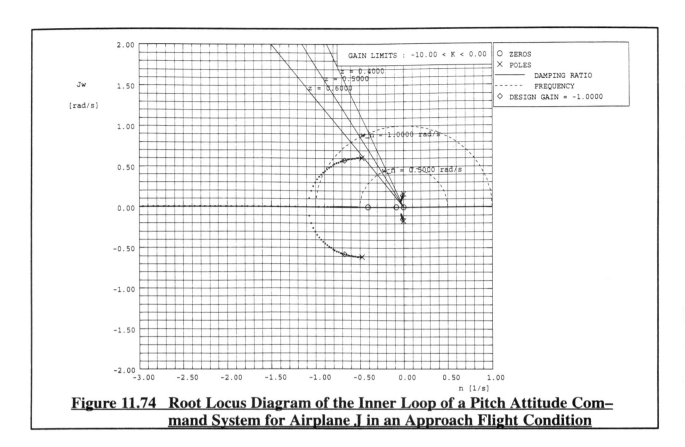

Figure 11.74 Root Locus Diagram of the Inner Loop of a Pitch Attitude Command System for Airplane J in an Approach Flight Condition

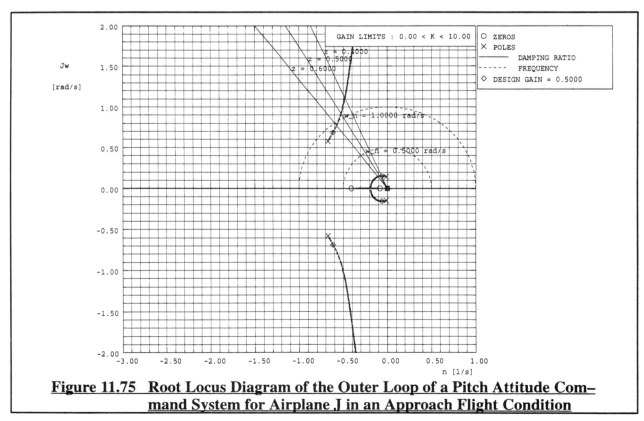

Figure 11.75 Root Locus Diagram of the Outer Loop of a Pitch Attitude Command System for Airplane J in an Approach Flight Condition

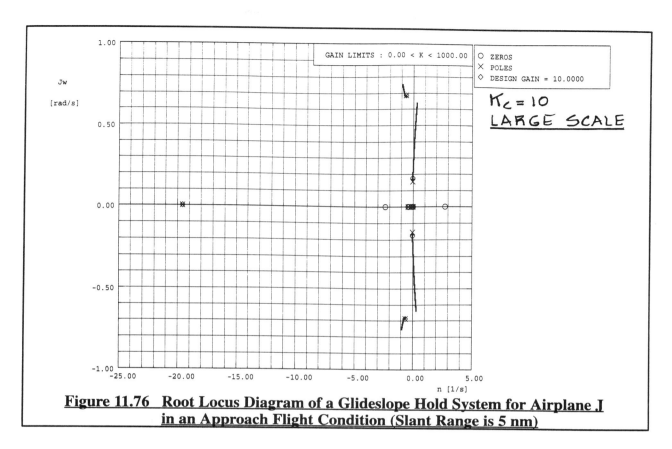

Figure 11.76 Root Locus Diagram of a Glideslope Hold System for Airplane J in an Approach Flight Condition (Slant Range is 5 nm)

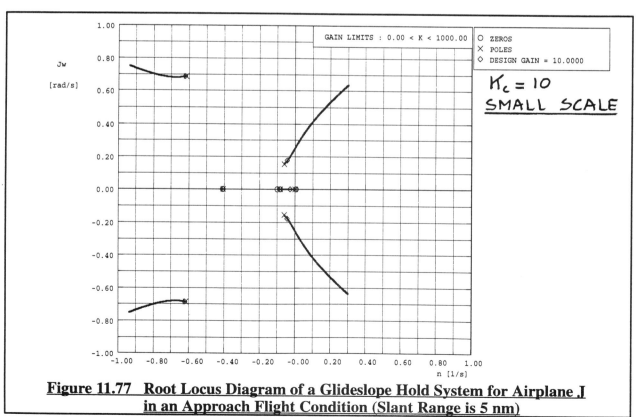

Figure 11.77 Root Locus Diagram of a Glideslope Hold System for Airplane J in an Approach Flight Condition (Slant Range is 5 nm)

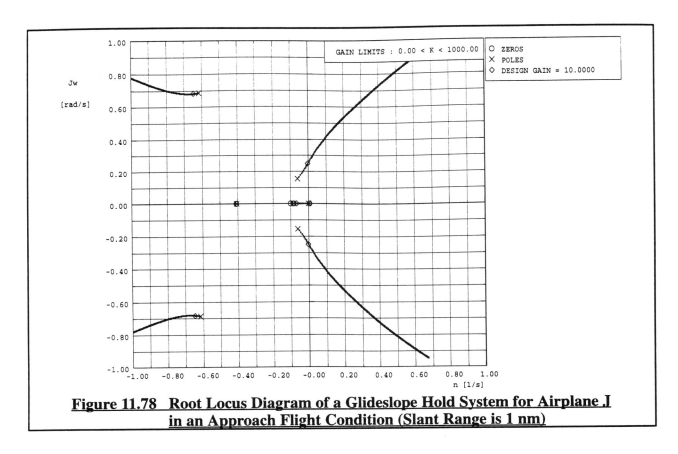

Figure 11.78 Root Locus Diagram of a Glideslope Hold System for Airplane J in an Approach Flight Condition (Slant Range is 1 nm)

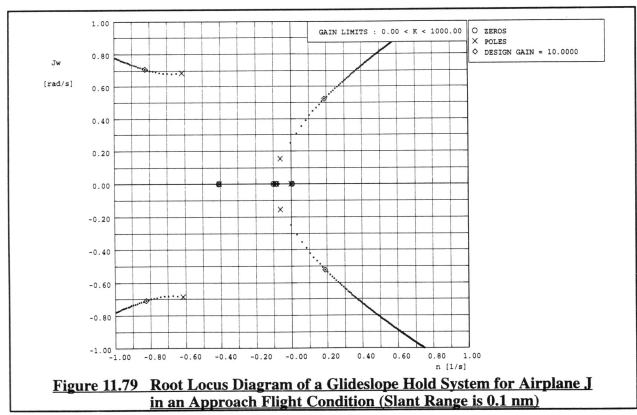

Figure 11.79 Root Locus Diagram of a Glideslope Hold System for Airplane J in an Approach Flight Condition (Slant Range is 0.1 nm)

One way to solve this problem is to adjust the coupler gain downward as the distance to the glideslope transmitter decreases (by using some form of D.M.E.). In older autopilots the coupler gain is adjusted downward as a result of a clock which starts when the airplane is over the outer marker. Another way is to add some form of compensation to the system. Figure 11.80 shows what happens at 5 nm slant range if a (10(s+0.3)/(s+3) compensator is added to the coupler transfer function. Note the favorable effect this has on the critical branch of the root locus.

Most autopilots with glideslope capability have what is referred to as a "glideslope intercept and hold feature". What has been discussed here is only the "hold" part of it. Figure 11.81 shows

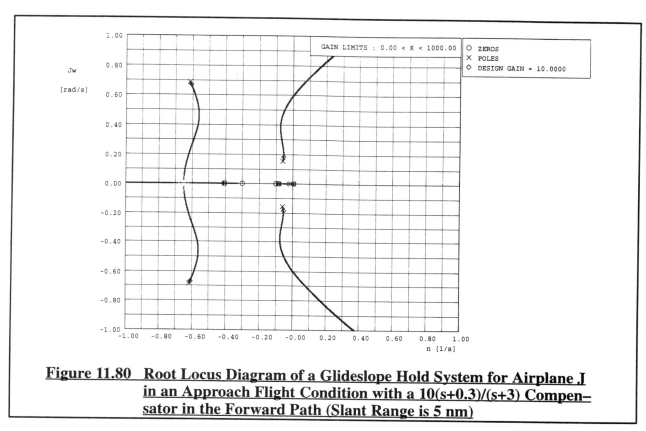

Figure 11.80   Root Locus Diagram of a Glideslope Hold System for Airplane J in an Approach Flight Condition with a 10(s+0.3)/(s+3) Compen-sator in the Forward Path (Slant Range is 5 nm)

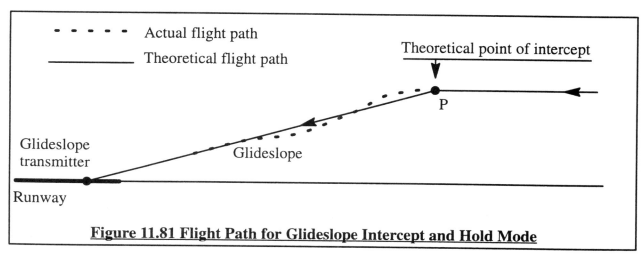

Figure 11.81 Flight Path for Glideslope Intercept and Hold Mode

a typical flight path which would arise if the autopilot is put in the intercept and hold mode.

At the intercept point, P, the autopilot would use its full authority to "nose the airplane down". Depending on the authority limit designed into the autopilot this could result in very unacceptable "g" excursions. Therefore, every intercept mode has a smoothing feature built in which limits these "g" excursions.

Obviously, in the real world many studies like those discussed here will have to be carried out (with different airplane c.g. locations, weights and speeds) to make sure that an overall acceptable solution has been found. Finally, time domain simulations in the presence of turbulence should also be conducted.

11.7.3 AUTOMATIC FLARE (LANDING) MODE

The allowable vertical touchdown velocity of an airplane onto the runway is determined by several factors:

a) Passenger and crew comfort: hard landings (touchdown rates of 6 ft/sec or more) are not acceptable for everyday operation. Firm landings (touchdown rates of 2–3 ft/sec) are desirable. The non–pilot reader should realize that so–called "egg–landings" with close to zero touchdown rates are also undesirable. The reason is that an inevitable consequence of very low touchdown rates is "floatation" of the airplane and lack of control over the touchdown point on the runway.

b) The landing gear and the attachment structure may incus damage if the touchdown rates are too high. Reference 11.6 contains detailed information about touchdown velocity design criteria depending on airplane type. For civil transports most landing gears are designed to withstand a vertical touchdown rate of at least 10 ft/sec. For certain carrier based airplanes the design touchdown rate can be as high as 25 ft/sec.

Table 11.5 shows the relationship between vertical touchdown velocity and forward airspeed if an airplane is on a (typical) 2.5 degree glideslope. It is clear that for most airplanes some type of flare maneuver is required.

The reader is reminded that carrier based airplanes do not flare when coming on board the carrier. These airplanes are "driven" straight into the deck (aiming for the number three arresting wire) along the glideslope.

Figure 11.82 shows the flight path followed by the airplane during the flare maneuver.

The following assumptions will be made:

1) The airplane will be controlled on the flare path by the pitch attitude command system of Figure 11.72.
2) The flare path starts at a height of h_{flare}
3) The intended point of touchdown is 1,100 ft from the glideslope transmitter (Fig. 11.82)

Table 11.5		Effect of Forward Airspeed on the Vertical Touchdown Velocity on a 21/2 Degree Glideslope		
Forward Velocity		Vertical touchdown velocity on a 2.5 degree glideslope		
Knots	Ft/sec	Ft/sec		
10	17	0.7		
20	34	1.5	"soft landings"	
40	68	3.0		
80	135	6.0		
120	203	9.0	"hard landings"	
160	270	12.0		

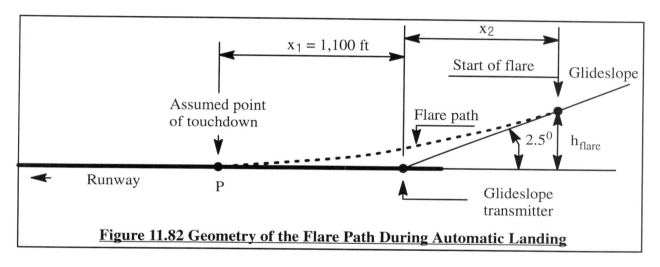

Figure 11.82 Geometry of the Flare Path During Automatic Landing

To simplify the derivation of the flare control law, a procedure used by Blakelock in Reference 11.7 will be used. Assume that the flare path can be approximated by a relationship which makes it tangential at point P:

$$h = h_{flare}e^{-t/\tau} \tag{11.33}$$

This equation represents the flare path control law. Clearly, h_{flare} and τ need to be determined first. The following example deals with Airplane J in the landing configuration. The airplane speed is assumed to be $U_1 = 221$ ft/sec. At the start of the flare, the rate of descent is given by:

$$\dot{h}_{at\ h_{flare}} = -\frac{2.5}{57.3}U_1 = \left(-\frac{2.5}{57.3}\right)221 = -9.64\ \text{ft/sec} \tag{11.34}$$

By differentiating Eqn (11.33) it follows that:

$$\dot{h} = -\frac{h_{flare}}{\tau}e^{-t/\tau} = -\frac{h}{\tau} \tag{11.35}$$

Assuming that the airplane touches down in $t = 4\tau$ it follows that:

$$x_1 + x_2 = 1,100 + x_2 = 4\tau U_1 = 4 \times 221 \times \tau = 884\tau \tag{11.36}$$

From this it follows that:

$$x_2 = 884\tau - 1,100 \tag{11.37}$$

However, from the geometry in Figure 11.82 it also follows that:

$$x_2 = \frac{h_{flare}}{\tan 2.5^0} \tag{11.38}$$

From Eqn (11.35) it follows that:

$$\dot{h}_{at\,h_{flare}} = -\frac{h_{flare}}{\tau} = -9.64\,\text{ft/sec} \tag{11.39}$$

Substituting Eqn (11.39) into Eqn (11.38):

$$x_2 = \frac{9.64\,\tau}{\tan 2.5} = 221\tau \tag{11.40}$$

By now equating Eqns (11.40) and (11.37) it is found that:

$$\tau = 1.66\ \text{sec} \tag{11.41}$$

The flare height, h_{flare}, from which the flare is begun is therefore: $9.64 \times 1.66 = 16$ ft.

The flare control law can now be expressed as:

$$\dot{h} = -\frac{h}{1.66} = -0.6h \tag{11.42}$$

During the flare, the rate of descent, $\dot{h}$, will be controlled with the pitch attitude command system of Figure 11.73. A block diagram showing the flare path control system is presented in Figure 11.83.

Note that $\dot{h}$ is also given by:

$$\dot{h} \approx U_1\gamma \quad (\gamma \text{ in radians}) \tag{11.43}$$

From this it follows that:

$$\frac{\dot{h}(s)}{\theta(s)} = \frac{\gamma(s)\ U_1}{\theta(s)\ 57.3} \quad (\gamma \text{ in deg.}) \tag{11.44}$$

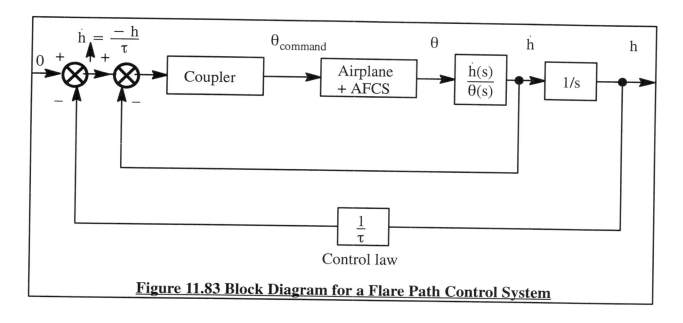

Figure 11.83 Block Diagram for a Flare Path Control System

The various transfer functions in Figure 11.83 will now be identified.

The first coupler transfer function to be tried is that of Eqn (11.30). The transfer function of the airplane plus its pitch attitude command system (AFCS) is that of Eqn (11.31). The rate–of–descent–to–pitch–attitude transfer function is given by Eqns (11.44) and (11.32) as:

$$\frac{\dot{h}(s)}{\theta(s)} = \left(\frac{221}{57.3}\right)\frac{(6.555s^3 - 2.4s^2 - 42.5s + 0.296)}{(- 91.01s^2 - 44.6s - 3.097)} \tag{11.45}$$

The value of τ in Figure 11.83 for the example airplane is 1.66 sec, according to Eqn (11.41).

Figures 11.84 and 11.85 show root locus diagrams for the flare path control system for $K_c = 0.1$ deg/ft/sec and $K_c = 1.0$ deg/ft/sec respectively. Observe the fact that the stability of the operating point is strongly influenced by the selection of the coupler gain. The reader is encouraged to find a lead–lag compensator which lowers this sensitivity.

The reader should appreciate the fact that autopilots carry out maneuvers with much greater accuracy than do human pilots. Therefore, the flare path control system will ensure runway damage by always touching airplanes down at point P in Figure 11.82. To avoid this in the real world, most flare control laws include some form of "Monte Carlo" scheme to vary the intended point of touchdown. This creates the type of touchdown dispersion which human pilots, because of their lack of repeatability, always exhibit.

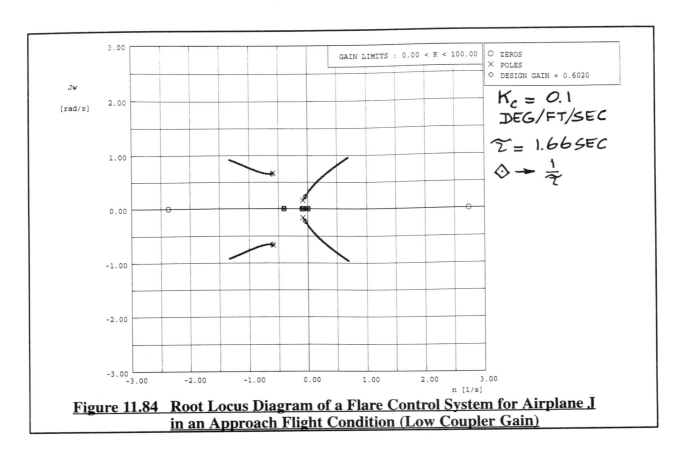

Figure 11.84 Root Locus Diagram of a Flare Control System for Airplane J in an Approach Flight Condition (Low Coupler Gain)

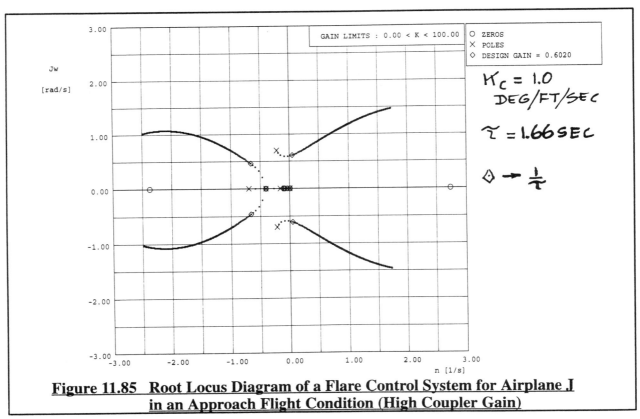

Figure 11.85 Root Locus Diagram of a Flare Control System for Airplane J in an Approach Flight Condition (High Coupler Gain)

11.8 LATERAL–DIRECTIONAL NAVIGATION MODES

Lateral–directional navigation modes are used to guide the airplane along pre–determined paths such as:

a) a localizer intercept and hold mode as part of an automatic I.L.S. (Instrument Landing System) approach.

b) a V.O.R. or other radio signal emitting station

c) an arbitrary waypoint

The types of guidance and control required to accomplish these tasks are similar in nature. For that reason only the localizer hold mode and the V.O.R. hold mode will be discussed.

11.8.1 LOCALIZER HOLD MODE

It will be assumed that the airplane already has a heading angle control system. Figure 11.86 shows the pertinent flight path geometry for a localizer hold mode.

Several aspects of Figure 11.86 must be explained:

a) the airplane localizer antenna is assumed to be coincident with the c.g.

b) the c.g. is supposed to be driven along the centerline of the localizer beam: intended path

c) the localizer error angle, λ, is sensed by a localizer receiver mounted on board the airplane

d) the airplane heading angle command system is used to keep the airplane on the centerline of the localizer beam. The localizer beam width is typically 5 degrees, 2.5 degrees on either side of the centerline

e) any speed and lift changes due to banking is automatically compensated for

The localizer guidance and control as treated here is assumed to be independent of any longitudinal control action.

The localizer error angle, λ, is determine from Figure 11.86 as:

$$\lambda \approx 57.3 \frac{d}{R} \tag{11.46}$$

Where, R is the slant range. The distance, d, from the centerline follows from:

$$d(s) = \frac{1}{s}\dot{d}(s) \tag{11.47}$$

where:

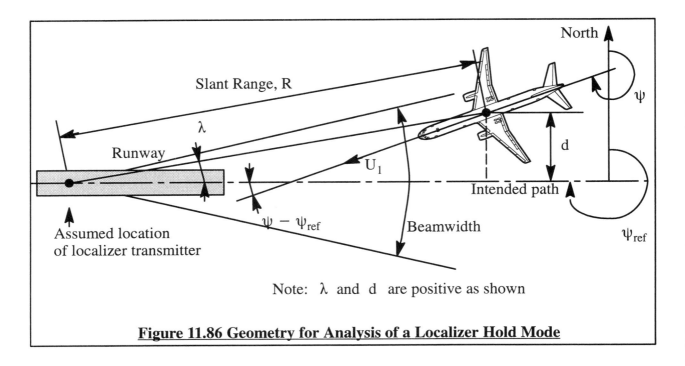

Note: λ and d are positive as shown

Figure 11.86 Geometry for Analysis of a Localizer Hold Mode

$$\dot{d} = U_1 \sin(\psi - \psi_{ref}) \approx U_1(\psi - \psi_{ref}) \quad (\Psi \text{ in radians}) \tag{11.48}$$

so that:

$$\dot{d}(s) \approx U_1\{\psi(s) - \psi_{ref}(s)\} \tag{11.49}$$

Figure 11.87 shows a block diagram corresponding to the localizer hold system. Equations (11.46), (11.47) and (11.49) are included in the transfer function box labeled "geometry of localizer intercept and hold mode". The reader should realize that this box of transfer functions is there only for purposes of analysis. The airplane merely has a localizer receiver (with antenna) on board.

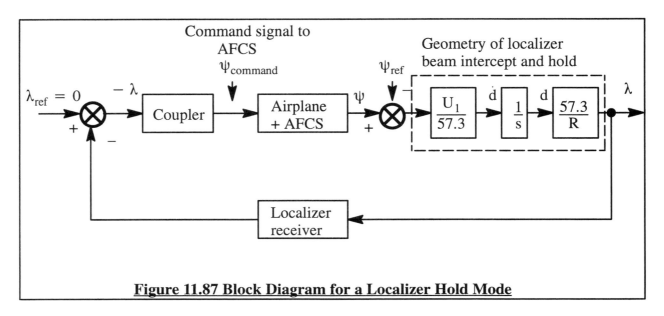

Figure 11.87 Block Diagram for a Localizer Hold Mode

Discussion of the system of Figure 11.87 begins with the box labeled "Airplane + AFCS". In this case this box represents the airplane plus heading command system. In most cases this system itself is a three–loop system, consisting of a roll damper in the inner loop, a bank angle control system in the middle loop and the heading angle control system as the outer loop. Figure 11.88 shows a block diagram for this system.

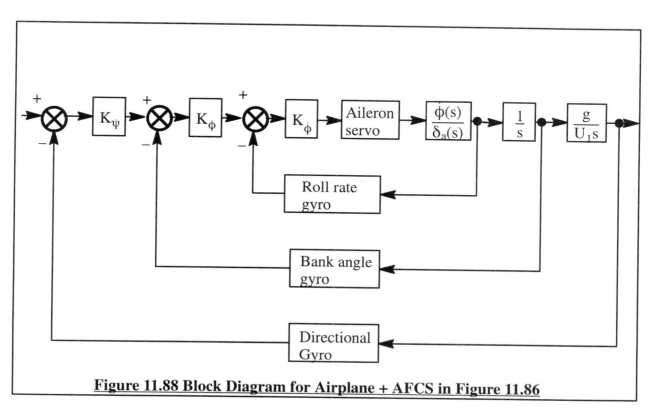

Figure 11.88 Block Diagram for Airplane + AFCS in Figure 11.86

As an example of the localizer hold synthesis procedure, Airplane J will be used in an approach flight condition. The heading angle command system of Figure 11.88 will be synthesized first. It will be assumed that Airplane J, on final approach will have a yaw damper in operation so that no significant yawing motions will interfere with the control of bank angle. This also means that the single degree of freedom roll–rate–to–aileron transfer function can be used. For the example airplane, using the data of Table B10 in Part I, the roll damper loop (inner loop) of Figure 11.88 takes the form of Figure 11.89.

A root locus diagram for the roll damper of Figure 11.89 is given in Figure 11.90.

Using the closed loop transfer function of the inner loop at a design gain of 10 deg/deg/sec the block diagram of the bank angle control system of Figure 11.91 can be drawn. A root locus diagram for the bank angle control system of Figure 11.91 is presented in Figure 11.92.

Selecting a bank angle control loop gain of 5 deg/deg for the system of Figure 11.91, the heading control loop of Figure 11.93 can now be analyzed.

A root locus diagram for the system of Figure 11.93 is given in Figure 11.94.

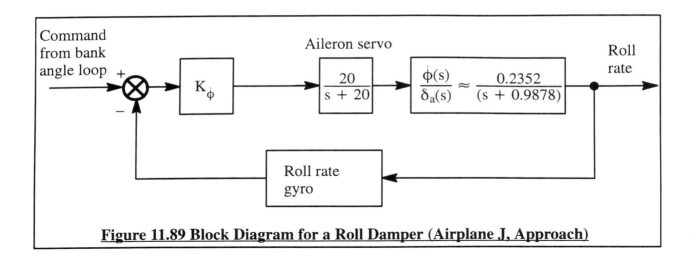

Figure 11.89 Block Diagram for a Roll Damper (Airplane J, Approach)

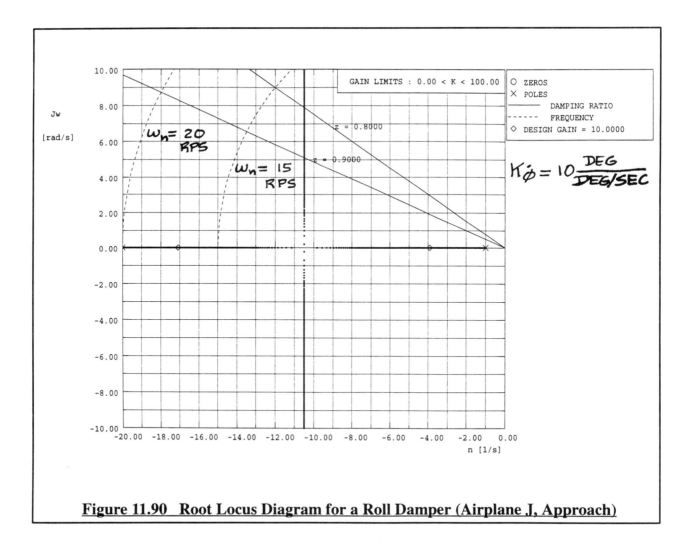

Figure 11.90   Root Locus Diagram for a Roll Damper (Airplane J, Approach)

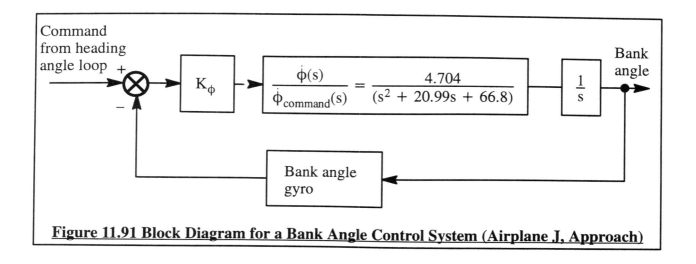

Figure 11.91 Block Diagram for a Bank Angle Control System (Airplane J, Approach)

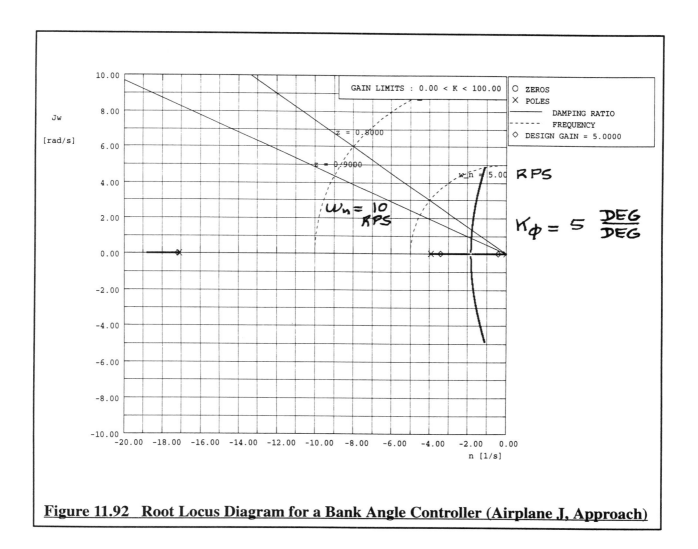

Figure 11.92   Root Locus Diagram for a Bank Angle Controller (Airplane J, Approach)

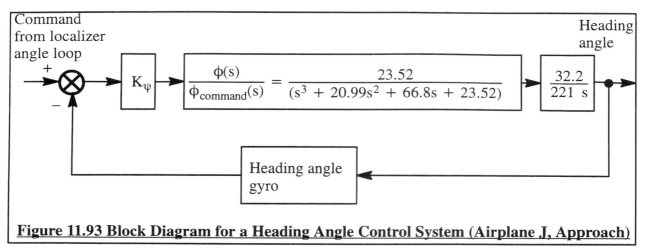

Figure 11.93 Block Diagram for a Heading Angle Control System (Airplane J, Approach)

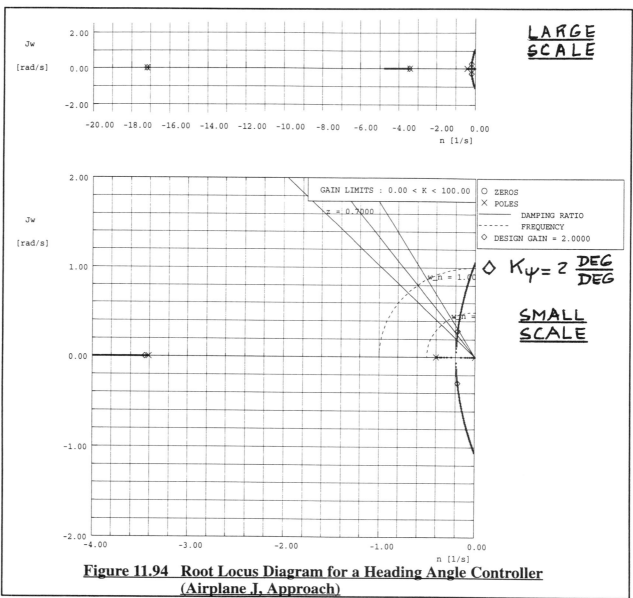

Figure 11.94   Root Locus Diagram for a Heading Angle Controller (Airplane J, Approach)

With a heading loop gain of 2 deg/deg the closed loop transfer function of the heading control system can be obtained. For Airplane J in the approach flight condition this transfer function has been inserted in the general block diagram of the localizer loop as given by Figure 11.87. The result is the computational block diagram of Figure 11.95.

To simplify the analysis the value for the reference heading angle was set at zero. A root locus diagram for this localizer control system is shown in Figure 11.96. The coupler gain was set at 10 deg/deg. The parameter 1/R acts as the variable gain in this system. The diamond symbols are indicative of the system stability for a slant range of 5 nm: 1/R = 0.000033 1/ft. At a slant range of 5 nm the system is stable. Figure 11.97 shows the same root locus: the diamond symbol in this case represents the situation at a slant range of 1 nm: 1/R = 0.0001645 1/ft. It is clear that the system is already unstable at the selected coupler gain of 10 deg/deg. The favorable effect of a compensating network (added to the coupler T.F.F.) on this system is shown in Figure 11.98 with the diamond symbols again representing the system stability at a slant range of R = 5 nm. For R = 1 nm, Figure 11.99 shows the same root locus diagram with the diamond symbols representing the stability of the system at R = 1 nm. Even at a slant range of 1.0 nm the system is still stable with the compensating network in place. Since the localizer is far down the runway, at a slant range of 1.0 miles the airplane should have already touched down so that the relative stability of the system at that small a slant range is probably not critical. Better stability can be obtained by adjusting the compensating network.

It must be noted that by varying the coupler gain as a function of slant range, a constant operating point can be obtained. Doing this requires distance measuring equipment (see page 851).

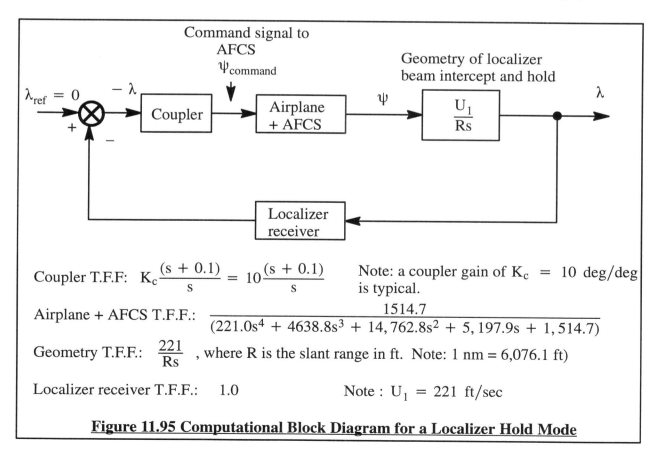

Coupler T.F.F: $K_c\frac{(s + 0.1)}{s} = 10\frac{(s + 0.1)}{s}$ Note: a coupler gain of $K_c = 10$ deg/deg is typical.

Airplane + AFCS T.F.F.: $\dfrac{1514.7}{(221.0s^4 + 4638.8s^3 + 14,762.8s^2 + 5,197.9s + 1,514.7)}$

Geometry T.F.F.: $\dfrac{221}{Rs}$, where R is the slant range in ft. Note: 1 nm = 6,076.1 ft)

Localizer receiver T.F.F.: 1.0   Note : $U_1 = 221$ ft/sec

Figure 11.95 Computational Block Diagram for a Localizer Hold Mode

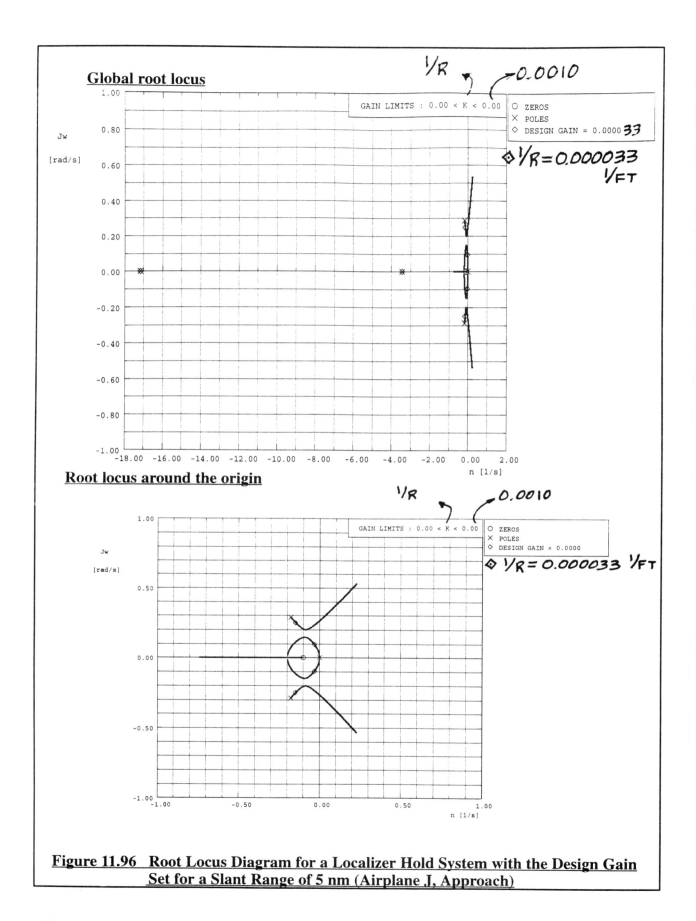

Figure 11.96   Root Locus Diagram for a Localizer Hold System with the Design Gain Set for a Slant Range of 5 nm (Airplane J, Approach)

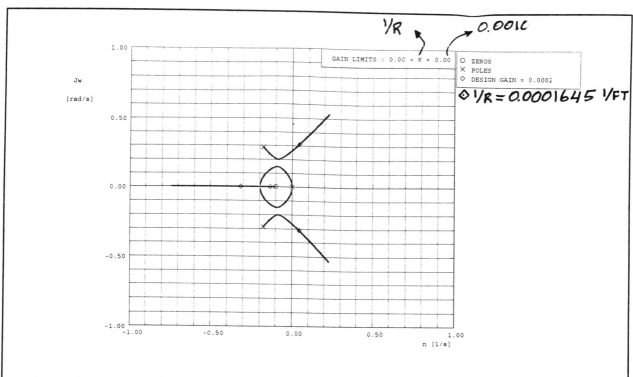

Figure 11.97   Root Locus Diagram for a Localizer Hold System with the Design Gain Set for a Slant Range of 1 nm (Airplane J, Approach)

Compensating network : $\dfrac{5(s^2 + 0.4s + 0.2)}{(s^2 + 2s + 1)}$ included in the coupler T.F.F.

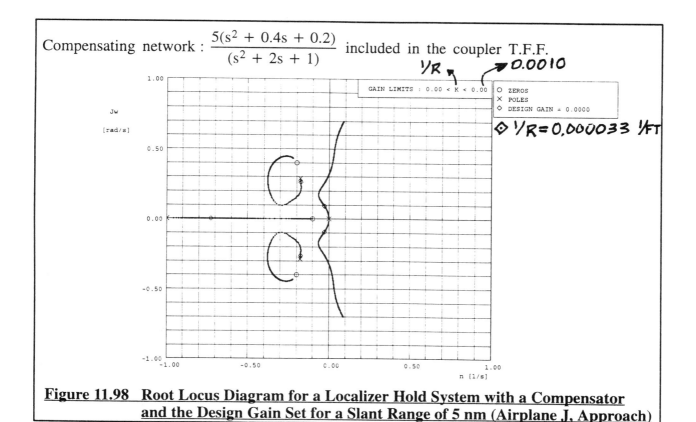

Figure 11.98   Root Locus Diagram for a Localizer Hold System with a Compensator and the Design Gain Set for a Slant Range of 5 nm (Airplane J, Approach)

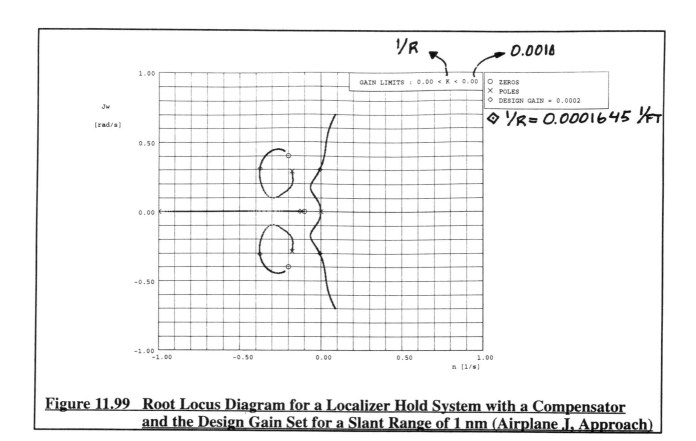

Figure 11.99 Root Locus Diagram for a Localizer Hold System with a Compensator and the Design Gain Set for a Slant Range of 1 nm (Airplane J, Approach)

11.8.2 V.O.R HOLD MODE

The synthesis of VOR (or other radio beacon centered navigation) modes is similar to that of the localizer hold mode discussed in Sub–section 11.8.1. The main difference is in the width of the beam coming from the VOR transmitter. The diagrams of Figure 11.86 and 11.88 apply without change to the VOR hold case. The range of numerical change in slant range will be much larger in the case of VOR hold than in the case of localizer hold. An example will be shown for Airplane A in a 5,000 ft cruise condition. Because of the excellent inherent roll damping of this airplane no roll damper will be used in the inner loop of the bank angle control system. The closed loop heading control system of Figure 11.65 will be used. At gains of K_ϕ = 0.5 deg/deg and K_ψ = 5 deg/deg the closed loop transfer function corresponding to the root locus of Figure 11.6 is:

$$\frac{\psi(s)}{\psi_{command}(s)} = \frac{60,455}{220.1s^4 + 5,062s^3 + 28,613s^2 + 82,648s + 60,455} \tag{11.50}$$

The VOR hold loop root locus diagram for this case is shown in Figure 11.100. Operating points are shown for R = 50 nm, R = 5 nm and R = 1 nm. At the 5,000 ft altitude the slant range can never be less than 5,000 ft. The system works well for this airplane even without adjustment to the coupler gain as a function of slant range. Note however, that at constant coupler gain the closed loop damping ratio greatly diminishes as the airplane approaches the VOR transmitter! That behavior is typical of constant gain loops.

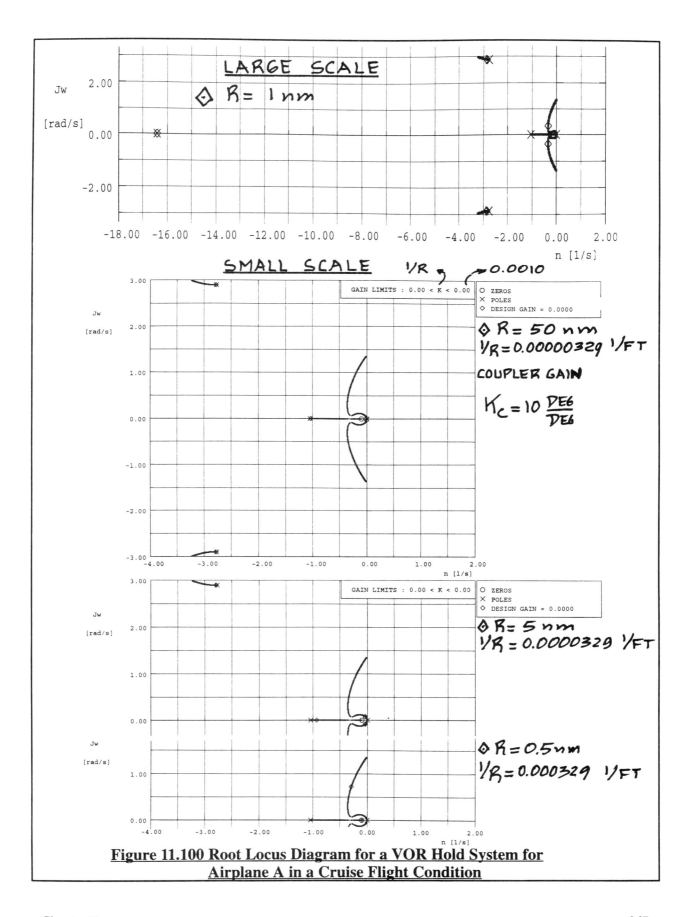

Figure 11.100 Root Locus Diagram for a VOR Hold System for Airplane A in a Cruise Flight Condition

11.9 MULTIPLE LOOP, MULTIPLE VARIABLE CONTROL SYSTEMS

In the discussion of feedback control systems only loop structures involving the feedback of one variable to one controller was considered at any time. In reality many situations arise where more than one variable is fed back to more than one controller at the same time. Figure 11.101 shows such a more general feedback loop arrangement. The reader should consult Reference 11.3 for a detailed discussion of such systems.

The purpose of this Section is to provide the reader with a general idea of the complexities involved in using classical control methods in the synthesis of such more general systems.

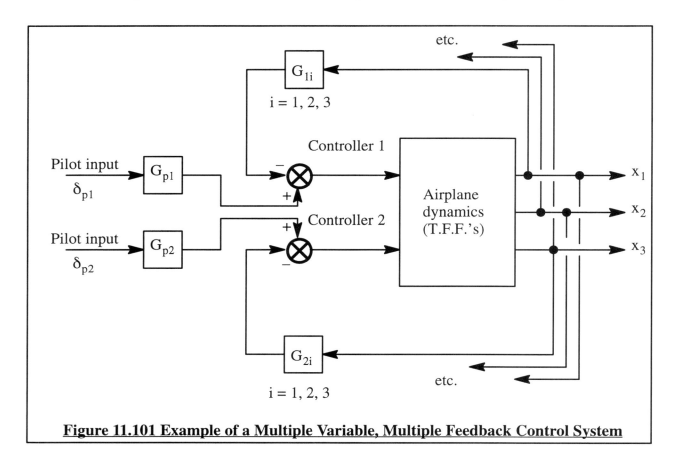

Figure 11.101 Example of a Multiple Variable, Multiple Feedback Control System

To synthesize systems such as depicted in Figure 11.101 requires that a closed loop transfer function be derived which accounts for all feedback loops to all controllers indicated in this figure. To illustrate the mathematical complexities involved, the transfer function derivation for two simplified systems will be presented.

First, consider the system of Figure 11.102. In this system two variables (angle of attack, α, and pitch attitude angle, θ) are fed back to only one controller, the elevator. For this analysis, the closed loop transfer functions desired are: $\alpha(s)/\delta_p(s)$ and $\theta(s)/\delta_p(s)$. Their derivation will now be presented.

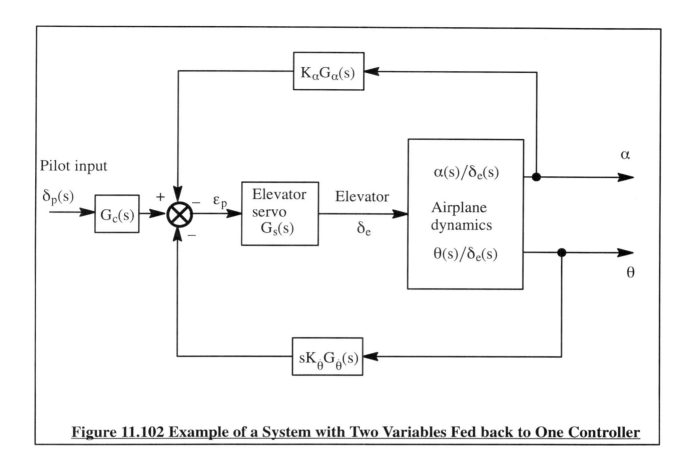

Figure 11.102 Example of a System with Two Variables Fed back to One Controller

The error Laplace transform, $\varepsilon_p(s)$, can be written as:

$$\varepsilon_p(s) = \delta_p(s)G_c(s) - K_\alpha G_\alpha(s)\alpha(s) - sK_{\dot\theta}G_{\dot\theta}(s)\theta(s) \qquad (11.51)$$

where:

$$\alpha(s) = \frac{\alpha(s)}{\delta_e(s)}\varepsilon_p(s)G_s(s) \qquad (11.52)$$

and

$$\theta(s) = \frac{\theta(s)}{\delta_e(s)}\varepsilon_p(s)G_s(s) \qquad (11.53)$$

To simplify the notation, the (s) designation will be omitted except from the input and output variables. Substitution of Eqns (11.52) and (11.53) into (11.51) yields:

$$\varepsilon_p(s) = \delta_P G_c\left(1 + K_\alpha G_\alpha G_s \frac{\alpha}{\delta_e} + sK_{\dot\theta}G_{\dot\theta}G_s \frac{\theta}{\delta_e}\right)^{-i} \qquad (11.54)$$

The closed loop system transfer function can now be found with the help of Eqns (11.52) and (11.53) as:

$$\frac{\alpha(s)}{\delta_p(s)} = \frac{G_s G_c \frac{\alpha}{\delta_e}}{\left(1 + K_\alpha G_\alpha G_s \frac{\alpha}{\delta_e} + s K_{\dot\theta} G_{\dot\theta} G_s \frac{\theta}{\delta_e}\right)} \tag{11.55}$$

and:

$$\frac{\theta(s)}{\delta_p(s)} = \frac{G_s G_c \frac{\theta}{\delta_e}}{\left(1 + K_\alpha G_\alpha G_s \frac{\alpha}{\delta_e} + s K_{\dot\theta} G_{\dot\theta} G_s \frac{\theta}{\delta_e}\right)} \tag{11.56}$$

The closed loop stability behavior of both transfer functions is determined by the roots of the characteristic equation formed by setting the denominator equal to zero:

$$\left(1 + K_\alpha G_\alpha G_s \frac{\alpha}{\delta_e} + s K_{\dot\theta} G_{\dot\theta} G_s \frac{\theta}{\delta_e}\right) = 0 \tag{11.57}$$

Observe that the numerator characteristics of both the angle of attack and the pitch attitude angle transfer functions are important in determining the roots of Eqn (11.57).

Second, consider the system of Figure 8.103.

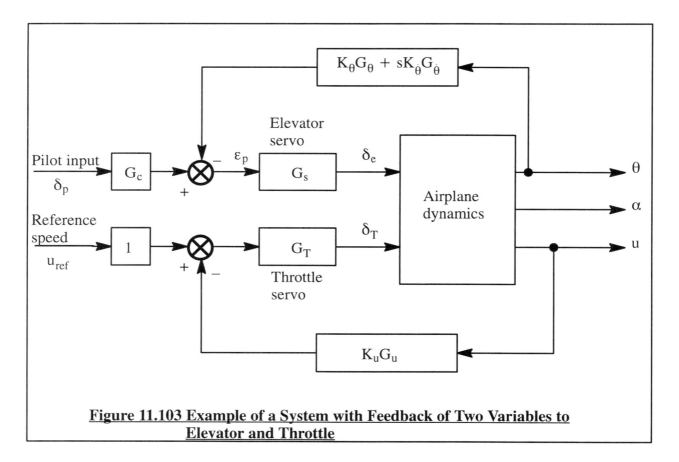

Figure 11.103 Example of a System with Feedback of Two Variables to Elevator and Throttle

Assume that the task is to derive an expression for the pitch attitude to pilot input transfer function. Leaving out the (s) notation for simplification it is observed that the three airplane output variables can be written as:

$$\theta = \delta_e(\theta/\delta_e) + \delta_T(\theta/\delta_T) \tag{11.58}$$

$$\alpha = \delta_e(\alpha/\delta_e) + \delta_T(\alpha/\delta_T) \tag{11.59}$$

$$u = \delta_e(u/\delta_e) + \delta_T(u/\delta_T) \tag{11.60}$$

From Figure 11.102 it can be seen that the error, ε_p, can be written as:

$$\varepsilon_p = \delta_p G_c - \theta \overline{G}_\theta \tag{11.61}$$

where:

$$\overline{G}_\theta = K_\theta G_\theta + s K_{\dot\theta} G_{\dot\theta} \tag{11.62}$$

The throttle deflection, δ_T, can be expressed as:

$$\delta_T = -G_T K_u G_u u \quad \text{iff } u_{ref} = 0 \tag{11.63}$$

The elevator deflection, δ_e is found as:

$$\delta_e = \varepsilon_p G_s \tag{11.64}$$

Combining Eqns (11.58) through (11.64) yields for the pitch attitude angle, θ:

$$\theta = G_s(\delta_p G_c - \theta \overline{G}_\theta)(\theta/\delta_e) - G_T K_u G_u u(\theta/\delta_T) \tag{11.65}$$

From Eqns (11.60) and (11.63) it follows that:

$$u = \delta_e(u/\delta_e) - G_T K_u G_u u(u/\delta_T) \tag{11.66}$$

From this, the speed perturbation, u, can be solved for as:

$$u = \frac{\delta_e(u/\delta_e)}{1 + G_T K_u G_u(u/\delta_T)} \tag{11.67}$$

Substituting Eqns (11.61) and (11.64) into Eqn (11.67) results in:

$$u = \frac{G_s(\delta_p G_c - \theta \overline{G}_\theta)(u/\delta_e)}{1 + G_T K_u G_u(u/\delta_T)} \tag{11.68}$$

Combining Eqns (11.68) and (11.65) yields:

$$\theta = G_sG_c(\theta/\delta_e)\delta_p - G_s\overline{G}_\theta(\theta/\delta_e)\theta - \frac{G_TK_uG_u(\theta/\delta_T)G_sG_c(u/\delta_e)\delta_p}{1 + G_TK_uG_u(u/\delta_T)} + \qquad (11.69)$$

$$+ \frac{G_TK_uG_u(\theta/\delta_T)G_s\overline{G}_\theta(u/\delta_e)\theta}{1 + G_TK_uG_u(u/\delta_T)}$$

The latter equation can be solved for the pitch–attitude–angle–to–pilot–input (θ/δ_p) transfer function. The result is:

$$\frac{\theta}{\delta_p} = \frac{G_sG_c(\theta/\delta_e) - \dfrac{G_TK_uG_u(\theta/\delta_T)G_sG_c(u/\delta_e)}{1 + G_TK_uG_u(u/\delta_T)}}{1 + G_s\overline{G}_\theta(\theta/\delta_e) - \dfrac{G_TK_uG_u(\theta/\delta_T)G_s\overline{G}_\theta(u/\delta_e)}{1 + G_TK_uG_u(u/\delta_T)}} \qquad (11.70)$$

This can be "cleaned up" to yield:

$$\frac{\theta}{\delta_p} = \frac{G_sG_c(\theta/\delta_e) + G_sG_c(\theta/\delta_e)G_TK_uG_u(u/\delta_T) - G_TK_uG_u(\theta/\delta_T)G_sG_c(u/\delta_e)}{\Delta} \qquad (11.71)$$

where:

$$\Delta = 1 + G_s\overline{G}_\theta(\theta/\delta_e) + G_TK_uG_u(u/\delta_T) + G_s\overline{G}_\theta(\theta/\delta_e)G_TK_uG_U(u/\delta_T) - G_TK_uG_u(\theta/\delta_T)G_s\overline{G}_\theta(u/\delta_e)$$

It is clear from Eqn (11.71) that the denominator of the closed loop system transfer function is affected by the speed feedback loop as well as by the pitch attitude (and pitch rate) feedback loop.

It is also clear that the closed loop analysis of multiple variable feedback to multiple controllers can be come very complicated. For a more systematic approach to this problem, using matrix algebra, the reader should consult Reference 11.3.

Another way around these mathematical problems is to employ so–called modern control theory. In modern control theory all equations are reduced to first order differential equations. Matrix methods are then used in their solution. A problem with this method is that direct contact with the physical world is easily lost because of the lack of transparency of large matrix operations.

11.10 SEPARATE SURFACE CONTROL SYSTEMS

11.10.1 INTRODUCTION AND DEFINITIONS

Figure 11.104 shows a conventional, cable driven flight control system with a tie–in for the autopilot servo. Most airplanes are equipped with systems similar to that shown in Figure 11.104. With the autopilot turned off the pilot controls the airplane with his control wheel. With the autopilot turned on the autopilot servo controls the airplane by dragging the entire system with it. Because flight control systems have their own inertia, friction and cable slack problems a fair amount of development testing is necessary to certify such systems. Also, a relatively large servo is required to drag the entire system with it.

Many airplanes require some form of stability augmentation (yaw damping and pitch damping are examples dealt with in Sections 11.1 and 11.2). If a pilot needs to control the airplane manually but with stability augmentation turned on, there is an annoying feedback from the SAS system to the cockpit controls because they move when the servo commands the flight control surfaces to move. One way to avoid such problems is to use a completely separate control surface which is dedicated to the autopilot and/or its stability augmentation functions. Figure 11.105 shows an example of such a system.

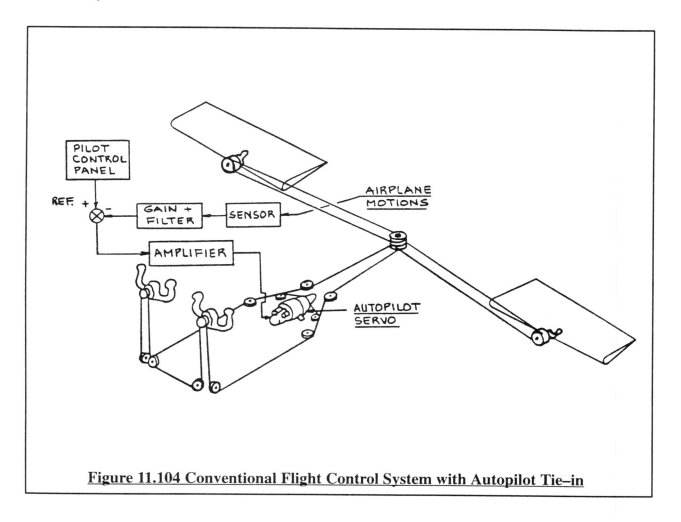

Figure 11.104 Conventional Flight Control System with Autopilot Tie–in

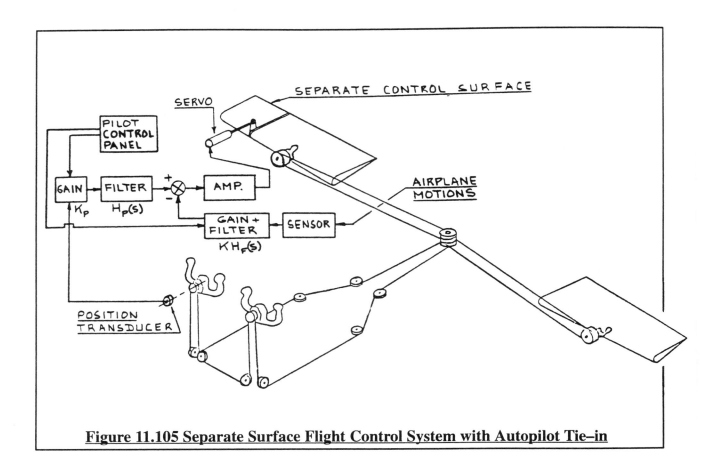

Figure 11.105 Separate Surface Flight Control System with Autopilot Tie–in

11.10.2 CLOSED LOOP ANALYSIS OF SEPARATE SURFACE CONTROL SYSTEMS

The closed loop analysis of a separate surface control system is done in a manner very similar to that of a conventional system. Figure 11.106 shows a block diagram of a separate surface feed-back system with the pilot in the loop as well.

In Figure 11.106 the pilot's wheel has an electrical pickup which is used to command the separate surface control loop. This feature is called "slaving". One advantage of slaving is that the pilot still has available the total aerodynamic control power designed into the airplane.

Checking with Figure 11.106 the separate surface deflection can be written as:

$$\delta_{ss}(s) = K_pH_p(s)G_{servo}(s)\delta_w - K_{ss}H_{ss}(s)G_{servo}(s)x(s) \tag{11.72}$$

The airplane motion variable(s), $x(s)$ can be expressed as:

$$x(s) = \delta_w(s)G_wG_p(s) + \delta_{ss}(s)G_{ss}(s) \tag{11.73}$$

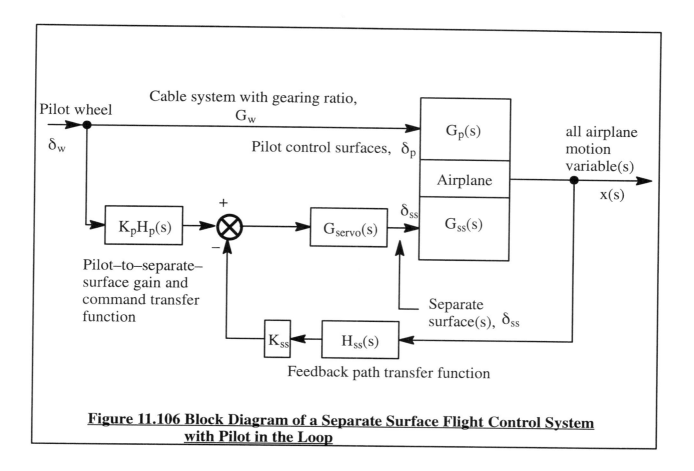

Figure 11.106 Block Diagram of a Separate Surface Flight Control System with Pilot in the Loop

Several observations are in order. First, the quantity G_w represents the gearing ratio from the pilot control wheel (or stick) to the pilot–controlled surfaces, δ_p. Second, the airplane open loop transfer function, $G_p(s)$, is taken with respect to the pilot–controlled surfaces only. Third, the airplane open loop transfer function, $G_{ss}(s)$, is taken with respect to the separate control surfaces only. Fourth, $G_p(s)$ and $G_{ss}(s)$ have identical denominators but different numerators. The reason for the latter is the fact that the control power magnitudes associated with the pilot–controlled surfaces and the separate control surfaces will, in general, be quite different. Obviously, the numerator of $G_p(s)$ contains the control power derivatives due to the pilot–controlled surfaces. Similarly, the numerator of $G_{ss}(s)$ contains the control power derivatives due to the separate control surfaces.

Solving Eqn (11.73) for $\delta_{ss}(s)$ yields:

$$\delta_{ss}(s) = \frac{x(s)}{G_{ss}(s)} - \frac{\delta_w(s)G_wG_p(s)}{G_{ss}(s)} \tag{11.74}$$

The closed loop transfer function with respect to pilot input, δ_w, can be found by substituting Eqn (11.74) into Eqn (11.72) and solving for $x(s)/\delta_w(s)$:

$$\frac{x(s)}{\delta_w(s)} = \frac{G_wG_p(s) + K_pH_p(s)G_{servo}(s)G_{ss}(s)}{1 + K_{ss}H_{ss}(s)G_{servo}(s)G_{ss}(s)} \qquad (11.75)$$

Several aspects of this transfer function are now discussed.

First, when $K_p = K_{ss} = 0$ (this implies no feedback loop and no separate surface slaving) the transfer function of Eqn (11.75) simplifies to:

$$\frac{x(s)}{\delta_w(s)} = G_wG_p(s) \qquad (11.76)$$

The reader will recognize this as the conventional airplane open loop transfer function of airplane output to pilot input. The dynamic stability characteristics of the airplane is then determined by:

$$\text{Denominator of } G_p(s) = 0 \qquad (11.77)$$

This is the open loop case which was extensively discussed in Chapter 5 of Part I.

Second, when $K_p = 0$ but $K_{ss} \neq 0$ the pilot has no direct control over the separate surface. However, the feedback loop does. In that case the closed loop transfer function of Eqn (11.75) is:

$$\frac{x(s)}{\delta_w(s)} = \frac{G_wG_p(s)}{1 + K_{ss}H_{ss}(s)G_{servo}(s)G_{ss}(s)} \qquad (11.78)$$

In this case the dynamic stability behavior of the airplane is governed by:

$$1 + K_{ss}H_{ss}(s)G_{servo}(s)G_{ss}(s) = 0 \qquad (11.79)$$

From this expression it is seen that for a given servo transfer function, $G_{servo}(s)$, the roots of Eqn (11.79) can be driven to desirable locations in the s–plane by selecting the separate surface feedback gain, K_{ss}, and the feedback path transfer function, $H_{ss}(s)$, in an appropriate manner. Because the separate surfaces do not feed back to the pilot's control wheel, this type of stability augmentation takes place without the pilot noticing any control wheel activity. Of course, if the pilot could see the separate surface from the cockpit he would see that surface move!

Third, with $K_p \neq K_{ss} \neq 0$ the benefit of stability augmentation is combined with the benefit of tailoring the numerator of the closed loop transfer function of Eqn (11.75). This way it is possible to achieve response tailoring as well as response quickening.

When an airplane equipped with the separate surface control system of Figure 11.106 is equipped with an autopilot, the control wheel stays inactive while the autopilot controls the separate surface(s). Figure 11.107 shows a block diagram of the system in such a mode.

The closed loop transfer function of such an autopilot mode can be written as:

$$\frac{x(s)}{x_{ref}(s)} = \frac{K_{ss}G_{servo}(s)G_{ss}(s)}{1 + K_{ss}H_{ss}(s)G_{servo}(s)G_{ss}(s)} \qquad (11.80)$$

The analysis and synthesis of this equation is identical to that discussed in previous sections of this chapter.

From a hardware viewpoint, depending on airplane mission and on detail design considerations separate control surfaces can be integrated into a configuration as suggested by the various ideas in Figures 11.108, 11.109 and 11.110.

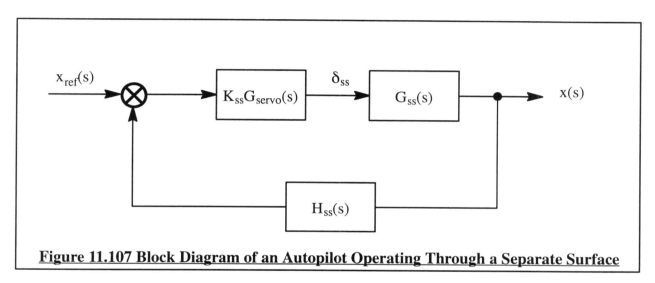

Figure 11.107 Block Diagram of an Autopilot Operating Through a Separate Surface

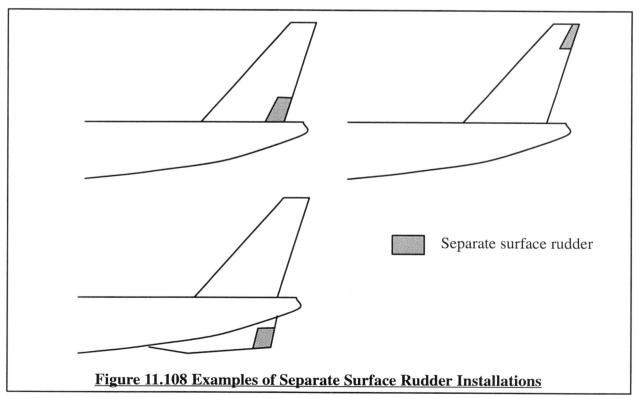

Figure 11.108 Examples of Separate Surface Rudder Installations

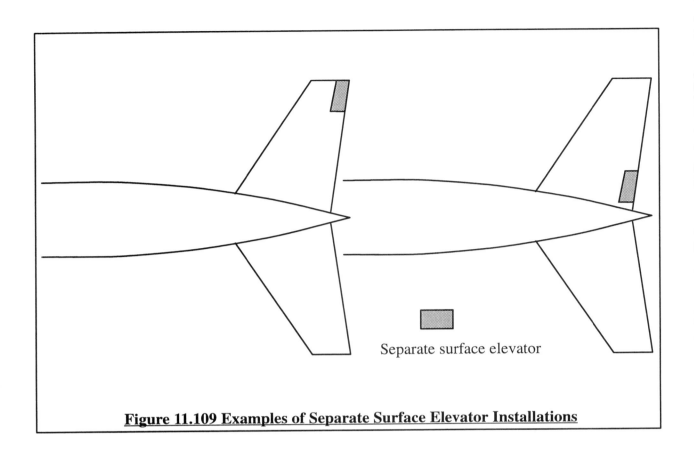

Figure 11.109 Examples of Separate Surface Elevator Installations

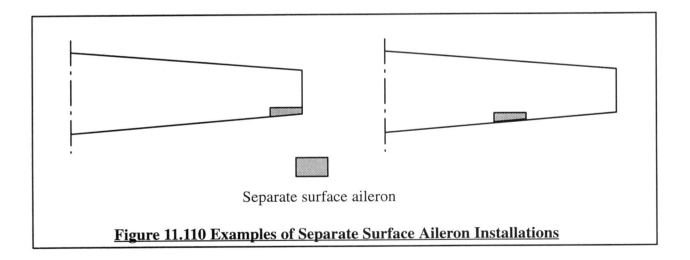

Separate surface aileron

Figure 11.110 Examples of Separate Surface Aileron Installations

11.11 SUMMARY FOR CHAPTER 11

In this chapter the reader has been introduced to the analysis and synthesis of stability augmentation systems: yaw dampers, pitch dampers, angle–of–attack feedback, acceleration feedback and angle–of–sideslip feedback. Such systems alter the apparent flying qualities of an airplane.

An introduction is also presented to the analysis and synthesis of various autopilot modes. Longitudinal as well as lateral–directional autopilot modes are presented. In all cases extensive use has been made of block diagrams to describe the flow of signals around the various feedback loop structures. Application of pitch attitude command systems and heading angle command systems to automatic landing problems is also discussed.

Root locus diagrams (and sometimes Bode diagrams) were used to determine desirable closed loop performance, gain margins and phase margins.

A brief introduction is presented to the problem of analyzing so–called multiple variable, multiple controller feedback systems.

Finally, the reader is introduced to the analysis and synthesis of separate surface flight control systems. The latter systems are useful in airplanes with reversible flight control systems.

11.12 PROBLEMS FOR CHAPTER 11

11.1   An airplane has a roll damper which actuates its ailerons through a servo with transfer function 10/(s+10). The airplane has a dimensional roll damping derivative of $L_p = -1.0 \ sec^{-1}$ at sealevel. Discuss the relative stability of the roll damper operation at 30,000 ft and 60,000 ft altitude. Assume that the spiral root stays at the origin.

11.2   Discuss qualitatively the effect of a yaw damper on spiral stability by examining the effect of the yaw damper on the "equivalent" values of the derivatives C_{l_p} and C_{n_p} .

11.3   Assume that the inherently unstable fighter of Table 5.5 in Part I is stabilized with a pure angle of attack feedback system. Assume further that the angle of attack sensor is repre–sented by a first order lag. How much lag can be tolerated (without compensation) and still achieve reasonable closed loop behavior?

11.4   Synthesize a pitch attitude command system for Airplane H in the approach and cruise flight condition. Discuss any need for a pitch damper in the inner loop. Also discuss any need for gain scheduling. Synthesize means: draw all appropriate block diagrams, root locus diagrams, Bode diagrams and identify clearly the various loop gains.

11.5   Synthesize a heading angle command system for Airplane H in the approach and cruise flight condition. Discuss any need for a roll damper in the inner loop. Also discuss any need for gain scheduling. Synthesize means: draw all appropriate block diagrams, root locus diagrams, Bode diagrams and identify clearly the various loop gains.

11.6   Synthesize a glideslope hold system for Airplane E in the approach flight condition. Synthesize means: draw all appropriate block diagrams, root locus diagrams, Bode diagrams and identify clearly the various loop gains.

11.7   Synthesize a localizer hold system for Airplane E in the approach flight condition. Synthesize means: draw all appropriate block diagrams, root locus diagrams, Bode diagrams and identify clearly the various loop gains.

11.8   Synthesize a yaw damper for Airplane I for the approach, subsonic cruise and supersonic cruise flight conditions. Use a tilted rate gyro and determine the required tilt angle. Also, identify the need for gain scheduling.

11.13 REFERENCES FOR CHAPTER 11

11.1   McRuer, D.T. and Johnston, D.E.; Flight Control Systems Properties and Problems, Volume 1; NASA–CR–2500, February 1975.

11.2   McRuer, D.T. and Johnston, D.E.; Flight Control Systems Properties and Problems, Volume 2, Block Diagram Compendium; NASA–CR–2500, February 1975.

11.3   McRuer, D.T., Ashkenas, I. and Graham, D.; Aircraft Dynamics and Automatic Control; Princeton University Press, 1973.

11.4   Anon.; Business and Commercial Aviation International; 1994 Planning & Purchasing Handbook; McGrawHill, N.Y. (Note: BCA is a monthly magazine. The Planning & Purchasing Handbook is issued once per year to subscribers.)

11.5   Anon.; 707 Mach Trim; Boeing Airliner Magazine, July 1959, p.3–7.

11.6   Roskam, J.; Airplane Design, Part IV, Layout Design of Landing Gear and Systems; Roskam Aviation and Engineering Corporation, c/o Design, Analysis and Research Corporation, 120 East Ninth Street, Suite 2, Lawrence, Kansas, 66044.

11.7   Blakelock, J.H.; Automatic Control of Aircraft and Missiles; Second Edition, John Wiley & Sons, N.Y., 1991.

11.8   Blakelock, J.H.; Automatic Control of Aircraft and Missiles; Second Edition, John Wiley & Sons, N.Y., 1965.

CHAPTER 12 FUNDAMENTALS OF DIGITAL CONTROL SYSTEM ANALYSIS

The methods presented in this text so far deal with systems and signals which are continuous functions of time. Nearly all high performance airplanes today are designed with some form of flight control system which utilizes digital computers. In digital computers time domain signals are not continuous but can be thought of as pulse trains. A key parameter in the analysis of such pulsed data streams is the so–called sampling rate. The sampling rate is the number of times per second that a continuous signal is being sampled for processing by the digital computer. If the sampling rate is very high, for all practical purposes, the system can still be analyzed as a continuous system and all methods discussed in this text more or less apply. However, if the sampling rate is not high a series of problems can arise.

The purpose of this chapter is to present a brief discussion of the fundamentals of digital control system analysis. For a fundamental treatment of this subject Reference 12.1 is recommended.

A brief introduction to sampling of signals is given in Section 12.1. Laplace transforms of sampled data systems are discussed in Section 12.2. To reconstruct continuous signals from digital signals certain "hold" devices are used. Two of these are discussed in Section 12.3.

A convenient method for analyzing digital systems is the so–called z–transform method. Section 12.4 contains a discussion of z–transforms. An example of their application is contained in Section 12.5.

The effect of sampling frequency on the stability of digital systems is briefly discussed in Section 12.6. Finally, an introduction to the so–called w–transformation method is given in Section 12.6.

12.1 INTRODUCTION TO SIGNAL SAMPLING

A very simple example of the application of a digital computer to the automatic control of an airplane is given in Figure 12.1. Except for the box labeled "digital/discrete" all elements of the block diagram in Figure 12.1 are analog (i.e. continuous) in nature.

The A/D (Analog–to–digital) device is, for all practical purposes, a data sampling device. The A/D converter translates an analog signal into a digital signal. The way the A/D converter operates can be thought of as multiplying the analog signal by a unit pulse train. Figure 12.2 shows conceptually what a sampler (A/D converter) looks like. Figure 12.3 indicates how, by multiplying an analog signal by a unit pulse train, the digital output (which is just another pulse train) comes about.

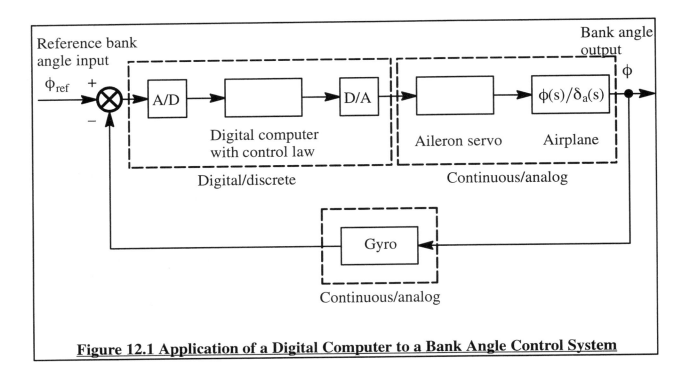

Figure 12.1 Application of a Digital Computer to a Bank Angle Control System

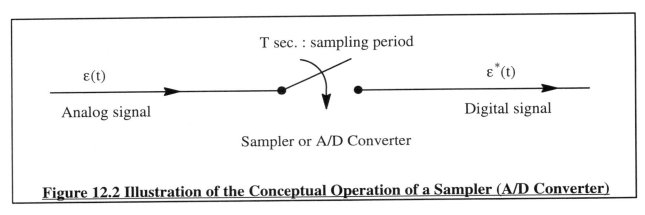

Figure 12.2 Illustration of the Conceptual Operation of a Sampler (A/D Converter)

Returning to Figure 12.1, the digital computer operates on the signal it receives from the A/D converter. The operation of the digital computer is governed by a control law which is programmed into the computer (software). The output of the digital computer is sent to a digital–to–analog (D/A) converter. The analog output of the D/A converter is normally sent to an amplifier which in turn sends its output to the aileron servo. The aileron servo moves the ailerons which in turn cause the airplane to change its bank angle. The bank angle is sensed by a gyro and its (analog) output is compared to a reference input (subtracted from a reference input) and the result forwarded to the A/D converter.

Now consider again Figure 12.3. The output signal, $\varepsilon^*(t)$, of the sampler (A/D converter) can be thought of as the product of the unit pulse train, $\delta_T(t)$, and the (analog) sampler input signal, $\varepsilon(t)$:

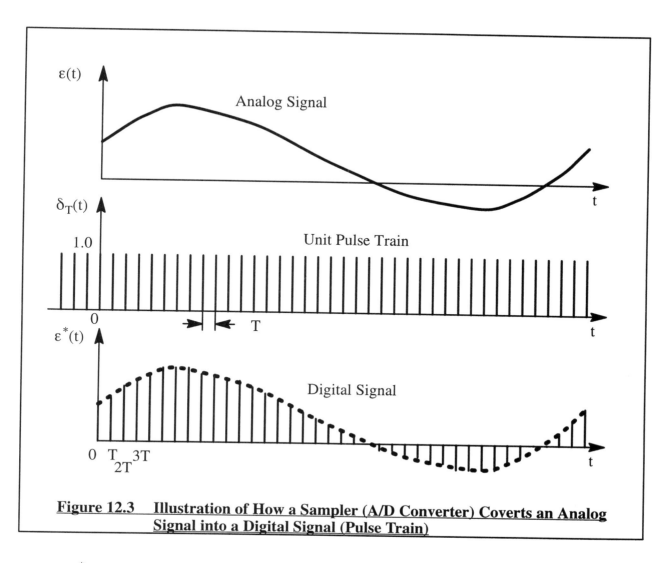

Figure 12.3   Illustration of How a Sampler (A/D Converter) Coverts an Analog Signal into a Digital Signal (Pulse Train)

$$\varepsilon^*(t) = \varepsilon(t) \, \delta_T(t) \tag{12.1}$$

where: the unit pulse train is defined by:

$$\delta_T(t) = \sum_{n=-\infty}^{\infty} \delta(t - nT) \tag{12.2}$$

where: $\delta(t - nT)$ represents an impulse of unit area at t=nT. The quantity T will be referred to as the sampling period. In current airplane systems the sampling period ranges from 1 sec. to 0.001 seconds depending on the frequency content of the data being processed. Evidently, the higher the frequency content of an airplane motion variable which needs to be controlled, the faster the sampling operation must be.

Combining Eqns (12.1) and (12.2) yields:

$$\varepsilon^*(t) = \varepsilon(t) \sum_{n=-\infty}^{\infty} \delta(t - nT) \tag{12.3}$$

or:

$$\varepsilon^*(t) = \sum_{n=-\infty}^{\infty} \varepsilon(nT) \ \delta(t - nT) \tag{12.4}$$

In nearly all airplane applications it is assumed that $\varepsilon(t) = 0$ for $t < 0$ so that Eqn (12.4) can be rewritten as:

$$\varepsilon^*(t) = \sum_{n=0}^{\infty} \varepsilon(nT) \ \delta(t - nT) \tag{12.5}$$

In the applications of feedback control discussed in Chapters 9, 10 and 11 the Laplace transformation was used. In Section 12.2 the application of Laplace transforms to sampled data systems is discussed.

12.2 LAPLACE TRANSFORMS AND SAMPLED DATA SYSTEMS

12.2.1 THE UNIQUENESS PROBLEM

The Laplace transform of a sampled signal, $\varepsilon^*(t)$, is defined as follows:

$$\varepsilon^*(s) = \pounds \ \left\{ \varepsilon^*(t) \right\} \tag{12.6}$$

Substituting Eqn (12.5) yields:

$$\varepsilon^*(s) = \pounds \ \left\{ \sum_{n=0}^{\infty} \varepsilon(nT) \ \delta(t - nT) \right\} \tag{12.7}$$

or:

$$\varepsilon^*(s) = \sum_{n=0}^{\infty} \varepsilon(nT) \ e^{-nTs} \tag{12.8}$$

because:

$$\pounds \ \left\{ \delta(t - nT) \right\} = \int_0^{\infty} e^{-st} \delta(t - nT)dt = e^{-nTs} \tag{12.9}$$

The following observation is of key importance. The sampled signal, $\varepsilon^*(t)$, describes the value of $\varepsilon(t)$ only at the sampling instants, nT. Therefore, the Laplace transform, $\varepsilon^*(s)$, does NOT contain any information on the value of $\varepsilon(t)$ during the sampling period ranging from nT to (n+1)T. Figure 12.4 illustrates the consequence of this observation: two totally different time domain signals can have the same samples data signals!

The signals $\varepsilon_1(t)$ and $\varepsilon_2(t)$ in Figure 12.4 are very different yet, they have the same sampled signal, $\varepsilon^*(t)$. Another way of putting this is: there is a uniqueness problem here. In most practical applications, particularly if the sampling period, T, is sufficiently small, this does not turn out to be a major problem.

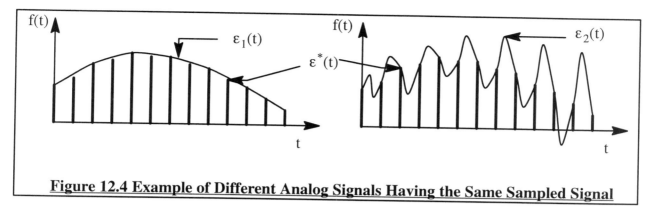

Figure 12.4 Example of Different Analog Signals Having the Same Sampled Signal

12.2.2 THE LAPLACE TRANSFORM OF THE SAMPLED UNIT STEP

It was seen in previous chapters that step inputs are frequently used to judge the response of both open and closed loop systems. The unit step is but a special case of the general step.

Consider the ideal sampler described by Eqn (12.4) as being subjected to a unit step input: $\varepsilon(t) = u(t)$ where $u(t)$ is assumed to have a constant magnitude of 1.0 at all times. The output of the sampler in this case is:

$$\varepsilon^*(t) = \sum_{n=0}^{\infty} \delta(t - nT) \tag{12.10}$$

Applying the Laplace transformation the result is:

$$\varepsilon^*(s) = \sum_{n=0}^{\infty} e^{-nTs} \tag{12.11}$$

This can be expanded to yield:

$$\varepsilon^*(s) = 1 + e^{-Ts} + e^{-2Ts} + e^{-3Ts} + ... = \frac{1}{1 - e^{-nTs}} \tag{12.12}$$

This result is valid as long as: $|e^{-Ts}| < 1$ is satisfied.

12.2.3 THE LAPLACE TRANSFORM OF THE SAMPLED FUNCTION: e^{-t}

Consider the ideal sampler described by Eqn (12.4) with the input: $\varepsilon(t) = e^{-t}$. The sampler output can be written as:

$$\varepsilon^*(t) = \sum_{n=0}^{\infty} e^{-t} \delta(t - nT) \tag{12.13}$$

Applying the Laplace transformation:

$$\varepsilon^*(s) = \sum_{n=0}^{\infty} e^{-nT} e^{-nTs} = \sum_{n=0}^{\infty} e^{-nT(1+s)} = \frac{1}{1 - e^{-T(s+1)}} \tag{12.14}$$

This result is valid as long as: $|e^{-T(s+1)}| < 1$ is satisfied.

12.2.4 ON THE PERIODICITY OF: $\varepsilon^*(s)$

It is not difficult to demonstrate that $\varepsilon^*(s)$ is itself a periodic function of the Laplace variable, s. One way to show this is to substitute for s:

$$s \rightarrow s + jm\omega_s \tag{12.15}$$

where: m is a positive integer and

$$\omega_s = \frac{2\pi}{T} \tag{12.16}$$

which is also called the sampling frequency.

Substitution of Eqn (12.15) into Eqn (12.8) results in:

$$\varepsilon^*(s + jm\omega_s) = \sum_{n=0}^{\infty} \varepsilon(nT) \; e^{-nT(s+jm\omega_s)} = \sum_{n=0}^{\infty} \varepsilon(nT) e^{-nTs} e^{-jnm2\pi} \tag{12.17}$$

According to DeMoivre's Theorem:

$$e^{-jnm2\pi} = \cos(k2\pi) - j \, \sin(k2\pi) = 1 \tag{12.18}$$

where: k, n and m are positive integers. Therefore:

$$\varepsilon^*(s + jm\omega_s) = \sum_{n=0}^{\infty} \varepsilon(nT) \; e^{-nTs} = \varepsilon^*(s) \tag{12.19}$$

This proves that $\varepsilon^*(s)$ is periodic in s. This property has a very important consequence. If $\varepsilon^*(s)$ is periodic in s, then: $\varepsilon^*(s = s_1)$ must have the same value at all $s = s_1 + jm\omega_s$. An illustration of this property is given in Figure 12.5. Another interesting consequence of this is the fact that if $\varepsilon(s)$ is the Laplace transform of $\varepsilon(t)$ and if this Laplace transform has a pole located at $s = s_1$, then $\varepsilon^*(s)$ has poles located at $s = s_1 + jm\omega_s$. This fact is also shown in Figure 12.5. Obviously this makes root loci of functions like $\varepsilon^*(s)$ a complicated task!

12.3   RECONSTRUCTION OF ANALOG DATA FROM SAMPLED DATA

12.3.1 INTRODUCTORY OBSERVATIONS

It can already be observed from Figure 12.1 that before a digital signal coming from a digital computer can actually be used it must be transformed into an analog signal, after which it is normally amplified to move some hardware component in the system. Figure 12.6 shows a simplified version of a block diagram of a digital flight control system.

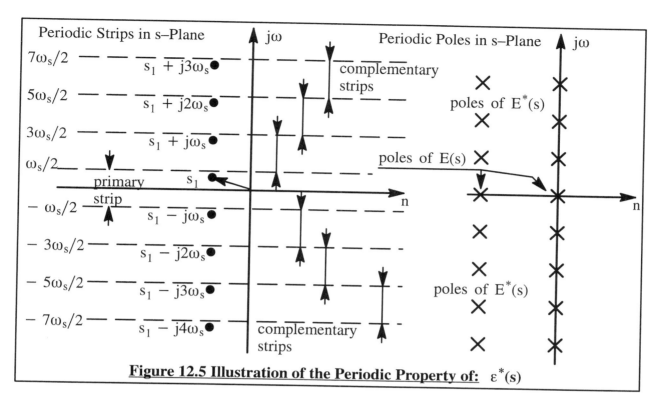

Figure 12.5 Illustration of the Periodic Property of: $\varepsilon^*(s)$

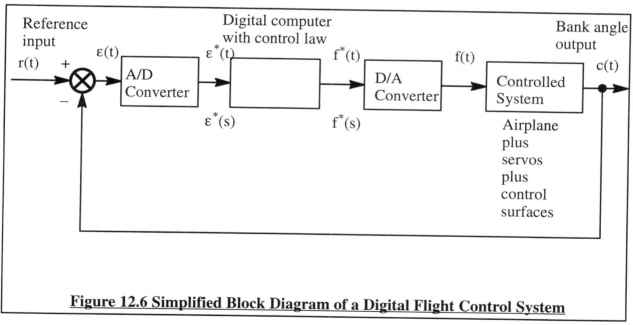

Figure 12.6 Simplified Block Diagram of a Digital Flight Control System

From Figure 12.6 it is seen that the D/A converter should regenerate a continuous time–domain signal from a sampled data signal. In other words: the D/A converter should regenerate the analog (continuous) signal, f(t) from the sampled signal, $f^*(t)$. Or, using the ε notation used before, the problem is to regenerate $\varepsilon(t)$ from $\varepsilon^*(t)$. The function $\varepsilon(t)$ in between two samples, nT and (n+1)T will be referred to as $\varepsilon_n(t)$. It is possible to expand $\varepsilon_n(t)$ in the following manner:

$$\epsilon_n(t) = \epsilon(nT) + \dot{\epsilon}(nT)(t - nT) + \frac{1}{2!}\ddot{\epsilon}(nT)(t - nT)^2 + ... \tag{12.20}$$

where: $\epsilon_n(t)$ is the value of $\epsilon(t)$ in between the sampling intervals nT and (n+1)T

$\epsilon(nT)$ is the value of $\epsilon(t)$ taken at t=nT

$\dot{\epsilon}(nT)$ is the first derivative of $\epsilon(t)$ taken at t=nT

$\ddot{\epsilon}(nT)$ is the second derivative of $\epsilon(t)$ taken at t=nT

The derivatives $\dot{\epsilon}(nT)$ and $\ddot{\epsilon}(nT)$ can be approximated with the help of numerical calculus in the following manner:

$$\dot{\epsilon}(nT) \approx \frac{1}{T}\Big[\epsilon(nT) - \epsilon\{(n - 1)T\}\Big] \tag{12.21}$$

and:

$$\ddot{\epsilon}(nT) \approx \frac{1}{T}\Big[\dot{\epsilon}(nT) - \dot{\epsilon}\{(n - 1)T\}\Big] \tag{12.22}$$

Substitution of Eqn (12.21) into Eqn (12.22) yields:

$$\ddot{\epsilon}(nT) \approx \frac{1}{T^2}\Big[\epsilon(nT) - 2\epsilon\{(n - 1)T\} + \epsilon\{(n - 2)T\}\Big] \tag{12.23}$$

To evaluate $\ddot{\epsilon}(nT)$ evidently requires knowledge of past values of $\epsilon(t)$. In a digital computer this problem is easily solved with the help of temporary data storage and retrieval.

From a pragmatic viewpoint only two types of D/A devices are of interest:

1) the zero–order hold
2) the first–order hold.

The s–domain characteristics of these two devices will be discussed in sub–sections 12.3.2 and 12.3.3 respectively.

12.3.2 THE ZERO ORDER HOLD

Figure 12.7 shows the ideal time domain behavior of a zero–order hold when the input is an ideal impulse. Note that this device holds the input constant during the sampling period, T.

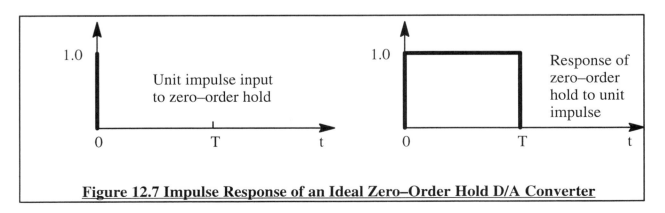

Figure 12.7 Impulse Response of an Ideal Zero–Order Hold D/A Converter

The output of a zero–order hold for a time varying series of impulses is shown in Figure 12.8. It is seen that as long as T is very small, the output signal of the zero order hold device will closely approximate the desired smooth continuous signal.

To perform frequency domain analyses on sampled data systems it is necessary to derive a transfer function for all components in the loop. The transfer function for the zero order hold can be inferred from its time domain response in Figure 12.7:

$$G_{ZOH}(s) = \frac{1}{s} - \frac{1}{s}e^{-sT} = \frac{1-e^{-sT}}{s} \tag{12.24}$$

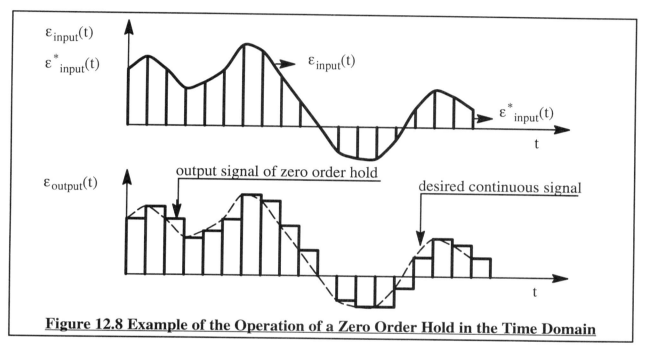

Figure 12.8 Example of the Operation of a Zero Order Hold in the Time Domain

The result stated in Eqn (12.24) is based upon a theorem in the theory of Laplace transforms which states that the Laplace transform of the unit impulse response of a system is the same as the transfer function of that system.

The frequency response of a zero order hold device can be obtained (as usual) by substituting s=jω into its transfer function. Doing this yields:

$$G_{ZOH}(j\omega) = \frac{1-e^{-j\omega T}}{j\omega} = \frac{2e^{-\frac{1}{2}j\omega T}\left(e^{\frac{1}{2}j\omega T} - e^{-\frac{1}{2}j\omega T}\right)}{2j\omega} \tag{12.25}$$

With DeMoivre's Theorem this can be cast into the following format:

$$G_{ZOH}(j\omega) = T\frac{\sin\frac{1}{2}\omega T}{\frac{1}{2}\omega T}\,e^{-\frac{1}{2}j\omega T} \tag{12.26}$$

From Eqn (12.16):

$$T = \frac{2\pi}{\omega_s} \tag{12.27}$$

Substitution into Eqn (12.26) results in:

$$G_{ZOH}(j\omega) = \frac{2\pi}{\omega_s} \frac{\sin \pi\left(\frac{\omega}{\omega_s}\right)}{\pi\left(\frac{\omega}{\omega_s}\right)} \, e^{-j\pi\left(\frac{\omega}{\omega_s}\right)} \tag{12.28}$$

From Eqn (12.28) the following gain and phase characteristics can be obtained:

$$|G_{ZOH}(j\omega)| = \frac{2\pi}{\omega_s} \frac{\sin \pi\left(\frac{\omega}{\omega_s}\right)}{\pi\left(\frac{\omega}{\omega_s}\right)} \tag{12.29}$$

$$\measuredangle\{G_{ZOH}(j\omega)\} = -\pi\left(\frac{\omega}{\omega_s}\right)\frac{\sin \pi \left(\frac{\omega}{\omega_s}\right)}{|\sin \pi \left(\frac{\omega}{\omega_s}\right)|} \tag{12.30}$$

Figure 12.9 presents a graphical representation of the zero order hold frequency response behavior. Some readers may recognize this behavior as similar to that of a low–pass filter.

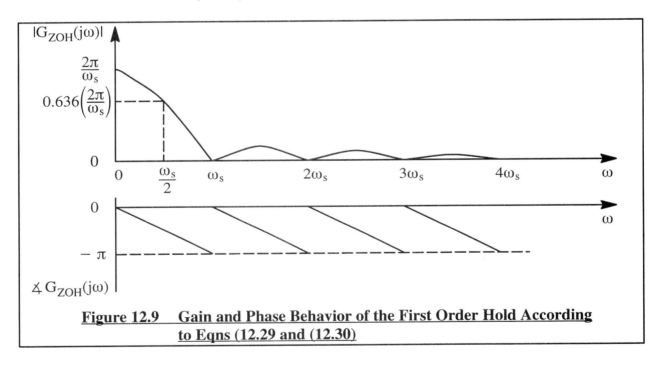

Figure 12.9   Gain and Phase Behavior of the First Order Hold According to Eqns (12.29 and (12.30)

12.3.3 THE FIRST ORDER HOLD

Figure 12.10 illustrates the time domain response behavior of an ideal first order hold device when subjected to a unit impulse.

It is seen from Figure 12.10 that before t=0 the response is equal to zero. For 0<t<T the response is the ramp function 1 + t/T. At t=T the response drops sharply to 0. For 2T>t>T the response is the ramp function –t/T. For t>2T the response is equal to zero.

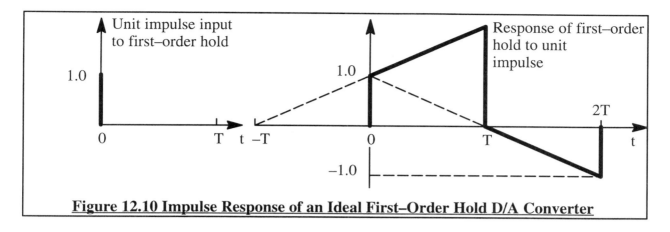

Figure 12.10 Impulse Response of an Ideal First–Order Hold D/A Converter

Because the transfer function of a system is equal to the Laplace transform of its unit impulse response, it is possible to infer the transfer function of the first order hold device from Figure 12.10 as:

$$G_{FOH}(s) = \frac{1}{s} + \frac{1}{Ts^2} - \frac{2}{s}e^{-Ts} - \frac{2}{Ts^2}e^{-Ts} + \frac{1}{s}e^{-2Ts} + \frac{1}{Ts^2}e^{-2Ts} \qquad (12.31)$$

This can be rearranged to yield:

$$G_{FOH}(s) = \left(\frac{1 + Ts}{T}\right)\left(\frac{1 - e^{-Ts}}{s}\right)^2 \qquad (12.32)$$

Figure 12.11 shows how a first order hold converter would reconstruct a pulse train. The spike during the interval $0<t<T$ is not normally a major concern. The reason is that in many cases the assumed condition that the input signal has the value of zero for $t=-T$ is not satisfied. The spike therefore will rarely occur.

The frequency response of the first order hold does give some reason for concern as will be shown next. Using the standard substitution $s=j\omega$ in the transfer function yields:

$$G_{FOH}(j\omega) = \left(\frac{1 + Tj\omega}{T}\right)\left(\frac{1 - e^{-Tj\omega}}{s}\right)^2 \qquad (12.33)$$

The reader is asked to show that the following expressions for magnitude and phase follow from Eqn (12.33):

$$|G_{FOH}(j\omega)| = \frac{2\pi}{\omega_s}\sqrt{\left(1 + \frac{4\pi^2\omega^2}{\omega_s^2}\right)}\left(\frac{\sin\frac{\pi\omega}{\omega_s}}{\frac{\pi\omega}{\omega_s}}\right)^2 \qquad (12.34)$$

and:

$$\angle G_{FOH}(j\omega) = \tan^{-1}\left(\frac{2\pi\omega}{\omega_s}\right) - \frac{2\pi\omega}{\omega_s} \qquad (12.35)$$

This frequency response behavior is illustrated in Figure 12.12. Two problems are the peak during the first frequency range and the large phase lag. For this reason and because of its greater simplicity the zero order hold device is used most frequently in digital systems.

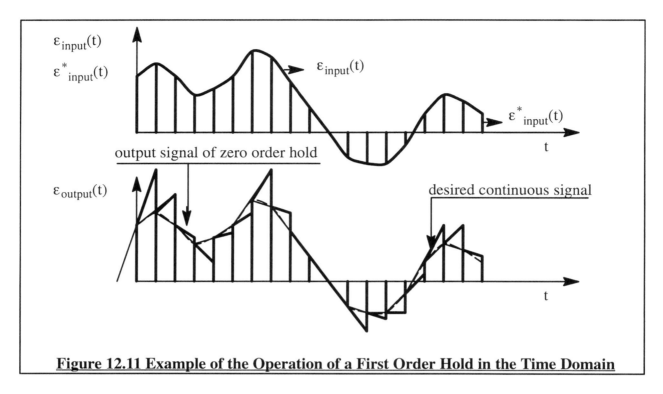

Figure 12.11 Example of the Operation of a First Order Hold in the Time Domain

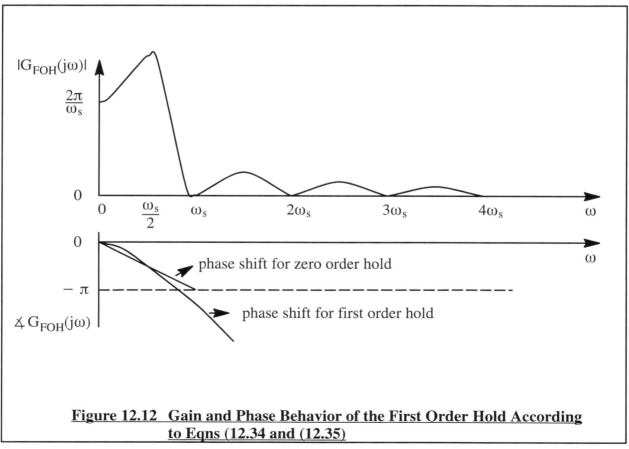

Figure 12.12   Gain and Phase Behavior of the First Order Hold According to Eqns (12.34 and (12.35)

12.4   FUNDAMENTALS OF Z–TRANSFORM THEORY

12.4.1   DEFINITION AND DERIVATION OF Z–TRANSFORMS

A disadvantage of the Laplace Transform method when used with sampled data systems is that such transforms in general are not algebraic because they contain powers of "e" involving the s–domain variable. This is already clear from the very definition of the Laplace transform of a pulsed variable, $\varepsilon^*(t)$:

$$\mathcal{L}\{\varepsilon(t)\} = \varepsilon^*(s) = \sum_{n=0}^{\infty} \varepsilon(nT) \; e^{-nTs} \tag{12.36}$$

For this reason, Laplace transforms of pulsed variables cannot be conveniently represented by ratios of polynomials with associated poles and zeros. This makes the formulation and use of transfer functions very difficult.

Some readers may wonder if the Pade approximation of Chapter 9 could not be used. The answer here is: no! The reason is the fact that because of the high sampling frequencies required, the bandwidth of the Pade transformation is not sufficient.

To eliminate this problem of the Laplace transformation the so–called z–transformation has been introduced. The z–transformation is obtained from the Laplace transformation by a simple substitution:

$$z = e^{Ts} \tag{12.37}$$

The inverse of this substitution is:

$$s = \frac{1}{T}\ln z \tag{12.38}$$

The new variable, z, is called the z–transform operator. With this operator the pulsed Laplace transform of Eqn (12.36) can be written as:

$$\varepsilon^*(s) = \varepsilon^*\left(s = \frac{1}{T}\ln z\right) = \varepsilon(z) = \sum_{n=o}^{\infty} \varepsilon(nT) \; z^{-n} \tag{12.39}$$

The function $\varepsilon(z)$ is called the z–transform of $\varepsilon(t)$. It should be understood that $\varepsilon(z)$ only defines $\varepsilon^*(t)$. As seen before, the continuous function, $\varepsilon(t)$ is not uniquely derivable from $\varepsilon(z)$.

The following three steps are required to find the z–transform of a time domain function:

Step 1: sample $\varepsilon(t)$ to obtain $\varepsilon^*(t)$

Step 2: find the Laplace transform $\varepsilon^*(s)$ from $\varepsilon^*(t)$

Step 3: find $\varepsilon(z)$ by substituting Eqn (12.37) into $\varepsilon^*(s)$

Five examples of z–transforms of frequently occurring time domain functions are now presented.

Example 1: Find the z–transform of a unit impulse function, $\delta(t)$.

Solution: When $\delta(t)$ is sampled by an ideal sampler, the result is:

$$\varepsilon^*(t) = \varepsilon(t) = \delta(t)$$

For that reason,

$$\varepsilon^*(s) = 1 \tag{12.40}$$

and:

$$\varepsilon(z) = 1 \tag{12.41}$$

Example 2: Find the z–transform of a unit impulse train, $\delta_T(t)$.

Solution: The unit impulse train can be written as:

$$\varepsilon(t) = \delta_T(t) = \sum_{n=0}^{\infty} \delta(t - nT)$$

By sending this function through an ideal sampler:

$$\varepsilon^*(t) = \varepsilon(t) \text{ and therefore:}$$

$$\varepsilon^*(s) = \sum_{n=0}^{\infty} e^{-nTs}$$

For that reason:

$$\varepsilon(z) = \sum_{n=0}^{\infty} z^{-n} = \frac{z}{z-1} \tag{12.42}$$

Example 3: Find the z–transform of a unit step, u(t).

Solution: Sending a unit step through an ideal sampler yields:

$$\varepsilon^*(t) = \sum_{n=0}^{\infty} \delta(t - nT)$$

According to Eqn (12.42):

$$\varepsilon(z) = \frac{z}{z-1} \tag{12.43}$$

This result should have been obvious! It also agrees with the non–uniqueness property of the z–transformation mentioned before. Figure 12.13 shows a visual representation of this result.

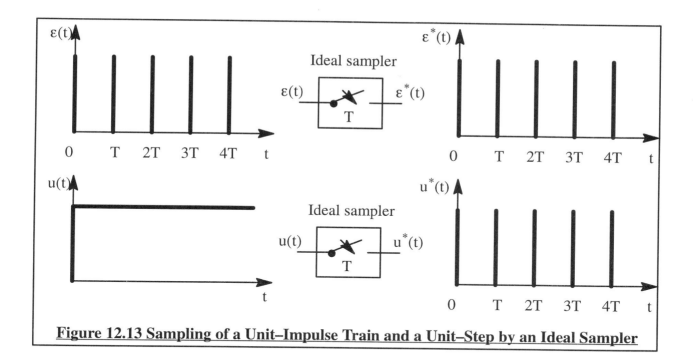

Figure 12.13 Sampling of a Unit–Impulse Train and a Unit–Step by an Ideal Sampler

Example 4:   Find the z–transform of the function $\varepsilon(t) = e^{-at}$.

Solution: Because $\varepsilon(nT) = e^{-anT}$ it is found that:

$$\varepsilon^*(s) = \sum_{n=0}^{\infty} e^{-anT}e^{-nTs} = 1 + e^{-aT}e^{-Ts} + e^{-2aT}e^{-2Ts} + ... = \qquad (12.44)$$

$$= \frac{1}{1 - e^{-(s+a)T}} \quad \text{for}: \quad |e^{-Ts}| < |e^{-aT}|$$

Therefore:

$$\varepsilon(z) = \frac{1}{1 - e^{-aT}z^{-1}} = \frac{z}{z - e^{-aT}} \quad \text{for}: \quad |z| < e^{-aT} \qquad (12.45)$$

Example 5:   Find the z–transform of the function $\varepsilon(t) = \sin \omega t$.

Solution: If $G(s) = N(s)/D(s)$ is the Laplace transform of some function, $g(t)$, then its s^* transform is found from:

$$G^*(s) = \sum_{n=1}^{k} \frac{N(\zeta_n)}{D'(\zeta_n)} \left\{ \frac{1}{1 - e^{-T(s - \zeta_n)}} \right\} \qquad (12.46)$$

where: k indicates the order of D(s) and where:

$$D'(\zeta_n) = \frac{dD(\zeta_n)}{d\zeta} \Big|_{\zeta = \zeta_n} \qquad (12.47)$$

The Laplace transform of $\sin \omega t$ is:

$$\varepsilon(s) = \frac{\omega}{s^2 + \omega^2} \tag{12.48}$$

This function has poles at: $s = \pm j\omega$ and therefore, since in this case:

$$N(\zeta) = \omega \qquad \text{and} \qquad D'(\zeta) = 2\zeta \qquad \text{it follows that:}$$

$$\varepsilon^*(s) = \sum_{n=1}^{2} \frac{\omega}{2\zeta_n} \left\{ \frac{1}{1 - e^{-T(s-\zeta_n)}} \right\}$$

$$= \frac{\omega}{2j\omega} \left\{ \frac{1}{1 - e^{-T(s-j\omega)}} \right\} - \frac{\omega}{2j\omega} \left\{ \frac{1}{1 - e^{-T(s+j\omega)}} \right\}$$

$$= \frac{1}{2j} \left\{ \frac{e^{-Ts}(-e^{-j\omega T} + e^{j\omega T})}{1 - e^{-Ts}(e^{j\omega T} + e^{-j\omega T}) + e^{-2Ts}} \right\}$$

$$= \frac{e^{-Ts} \sin \omega T}{e^{-2Ts} - 2e^{-Ts} \cos \omega T + 1} \tag{12.49}$$

Next, using the substitution: $z = e^{Ts}$ it is found that:

$$\varepsilon(z) = \frac{z \sin \omega T}{z^2 - 2z \cos \omega T + 1} \tag{12.50}$$

Deriving z–transforms can involve quite a bit of algebra. Table 12.1 presents z–transforms of frequently occurring functions.

An advantage of the z–transform method is that poles and zeros from the s–domain map into similar poles and zeros in the z–domain. A problem which must be overcome is: how does the s–plane map into the z–plane. This is particularly important in regard the definition of stable and unstable areas and lines of constant damping ratio and undamped natural frequency. The mapping of the s–plane into the z–plane is discussed in Sub–section 12.4.2.

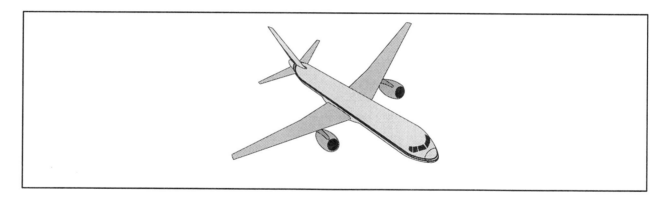

Fundamentals of Digital Control System Analysis

Table 12.1 Table of Laplace Transforms and z-Transforms

	Laplace Transform	Time Domain Function	z-Transform
	$E(s)$	$e(t)$	$E(z)$
1	1	$\delta(t)$ unit impulse at $t=0$	1
2	e^{-nTs}	$\delta(t-nT)$	z^{-n}
3	$\dfrac{1}{s}$	$u(t)$ unit step at $t=0$	$\dfrac{z}{z-1}$
4	$\dfrac{1}{s^2}$	t	$\dfrac{Tz}{(z-1)^2}$
5	$\dfrac{2!}{s^3}$	t^2	$\dfrac{T^2z(z+1)}{(z-1)^3}$
6	$\dfrac{(n-1)!}{s^n}$	$t^{(n-1)}$	$\lim_{a\to0}(-1)^{(n-1)}\dfrac{\partial^{(n-1)}}{\partial a^{(n-1)}}\left(\dfrac{z}{z-e^{-aT}}\right)$
7	$\dfrac{1}{s+a}$	e^{-at}	$\dfrac{z}{z-e^{-aT}}$
8	$\dfrac{1}{(s+a)(s+b)}$	$\dfrac{1}{(b-a)}(e^{-at}-e^{-bt})$	$\dfrac{1}{(b-a)}\left(\dfrac{z}{z-e^{-aT}}-\dfrac{z}{z-e^{-bT}}\right)$
9	$\dfrac{1}{s(s+a)}$	$\dfrac{1}{a}(u(t)-e^{-at})$	$\dfrac{1}{a}\left\{\dfrac{(1-e^{-aT})z}{(z-1)(z-e^{-aT})}\right\}$
10	$\dfrac{1}{s^2(s+a)}$	$\dfrac{1}{a}\left(t-\dfrac{1-e^{-at}}{a}\right)$	$\dfrac{1}{a}\left\{\dfrac{Tz}{(z-1)^2}-\dfrac{(1-e^{-aT})z}{a(z-1)(z-e^{-aT})}\right\}$
11	$\dfrac{s+b}{s^2(s+a)}$	$\dfrac{(a-b)}{a^2}u(t)+\dfrac{b}{a}t+\dfrac{1}{a}\left(\dfrac{b}{a}-1\right)e^{-aT}$	$\dfrac{1}{a}\left\{\dfrac{bTz}{(z-1)^2}+\dfrac{(a-b)(1-e^{-aT})z}{a(z-1)(z-e^{-aT})}\right\}$

Table 12.1 (Cont'd) Table of Laplace Transforms and z-Transforms

	Laplace Transform $E(s)$	Time Domain Function $e(t)$	z-Transform $E(z)$
12	$\dfrac{1}{s(s+a)(s+b)}$	$\dfrac{1}{ab}\left\{u(t) + \dfrac{b}{a-b}e^{-at} - \dfrac{a}{a-b}e^{-bt}\right\}$	$\dfrac{1}{ab}\left\{\dfrac{z}{z-1} + \dfrac{bz}{(a-b)(z-e^{-aT})} - \dfrac{1}{ab}\left[\dfrac{az}{(a-b)(z-e^{-bT})}\right]\right\}$
13	$\dfrac{1}{(s+a)^2}$	te^{-at}	$\dfrac{Tze^{-aT}}{(z-e^{-aT})^2}$
14	$\dfrac{1}{s^3(s+a)}$	$\dfrac{1}{2a}\left\{t^2 - \dfrac{2}{a}t + \dfrac{2}{a^2}u(t) - \dfrac{2}{a^2}e^{-at}\right\}$	$\dfrac{1}{a}\left\{\dfrac{T^2z}{(z-1)^3} + \dfrac{(aT-2)Tz}{2a(z-1)^2} + \dfrac{z}{a^2(z-1)} - \dfrac{1}{a}\left[\dfrac{z}{a^2(z-e^{-aT})}\right]\right\}$
15	$\dfrac{a}{s^2+a^2}$	$\sin at$	$\dfrac{z\sin aT}{z^2 - 2z\cos aT + 1}$
16	$\dfrac{s}{s^2+a^2}$	$\cos at$	$\dfrac{z(z-\cos aT)}{z^2 - 2z\cos aT + 1}$
17	$\dfrac{1}{(s+a)^2+b^2}$	$\dfrac{1}{b}e^{-at}\sin bt$	$\dfrac{1}{b}\left(\dfrac{ze^{-aT}\sin bT}{z^2 - 2ze^{-aT}\cos bT + e^{-2aT}}\right)$
18	$\dfrac{s+a}{(s+a)^2+b^2}$	$e^{-at}\cos bt$	$\left(\dfrac{z^2 - ze^{-aT}\cos bT}{z^2 - 2ze^{-aT}\cos bT + e^{-2aT}}\right)$
19	$\dfrac{1}{s\{(s+a)^2+b^2\}}$	$\dfrac{1}{a^2+b^2}\{1 - e^{-at}\sec\phi\cos(bt+\phi)\}$ with: $\phi = \tan^{-1}\left(\dfrac{-a}{b}\right)$	$\dfrac{1}{a^2+b^2}\left(\dfrac{z}{z-1} - \dfrac{z^2 - ze^{-aT}\sec\phi\cos(bT-\phi)}{z^2 - 2ze^{-aT}\cos bT + e^{-2aT}}\right)$

12.4.2 MAPPING OF THE S–PLANE INTO THE Z–PLANE

In the open and closed loop analysis of airplanes and control systems it was seen that four lines in the s–plane play a dominant role in determining flying qualities:

1) lines parallel to the imaginary axis (i.e. lines for which the real part of complex poles or zeros is constant).
2) lines parallel to the real axis (i.e. lines of constant frequency).
3) lines passing through the origin (i.e. lines of constant damping ratio).
4) circles around the origin (i.e. paths of constant undamped natural frequency).

Several specifications of flying qualities deal with the properties of these lines. It is therefore logical to inquire how these lines map from the s–plane into the z–plane.

Figure 12.14 shows how lines parallel to the imaginary axis in the s–plane and lines parallel to the real axis in the s–plane map into the z–plane. This mapping can be easily understood by tracing five paths in the s–plane and establishing their mappings in the z–plane. These paths are: $1\rightarrow2, 2\rightarrow3, 3\rightarrow4, 4\rightarrow5$ and $5\rightarrow1$. The mappings of these five paths will be discussed one by one. Once this mapping is understood it should be easy to determine how any given pole or zero in the s–plane maps into the z–plane.

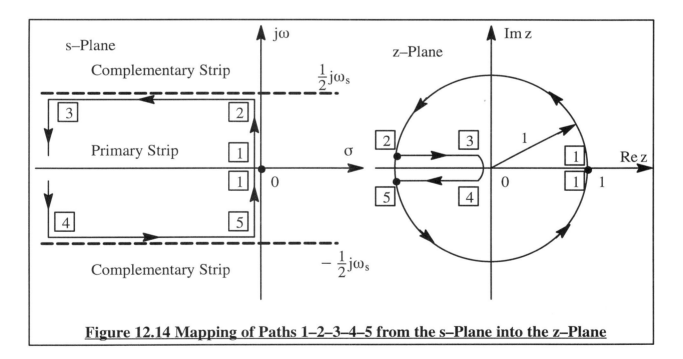

Figure 12.14 Mapping of Paths 1–2–3–4–5 from the s–Plane into the z–Plane

To discuss the mapping properties use will be made of Eqn (12.37) which is repeated here for convenience:

$$z = e^{Ts} \tag{12.51}$$

Note in Figure 12.14 that the s–plane is broken up into a primary and complementary strips.

The primary strip runs from: $s = -\omega_s/2$ to $s = +\omega_s/2$. The path 1–2–3–4–5–1 in the complementary strip in the s–plane (see Figure 12.14) will now be mapped piece–by–piece into the z–plane.

Path 1–2

Along path 1–2 it is seen that: $s = j\omega$ so that Eqn (12.51) yields: $z = e^{jT\omega}$. This latter expression represents a unit circle in the positive half of the z–plane. Note that when:

$$\omega = +\omega_s/2 = \frac{\pi}{T},$$ z is given by: $z = e^{j\pi}$. The latter represents point 2 in the z–plane. Also note, that when $\omega = 0$, z=1. Therefore, the origin in the s–plane maps into the point z=1 in the z–plane.

Path 2–3

Along path 2–3 it is seen that: $s = -k + j\omega_s/2$, where k is any positive number. Therefore, Eqn (12.51) yields: $z = e^{-Tk} e^{j\pi}$. This latter expression represents the left real axis in the z–plane. When k approaches zero, z is seen to approach the value 1.0. When k approaches $+\infty$, z approaches zero.

Path 3–4

Along path 3–4, $k = +\infty$, and therefore, z=0. This is the origin in the z–plane.

Path 4–5

Along path 4–5 it is clear that: $s = -k - j\omega_s/2$. Therefore, Eqn (12.51) yields: $z = e^{-Tk} e^{-j\pi}$. By analogy to path 2–3 this represents the left real axis in the z–plane.

Path 5–1

Along path 5–1 it is seen that: $s = -j\omega$ so that Eqn (12.51) yields: $z = e^{-jT\omega}$. This latter expression represents a unit circle in the negative half of the z–plane.

Conclusion: the area surrounded by path 1–2–3–4–5–1 in the s–plane maps into the interior of a unit circle in the z–plane.

If n is a positive integer, then: $e^{s+jn\omega_s T} = e^{Ts}e^{2\pi jn} = e^{Ts}$ for any integer value of n. This result implies that all complementary strips in the left side of the s–plane also map into the interior of the unit circle in the z–plane. Therefore, the entire left side of the s–plane maps into the interior of the unit circle in the z–plane.

The reader is asked to prove that the entire imaginary axis in the s–plane maps into the unit circle in the z–plane. The reader is also asked to verify that the entire right side of the s–plane maps into the entire z–plane outside the unit circle.

From a stability/instability viewpoint this can be depicted as in Figure 12.15.

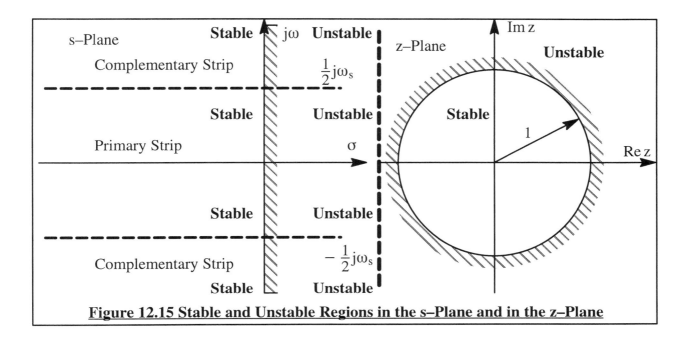

Figure 12.15 Stable and Unstable Regions in the s–Plane and in the z–Plane

12.4.3 MAPPING OF CONSTANT DAMPING LOCI

Figure 12.16 shows two constant damping (i.e. constant real part of complex root) loci in the s–plane. These loci are represented by: $s = \sigma + j\omega$ in the s–plane, where σ is a constant. The mapping of these loci into the z–plane will now be derived. The corresponding z–plane loci are also shown in Figure 12.16.

Because of Eqn (12.51): $z = e^{Ts} = e^{T\sigma}e^{jT\omega}$. Clearly this latter expression represents circles around the origin in the z–plane. If $\sigma<0$, then $e^{T\sigma} < 1.0$ and the circle is within the unit circle. If $\sigma>0$, then $e^{T\sigma} > 1.0$ and the circle is outside the unit circle . Finally, if $\sigma=0$ then $z = e^{jT\omega}$ is the unit circle itself.

12.4.4 MAPPING OF CONSTANT FREQUENCY LOCI

Figure 12.17 shows two constant frequency (i.e. constant imaginary part of complex root) loci in the s–plane. These loci are represented by: $s = \sigma + j\omega$ in the s–plane, where ω is a constant.

The mapping of these loci into the z–plane will now be derived. The corresponding z–plane loci are also shown in Figure 12.17.

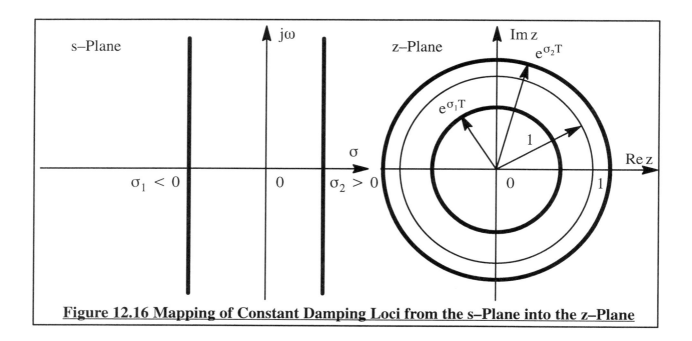

Figure 12.16 Mapping of Constant Damping Loci from the s–Plane into the z–Plane

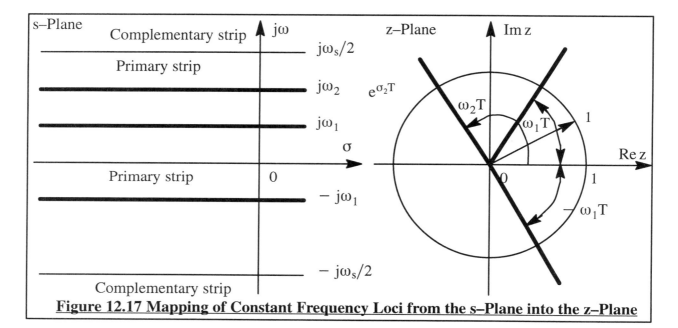

Figure 12.17 Mapping of Constant Frequency Loci from the s–Plane into the z–Plane

Because of Eqn (12.51): $z = e^{Ts} = e^{T\sigma}e^{jT\omega}$. If ω is a constant, the quantity $e^{jT\omega}$ repre-sents a constant angle. Since $e^{T\sigma}$ varies with σ it is seen that the result is straight lines through the origin at different angles, depending on ω.

12.4.5 MAPPING OF CONSTANT DAMPING RATIO LOCI

Figure 12.18 shows a line of constant damping ratio in the s–plane. This line makes an angle, β with the imaginary axis. Therefore, the constant damping ratio line can be expressed as:

$$s = -\omega \tan \beta + j\omega \tag{12.52}$$

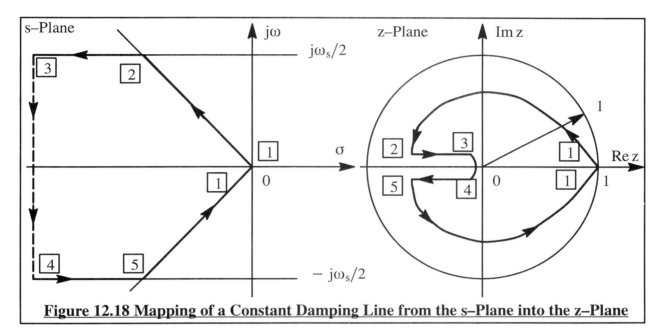

Figure 12.18 Mapping of a Constant Damping Line from the s–Plane into the z–Plane

The corresponding value of the damping ratio, ζ, is seen to be:

$$\zeta = \frac{\tan \beta}{\sqrt{\tan^2 \beta + 1}} \tag{12.53}$$

Using Eqn (12.51) the s–plane constant damping ratio line maps into:

$$z = e^{Ts} = e^{(-\omega \tan \beta + j\omega)T} \tag{12.54}$$

The latter expression can also be written as:

$$z = \left(e^{\left(\frac{-2\pi\omega \tan \beta}{\omega_s} \right)} \right) \angle \left(\frac{2\pi\omega}{\omega_s} \right) \tag{12.55}$$

where it should be remembered that β is a constant which depends on the damping ratio, as seen by Eqn (12.53).

Inspection of Eqn (12.55) shows that, as ω is varied from 0 to $+\infty$, the magnitude of z varies from 1.0 to zero while the angle of z varies from 0 degrees to 360 degrees. Therefore, a logarithmic spiral is traced around the origin of the z–plane. From Figure 12.18 it may be surmised that for each half revolution in the z–plane, the constant damping ratio path in the s–plane has moved along one increment of $\omega_s/2$ in the s–plane. Since for all practical purposes the sampling rate in a digital system will be very high compared to the highest motion frequency being controlled, only the first part of the spiral in the z–plane is of significance.

Figure 12.19 shows what typical constant damping ratio paths (in the s–plane) are like in the z–plane. From a pragmatic viewpoint, only frequency–to–sampling–frequency ratios below 0.1 are of interest. The reader should observe that line AB in Figure 12.19 is the equivalent of the negative real axis in the s–plane.

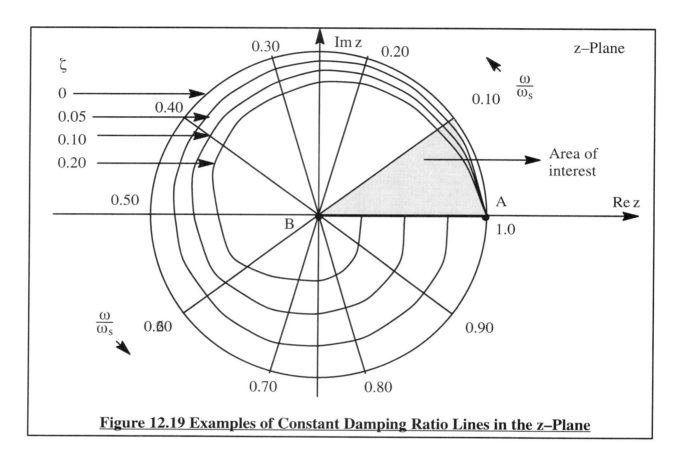

Figure 12.19 Examples of Constant Damping Ratio Lines in the z–Plane

12.4.6 MAPPING OF CONSTANT UNDAMPED NATURAL FREQUENCY LOCI

Constant undamped frequency loci in the s–plane are circles around the origin. Any point s, can be written as: $s = \sigma + j\omega$. For constant undamped natural frequency, ω_n the following relation must hold:

$$\sigma^2 + \omega^2 = \omega_n^2 \tag{12.56}$$

Eqn (12.56) can also be represented by the following two equations:

$$\sigma = \omega_n \cos \phi \tag{12.57}$$

$$\omega = \omega_n \sin \phi \tag{12.58}$$

In the z–plane, with Eqn (12.51) this yields:

$$z = e^{Ts} = e^{T(\omega_n \cos\phi + j\omega_n \sin\phi)} = \left(e^{T\omega_n \cos\phi}\right)\left(e^{jT\omega_n \sin\phi}\right)$$

$$= e^{T\omega_n \cos\phi} \;\measuredangle\, (T\omega_n \sin\phi)$$

$$= e^{\left(\frac{\omega_n}{\omega_s}\right)2\pi \cos\phi} \;\measuredangle\, \left\{\left(\frac{\omega_n}{\omega_s}\right)2\pi \sin\phi\right\} \qquad (12.59)$$

From Eqn (12.59) it is seen that z behaves as a function of ϕ. A numerical example of this behavior is presented in Table 12.2. Figure 12.20 shows several z– plane loci for various values of ω_n/ω_s and for various values of ϕ. The reader should recognize the fact that in the first stable quadrant of the s–plane, ϕ ranges from 90 degrees to 180 degrees.

Table 12.2 Variation of z with ϕ		
ϕ	$\|z\| = e^{\left(\frac{\omega_n}{\omega_s}\right)2\pi \cos\phi}$	$\measuredangle\left\{\left(\frac{\omega_n}{\omega_s}\right)2\pi \sin\phi\right\}$
0^0	$\|z\| = e^{\left(\frac{\omega_n}{\omega_s}\right)2\pi}$	0
90^0	$\|z\| = 1$	$\measuredangle\left\{\left(\frac{\omega_n}{\omega_s}\right)2\pi\right\}$
180^0	$\|z\| = 1/\left(e^{\left(\frac{\omega_n}{\omega_s}\right)2\pi}\right)$	0

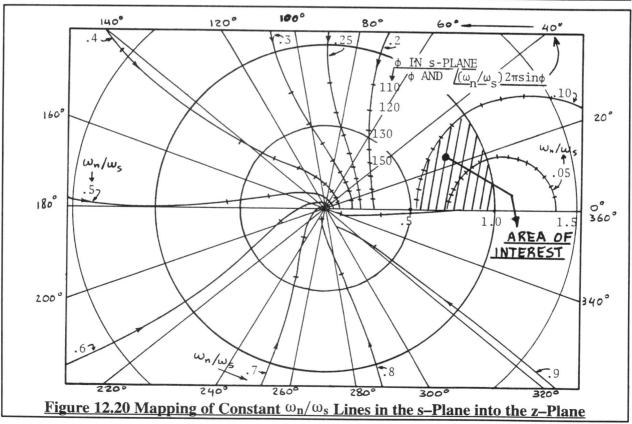

Figure 12.20 Mapping of Constant ω_n/ω_s Lines in the s–Plane into the z–Plane

12.4.7 INVERSE Z–TRANSFORMS

It was seen on page 892 that the z–transform is not unique. Several different time domain functions can have the same z–transform. This must be considered when taking the inverse of a function in the z–domain. Two methods for finding the inverse of z–transforms will be presented:

1. The partial fraction expansion method
2. The power series expansion method

1. The partial fraction expansion method

In the s–domain a common expression used for partial fraction expansion was:

$$\varepsilon(s) = \frac{A}{s + a} + \frac{B}{s + b} + \frac{C}{s + c} + \; ....$$ (12.60)

Such an expansion is easily converted to the time domain. It would perhaps be reasonable to expect a similar expansion to work in the z–domain:

$$\varepsilon(z) = \frac{A}{z + a} + \frac{B}{z + b} + \frac{C}{z + c} + \; ....$$ (12.61)

However, when inspecting the z–transform expressions in Table 12.1 it is seen that z–transforms only occur with z/z+x type terms. For that reason it is generally best to find a partial fraction expansion for $\varepsilon(z)/z$, then multiply by z and next, invert to the time domain. An example will illustrate this procedure.

Consider the following function of z:

$$\varepsilon(z) = \frac{\left(1 - e^{-aT}\right)z}{(z - 1)(z - e^{-aT})}$$ (12.62)

After dividing by z this yields:

$$\frac{\varepsilon(z)}{z} = \frac{\left(1 - e^{-aT}\right)}{(z - 1)(z - e^{-aT})}$$ (12.63)

This can be partially expanded to yield:

$$\frac{\varepsilon(z)}{z} = \frac{1}{z - 1} - \frac{1}{z - e^{-aT}}$$ (12.64)

From Table 12.1 the inverse of this z–transform is:

$$\varepsilon^*(t) = \sum_{n=0}^{\infty} \delta(t - nT)(1 - e^{-anT})$$ (12.65)

2. The power series expansion method

In general, the z–transform, $\varepsilon(z)$ can be cast in the following polynomial form:

$$\varepsilon(z) = \frac{a_m z^m + a_{m-1} z^{m-1} + a_{m-2} z^{m-2} + \ldots\ldots + a_1 z + a_0}{b_n z^n + b_{n-1} z^{n-1} + \ldots\ldots + b_1 z + b_0} \tag{12.66}$$

In physically realizable systems the condition $n \geq m$ is a necessary constraint. The reader is reminded that this was also the case in the s–domain.

By long division it is possible to write Eqn (12.66) as follows:

$$\varepsilon(z) = C_1 z^{m-n} + C_2 z^{m-n-1} + C_2 z^{m-n-2} + \ldots \tag{12.67}$$

Next, recall Eqn (12.39) and observe that:

$$\varepsilon(z) = \sum_{n=0}^{\infty} \varepsilon(nT) z^{-n} \tag{12.68}$$

By equating Eqn (12.68) to Eqn (12.67) it is seen that:

$$C_1 = \varepsilon(m-n)T \qquad C_2 = \varepsilon(m-n-1)T \qquad C_2 = \varepsilon(m-n-2)T \text{ , etc.} \tag{12.69}$$

Evidently, the C–coefficients in the long division result as represented by Eqn (12.67) are themselves the time domain values in the pulse train of data represented by the z–transform of the output of the sampled data system! The C–coefficients can be cast in a more convenient recurrence relationship as follows:

$$C_i = \frac{1}{B_m}\left\{ A_{n-i+1} - \sum_{j=0}^{n-1}\left(B_j C_{i-m+j}\right) \right\} \qquad \begin{array}{l} A_i = B_i = 0 \text{ for : } i < 0 \\[2mm] C_i = 0 \text{ for : } j \leq 0 \end{array} \tag{12.70}$$

An example will be used to illustrate an application of this method. Consider Eqn (12.62) but with the denominator expanded:

$$\varepsilon(z) = \frac{\left(1 - e^{-aT}\right)z}{\left\{z^2 - (1 + e^{-nT})z + e^{-aT}\right\}} \tag{12.71}$$

By applying the long division process with the help of Eqn (12.70) it is found that:

$$\varepsilon(z) = (1 - e^{-aT})z^{-1} + (1 - e^{-2aT})z^{-2} + (1 - e^{-3aT})z^{-3} + \ldots\ldots \tag{12.72}$$

The time domain inverse of this z–transform is:

$$\varepsilon^*(t) = (1 - e^{-aT})\delta(t - T) + (1 - e^{-2aT})\delta(t - 2T) + \ldots\ldots \tag{12.73}$$

This can be rewritten as:

$$\varepsilon^*(t) = \sum_{n=0}^{\infty} (1 - e^{-anT})\delta(t - nT) \tag{12.74}$$

The latter result will be recognized as being identical to Eqn (12.65).

12.4.8 IMPORTANT Z–TRANSFORM PROPERTIES

The z–transform of an s–domain function, just like the s–transform of a time domain function has the standard addition and multiplication properties of a linear operator. In the s–domain the initial and final value theorems were found to be useful. Similar theorems exist for z–transforms. Because of their importance these theorems will be stated and proven in the following.

Initial Value Theorem:

Theorem: If $\mathscr{Z}\{\varepsilon(t)\} = \varepsilon(z)$ and if $\lim_{z\to\infty} \varepsilon(z)$ exists, then:

$$\lim_{t\to 0} \varepsilon^*(t) = \lim_{z\to\infty} \varepsilon(z)$$

Proof: The z–transform of $\varepsilon(t)$ can be written as:

$$\varepsilon(z) = \sum_{n=0}^{\infty} \varepsilon(nT)z^{-n} = \tag{12.75}$$

$$= \varepsilon(0) + \varepsilon(T)z^{-1} + \varepsilon(2T)z^{-2} + \dots$$

Therefore, $\lim_{z\to\infty} \varepsilon(z) = \varepsilon(0) = \lim_{t\to 0} \varepsilon^*(t)$ Q.E.D.

Final Value Theorem:

Theorem: If $\mathscr{Z}\{\varepsilon(t)\} = \varepsilon(z)$ and if $(1 - z^{-1})\,\varepsilon(z)$ has no poles on or outside the unit circle in the z–plane, then:

$$\lim_{t\to\infty} \varepsilon^*(t) = \lim_{n\to\infty} \varepsilon(nT) = \lim_{z\to 1} (1 - z^{-1})\,\varepsilon(z)$$

Proof: Consider the following expansions:

$$\sum_{k=0}^{n} \varepsilon(kT)\,z^{-k} = \varepsilon(0) + \varepsilon(T)z^{-1} + \dots + \varepsilon(nT)z^{-n} \tag{12.76}$$

and:

$$\sum_{k=0}^{n} \varepsilon\{(k-1)T\}\,z^{-k} = \varepsilon(0)z^{-1} + \varepsilon(T)z^{-2} + \dots + \varepsilon\{(n-1)T\}z^{-n} \tag{12.77}$$

Observe that for k=0, $\varepsilon\{(k-1)T\} = \varepsilon(-T)$. However, $\varepsilon(-T) = 0$ because $\varepsilon(t)$ is defined only for $t \geq 0$. Comparing Eqns (12.76) and (12.77) it is possible to rewrite Eqn (12.77) as:

$$\sum_{k=0}^{n} \varepsilon\{(k-1)T\}\,z^{-k} = z^{-1} \sum_{k=0}^{n-1} \varepsilon(kT)z^{-k} \tag{12.78}$$

Subtracting Eqn (12.78) from Eqn (12.76) yields:

$$\left\{ \sum_{k=0}^{n} \varepsilon(kT) \, z^{-k} - z^{-1} \sum_{k=0}^{n-1} \varepsilon(kT) z^{-k} \right\} \tag{12.79}$$

The limit of Expression (12.79) for $z \to 1$ can be written as:

$$\lim_{z \to 1} \left\{ \sum_{k=0}^{n} \varepsilon(kT) \, z^{-k} - z^{-1} \sum_{k=0}^{n-1} \varepsilon(kT) z^{-k} \right\} =$$

$$= \sum_{k=0}^{n} \varepsilon(kT) - \sum_{k=0}^{n-1} \varepsilon(kT) = \varepsilon(nT) \tag{12.80}$$

The limit of Expression (12.80) for $n \to \infty$ can be written as:

$$\lim_{n \to \infty} \varepsilon(nT) = \lim_{n \to \infty} \lim_{z \to 1} \left\{ \sum_{k=0}^{n} \varepsilon(kT) \, z^{-k} - z^{-1} \sum_{k=0}^{n-1} \varepsilon(kT) z^{-k} \right\} =$$

$$= \lim_{z \to 1} \lim_{n \to \infty} \left\{ \sum_{k=0}^{n} \varepsilon(kT) \, z^{-k} - z^{-1} \sum_{k=0}^{n-1} \varepsilon(kT) z^{-k} \right\} = \tag{12.81}$$

Clearly, the following must be correct:

$$\lim_{n \to \infty} \sum_{k=0}^{n} \varepsilon(kT) z^{-k} = \lim_{n \to \infty} \sum_{k=0}^{n-1} \varepsilon(kT) z^{-k} \tag{12.82}$$

Also:

$$\lim_{n \to \infty} \sum_{k=0}^{n} \varepsilon(kT) z^{-k} = \sum_{n=0}^{\infty} \varepsilon(nT) z^{-n} = \varepsilon(z) \tag{12.83}$$

Because of Eqns (12.83) and (12.81) it now follows that:

$$\lim_{n \to \infty} \varepsilon(nT) = \lim_{z \to 1} (1 - z^{-1}) \, \varepsilon(z) \qquad \text{Q.E.D.} \tag{12.84}$$

The power of the initial and final value theorems lies in the fact that it is possible to predict initial and final time domain quantities directly from the z–transforms.

It is useful to consider an example. Assume that a signal $\varepsilon(t)$ has the following z–transform:

$$\varepsilon(z) = \frac{0.792 \, z^2}{(z - 1)(z^2 - 0.416z + 0.208)} \tag{12.85}$$

According to the final value theorem the final value of $\varepsilon(t)$ is found as follows:

$$\varepsilon(\infty) = \lim_{z \to 1}(1 - z^{-1})\varepsilon(z) = \lim_{z \to 1}\left\{\frac{0.792\,z}{(z^2 - 0.416z + 0.208)}\right\} \tag{12.86}$$

The poles of the z–transform defined by Eqn (12.86) are seen to be inside the unit circle:

$$z_{1,2} = 0.208 \pm j(0.329) \tag{12.87}$$

From Eqn (12.86) it is seen that: $\varepsilon(\infty) = 1.0$.

This result can be verified with the long division method discussed in Sub–section 12.4.7. Rewriting Eqn (12.85) it is seen that:

$$\varepsilon(z) = \frac{0.792\,z^2}{(z^3 - 1.416z^2 + 0.624z - 0.208)} \tag{12.88}$$

Invoking the recurrence equation (12.70) the following coefficient values can be found:

$$A_2 = 0.792 \qquad A_1 = 0 \qquad A_0 = 0 \tag{12.89}$$

$$B_3 = 1 \qquad B_2 = -1.416 \qquad B_1 = 0.624 \qquad B_0 = -0.208$$

From Eqn (12.70):

$$C_i = \frac{1}{B_m}\left\{A_{n-i+1} - \sum_{j=0}^{n-1}\left(B_j C_{i-m+j}\right)\right\} \tag{12.90}$$

with m=3 and m=2 respectively it follows that:

$C_1 = A_2 = 0.792$

$C_2 = A_1 - B_2 C_1 = 1.121$

$C_3 = A_0 - B_1 C_1 - B_2 C_2 = 1.093$

$C_4 = -B_0 C_1 - B_1 C_2 - B_2 C_3 = 1.013 \tag{12.91}$

$C_5 = -B_0 C_2 - B_1 C_3 - B_2 C_4 = 0.986$

$C_6 = -B_0 C_3 - B_1 C_4 - B_2 C_5 = 0.991$

$C_7 = -B_0 C_4 - B_1 C_5 - B_2 C_6 = 0.999$

It is clear that $\lim_{t \to \infty} C_i = 1.0$. This agrees with the previous result.

12.5 AN APPLICATION OF Z–TRANSFORMS

In this section the z–transform method will be applied to a sampled data system. A problem which will emerge is the fact that the pule transform of a cascaded system is not simply obtained as the product of the pulse transform elements in the cascade. This problem is discussed in Sub–section 12.5.1.

It also emerges that the z –transform of closed loop systems depends on where in the system the sampling devices are located. This problem is discussed in Sub–section 12.5.2.

An application to a simple bank angle hold system is presented in Sub–section 12.5.3.

12.5.1 THE PULSE TRANSFER FUNCTION OF SAMPLED DATA SYSTEMS

For a continuous (or analog) system, the time domain and s–domain notations associated with a simple system are illustrated in Figure 12.21.

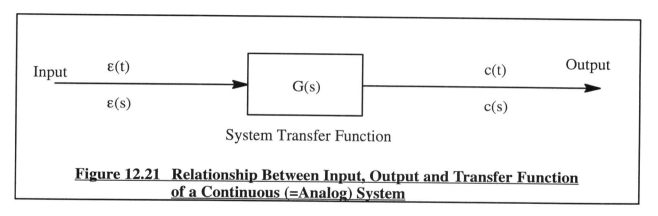

Figure 12.21   Relationship Between Input, Output and Transfer Function of a Continuous (=Analog) System

The system output is found from:

$$c(s) = \varepsilon(s)G(s) \tag{12.92}$$

For a similar discrete system (sampled data system) the same time domain and s–domain notations associated with the system are summarized in Figure 12.22.

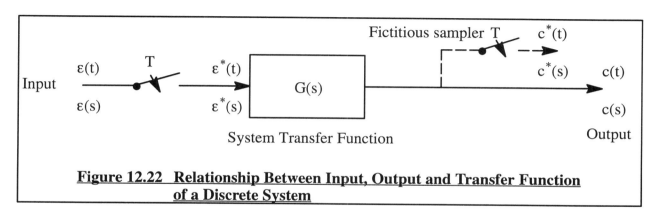

Figure 12.22   Relationship Between Input, Output and Transfer Function of a Discrete System

Using the conventional transform rules it follows for Figure 12.22 that:

$$c(s) = \varepsilon^*(s)G(s) \tag{12.93}$$

Obviously, the output in Figure 12.22 will be a series of pulses because of the existence of the sampler ahead of G(s). For that reason the idea of a "fictitious sampler" is introduced. The pulse transform of c(s) can therefore be written as:

$$c^*(s) = \varepsilon^*(s)G^*(s) \tag{12.94}$$

Transformation to the z–domain leads to:

$$c(z) = \varepsilon(z)G(z) \tag{12.95}$$

The function $G^*(s)$ is referred to as the pulse transfer function of G(s). The operation implied by Eqn (12.94) is referred to as taking the pulse transform of Eqn (12.93).

Next, these ideas will be applied to a cascaded system such as sketched in Figure 12.23.

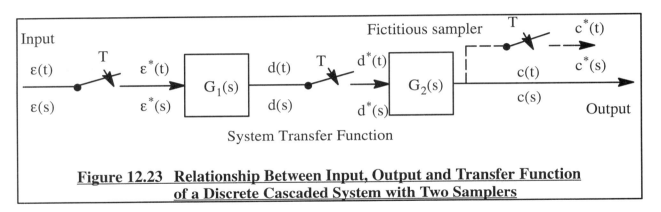

Figure 12.23   Relationship Between Input, Output and Transfer Function of a Discrete Cascaded System with Two Samplers

It will be assumed, that the two samplers operate synchronously. Referring to Figure 12.23 it is seen that the output of the first transfer function, $G_1(s)$, can be written as:

$$d(s) = G_1(s)\varepsilon^*(s) \tag{12.96}$$

The output of the second transfer function, $G_2(s)$, can be written as:

$$c(s) = G_2(s)d^*(s) \tag{12.97}$$

Taking the pulse transform of Eqn (12.96) yields:

$$d^*(s) = G_1^*(s)\varepsilon^*(s) \tag{12.98}$$

Substitution of this result into Eqn (12.97) yields:

$$c(s) = G_2(s)G_1^*(s)\varepsilon^*(s) \tag{12.99}$$

Taking the pulse transform of this result produces:

$$c^*(s) = G_2^*(s)G_1^*(s)\varepsilon^*(s) \tag{12.100}$$

Transformation to the z–domain yields:

$$c(z) = G_2(z)G_1(z)\varepsilon(z) \tag{12.101}$$

This result will now be compared with the result of a cascaded system which differs from the one in Figure 12.23 only in that there is no sampler between $G_1(s)$ and $G_2(s)$. Such a system is sketched in Figure 12.24.

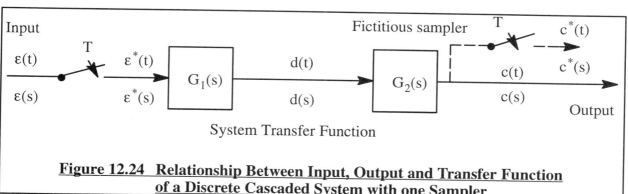

Figure 12.24   Relationship Between Input, Output and Transfer Function of a Discrete Cascaded System with one Sampler

For the system of Figure 12.24 the output can be written as:

$$c(s) = G_1(s)G_2(s)\varepsilon^*(s) \tag{12.102}$$

Taking the pulse transform yields:

$$c^*(s) = G_1G_2^*(s)\varepsilon^*(s) \tag{12.103}$$

where:

$$G_1G_2^*(s) = \left\{G_1(s)G_2(s)\right\}^* = \frac{1}{T}\sum_{n=-\infty}^{\infty}G_1(s + jn\omega_s)G_2(s + jn\omega_s) \tag{12.104}$$

The reader should remember that apparently:

$$G_1G_2^*(s) \neq G_1^*(s)G_2^*(s) \tag{12.105}$$

Taking the z–transform of Eqn (12.102) yields:

$$c(z) = G_1G_2(z)\varepsilon(z) \tag{12.106}$$

where the notation: $G_1G_2(z)$ implies:

$$G_1G_2(z) = \mathscr{Z}\left\{G_1(s)G_2(s)\right\} \tag{12.107}$$

It is useful and instructive to consider a numerical example. Figure 12.25 shows two types of cascaded system, one with one sampler, the other with two samplers.

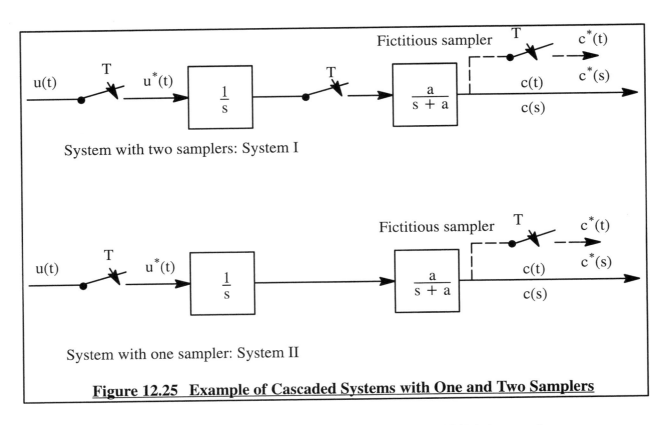

Figure 12.25 Example of Cascaded Systems with One and Two Samplers

In the case of the System I (two samplers) using Eqn (12.101) it is seen that:

$$c(z) = G_2(z)G_1(z)\varepsilon(z) = \qquad\qquad (12.108)$$

$$= \left(\frac{z}{z-1}\right)\left(\frac{az}{z-e^{-aT}}\right)\left(\frac{z}{z-1}\right) = \frac{az^3}{(z-1)^2(z-e^{-aT})}$$

In the case of System II (one sampler) using Eqn (12.106) is is seen that:

$$c(z) = G_1G_2(z)\varepsilon(z) = \qquad\qquad (12.109)$$

$$= \mathcal{Z}\left\{\frac{a}{a(s+a)}\varepsilon(z)\right\} = \frac{z^2(1-e^{-aT})}{(z-1)^2(z-e^{-aT})}$$

The reader will agree that the output transforms of the two systems are indeed different. In the analysis of digital systems it is therefore important to know the location of the samplers in the system before determining the mathematical format of the z–transform of the system output.

In the next Sub–section it will be shown that similar caution should be exercised in determining the closed loop z–transform of a system.

12.5.2 CLOSED LOOP SAMPLED DATA SYSTEMS

Figure 12.26 shows a digital control system with an A/D device in the error signal path.

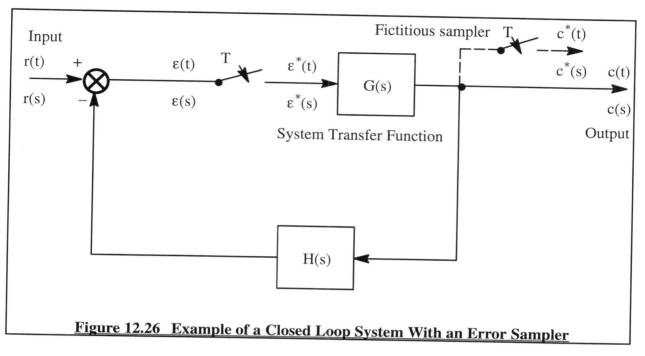

Figure 12.26   Example of a Closed Loop System With an Error Sampler

The output Laplace transform of this system, c(s) may be written as:

$$c(s) = G(s)\varepsilon^*(s) \tag{12.110}$$

To get $\varepsilon^*(s)$ first consider $\varepsilon(s)$:

$$\varepsilon(s) = r(s) - c(s)H(s) \tag{12.111}$$

Substitution of Eqn (12.110) into (12.111) yields:

$$\varepsilon(s) = r(s) - G(s)H(s)\varepsilon^*(s) \tag{12.112}$$

Taking the pulse Laplace transform results in:

$$\varepsilon^*(s) = r^*(s) - GH^*(s)\varepsilon^*(s) \tag{12.113}$$

This equation can be solved for $\varepsilon^*(s)$:

$$\varepsilon^*(s) = \frac{R^*(s)}{1 + GH^*(s)} \tag{12.114}$$

Substitution of this result into Eqn (12.110) produces:

$$c(s) = \frac{G(s)R^*(s)}{1 + GH^*(s)} \tag{12.115}$$

Upon taking the z–transform it is found that:

$$c(z) = \frac{G(z)}{1 + GH(z)} R(z) \qquad (12.116)$$

Next, it will be shown that if the samplers are located differently in the system, the output z–transform will also be different. To that end, consider Figure 12.27.

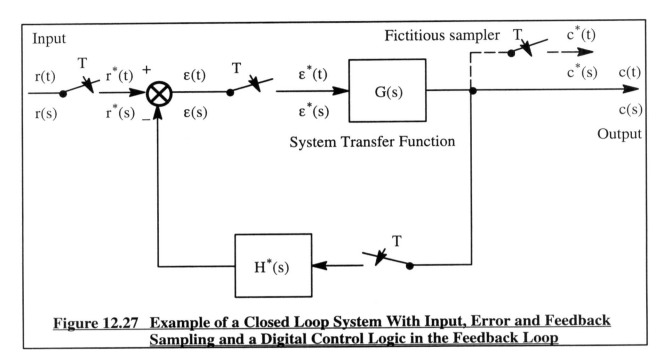

Figure 12.27 Example of a Closed Loop System With Input, Error and Feedback Sampling and a Digital Control Logic in the Feedback Loop

Observe in Figure 12.27 that the error sampler could be left out of the system without any change, provided all samplers are perfectly synchronized. The pulse transform of the error signal can be written as:

$$\varepsilon^*(s) = r^*(s) - c^*(s)H^*(s) \qquad (12.117)$$

The system output can be cast in the following form:

$$c(s) = \varepsilon^*(s)G(s) \qquad (12.118)$$

After taking the pulse transform:

$$c^*(s) = \varepsilon^*(s)G^*(s) \qquad (12.119)$$

Substitution of Eqn (12.119) into Eqn (12.117) yields:

$$\varepsilon^*(s) = r^*(s) - \varepsilon^*(s)G^*(s)H^*(s) \qquad (12.120)$$

Solving for $\varepsilon^*(s)$:

$$\varepsilon^*(s) = \frac{R^*(s)}{1 + G^*(s)H^*(s)} \qquad (12.121)$$

Therefore:

$$c^*(s) = \frac{G^*(s)R^*(s)}{1 + G^*(s)H^*(s)}$$

(12.122)

Taking the z–transform now yields:

$$c(z) = \frac{G(z)R(z)}{1 + G(z)H(z)}$$

(12.123)

By comparing Eqn (12.123) with Eqn (12.116) it is seen that the system transfer functions in the z–domain are indeed different! Therefore, again in digital control systems the location and the number of samplers both play a role in determining the system behavior.

12.5.3 A SIMPLE BANK ANGLE CONTROL SYSTEM

At this point a simple application to a bank–angle control system will be discussed. To set the stage an analog version of such a system will be presented first. Consider Figure 12.28 which shows a block diagram of a bank–angle control system. For simplicity in the mathematics a "fast" servo (with negligible dynamics) is assumed.

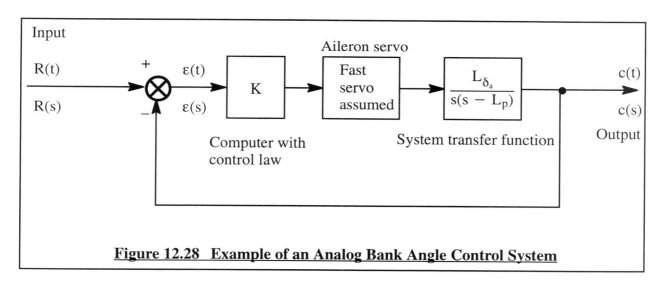

Figure 12.28 Example of an Analog Bank Angle Control System

The closed loop transfer function of this system can be shown to be:

$$W(s) = \frac{K\,L_{\delta_a}}{s^2 - L_p s + K L_{\delta_a}}$$

(12.124)

It will be assumed that: $L_{\delta_a} = 60$ sec^{-2} and $L_p = -10$ sec^{-1}, while K has been selected as K=1.5 deg/deg. The corresponding s–domain root locus is shown in Figure 12.29.

For a unit step input, the Laplace transform of aileron deflection is: $\delta_a(s) = \frac{1}{s}$. The system output Laplace transform then is:

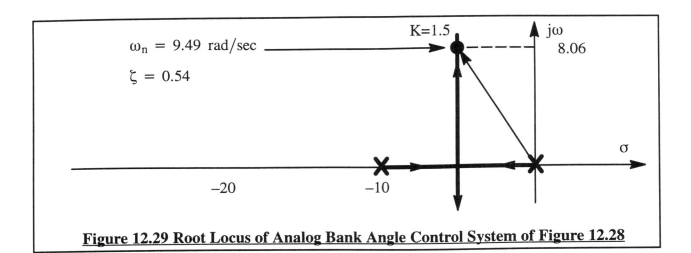

Figure 12.29 Root Locus of Analog Bank Angle Control System of Figure 12.28

$$C(s) = \frac{90}{s\left\{(s + 5)^2 + 65\right\}} \tag{12.125}$$

The time domain inverse of this output is:

$$C(t) = \left\{1 - e^{-5t}\sec \phi \cos (8.06t + \arctan \phi)\right\} \tag{12.126}$$

where: $\phi = \arctan \dfrac{-5}{8.06} = -0.56$

The time domain response of this analog system is shown in Figure 12.30 by the solid line. Note that the system response to the unit step is rather well behaved.

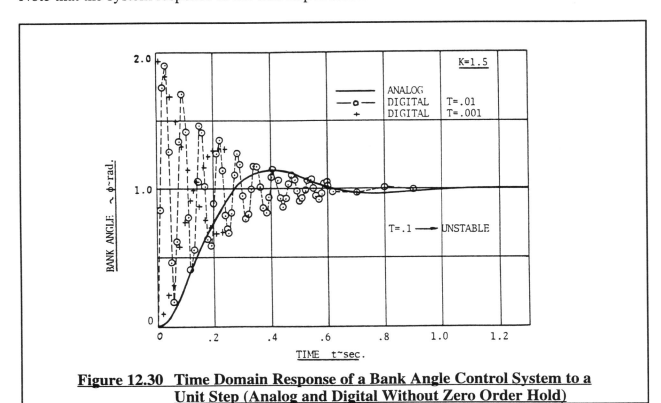

Figure 12.30 Time Domain Response of a Bank Angle Control System to a Unit Step (Analog and Digital Without Zero Order Hold)

Now consider a digital version of the system of Figure 12.28. A block diagram of this system with two samplers and NO D/A device is shown in Figure 12.31.

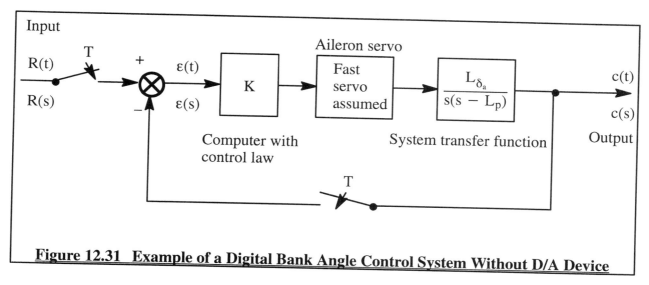

Figure 12.31   Example of a Digital Bank Angle Control System Without D/A Device

According to Eqn (12.123) the system transfer function in the z–domain is:

$$W(z) = \frac{KG(z)}{1 + KG(z)} \tag{12.127}$$

where:

$$G(z) = \mathscr{Z}\left\{\frac{L_{\delta_a}}{s(s - L_p)}\right\} = \left(\frac{L_{\delta_a}}{-L_p}\right)\frac{(1 - e^{L_p T})z}{(z - 1)(z - e^{L_p T})} \tag{12.128}$$

The system output to a unit step is given by:

$$\phi(z) = \frac{z}{z - 1}W(z) \tag{12.129}$$

$$= \frac{\left(L_{\delta_a}/ - L_p\right)K\left(1 - e^{L_p T}\right)z^2}{(z - 1)\left\{(z - 1)(z - e^{L_p T}) + \left(L_{\delta_a}/ - L_p\right)K\left(1 - e^{L_p T}\right)z\right\}}$$

Using $L_{\delta_a} = 60$ sec^{-2} and $L_p = -10$ sec^{-1} as in the analog system of Figure 12.28 this yields:

$$\phi(z) = \tag{12.130}$$

$$= \frac{6K(1 - e^{-10T})z^2}{\left[z^3 + z^2\left\{6K(1 - e^{-10T}) - e^{-10T} - 2\right\} + z\left\{2e^{-10T} + 1 - 6K(91 - e^{-10T})\right\} - e^{-10T}\right]}$$

The time domain inverse of this z–domain output is most conveniently obtained by using the long division method discussed in Sub–section 12.4.7. With that method it is seen that it is possible to write:

$$\phi(z) = \frac{a_m z^m + a_{m-1} z^{m-1} + a_{m-2} z^{m-2} + \dots\dots + a_1 z + a_0}{b_n z^n + b_{n-1} z^{n-1} + \dots\dots + b_1 z + b_0} \qquad (12.131)$$

$$= C_1 z^{-1} + C_2 z^{-2} + C_3 z^{-3} + \dots\dots + C_i z^{-i}$$

where:

$$C_i = \frac{1}{B_m} \left\{ A_{n-i+1} - \sum_{j=0}^{n-1} \left(B_j C_{i-m+j} \right) \right\} \qquad \begin{array}{l} A_i = B_i = 0 \text{ for : } i < 0 \\[2mm] C_i = 0 \text{ for : } j \le 0 \end{array} \qquad (12.132)$$

In this case, comparison with Eqn (12.130), while observing that n=3 and m=2, results in:

$$C_i = \frac{1}{B_3} \left[A_{3-i} - \sum_{j=0}^{2} B_j C_{i-3+j} \right] \qquad (12.133)$$

This yields:

$$C_1 = A_2 \qquad (12.134)$$
$$C_2 = A_1 - B_2 C_1$$
$$C_3 = A_0 - B_1 C_1 - B_2 C_2$$
$$C_4 = -B_0 C_1 - B_1 C_2 - B_2 C_3$$
$$C_5 = -B_0 C_2 - B_1 C_3 - B_2 C_4$$

Three observations are useful:

1) all coefficients with a negative subscript are assumed to have the value of zero

2) Eqns (12.134) can be readily programmed on a digital computer

3) because Eqn (12.131) inverts to the time domain as:

$$\phi^*(t) = \phi(0)\delta(0) + \phi(T)\delta(t - T) + \phi(2T)\delta(t - 2T) + \dots. \qquad (12.135)$$

where:

$$\phi(0) = C_1 \qquad (12.136)$$
$$\phi(T) = C_2$$
$$\phi(2T) = C_3, \text{ etc.}$$

As expected, the coefficients of Eqn (12.131) are in fact the values of $\phi^*(t)$ at the sampling intervals! Observe from Eqn (12.130) that:

$$A_2 = 6K(1 - e^{-10T}) \qquad\qquad A_1 = 0 \qquad\qquad A_0 = 0 \qquad\qquad (12.137)$$

$$B_3 = 1 \qquad\qquad\qquad B_2 = \left\{6K(1 - e^{-10T}) - 2\right\}$$

$$B_1 = \left\{2e^{-10T} + 1 - 6K(1 - e^{-10T})\right\} \qquad\qquad B_0 = -e^{-10T}$$

By "programming" the coefficients A_i and B_i for ranges of values for the gain, K, and for the sampling period, T, the discrete time domain response of the system can be obtained. Figure 12.30 shows these responses as well as the response of the analog system. The solution for T=0.1 sec. was found to be unstable and was not plotted for that reason. Solutions for T=0.01 sec. and T=0.001 sec. are shown and, although stable, these solutions are clearly undesirable: their oscillatory nature (buzz) would not be acceptable. Note that both digital system solutions do approach the analog solution eventually.

The main reason for the oscillatory response of the system is the fact that it lacks a D/A device. Figure 12.32 shows what the system would be like with a D/A device in the forward path, to command the actuator with a continuous rather than a discontinuous signal.

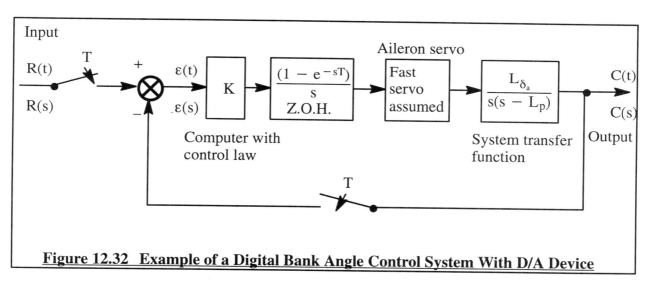

Figure 12.32 Example of a Digital Bank Angle Control System With D/A Device

The forward path transfer function of the system of Figure 12.32 is:

$$G(s) = \left(\frac{1 - e^{-sT}}{s}\right)\left(\frac{L_{\delta_a}}{s(s - L_p)}\right) \qquad\qquad (12.138)$$

Transformation to the z–domain yields:

$$G(z) = (1 - z^{-1})\, \mathcal{Z}\left\{\frac{L_{\delta_a}}{s^2(s - L_p)}\right\} = \qquad\qquad (12.139)$$

$$= \left(\frac{z - 1}{z}\right)\left(\frac{L_{\delta_a}}{-L_p}\right)\left\{\frac{Tz}{(z - 1)^2} - \frac{(1 - e^{L_pT})z}{-L_p(z - 1)(z - e^{L_pT})}\right\}$$

The response of the system to a unit step input is:

$$\phi(z) = \left(\frac{z}{z-1}\right)W(z) = \left(\frac{z}{z-1}\right)\left(\frac{KG(z)}{1+KG(z)}\right) \tag{12.140}$$

Substitution of Eqn (12.139) into (12.140) produces the following result:

$$\phi(z) = \left[\frac{\dfrac{KL_{\delta_a}}{-L_p^2}\left\{z^2\left(TL_p + 1 - e^{L_pT}\right) + z\left(-TL_p e^{L_pT} - 1 + e^{L_pT}\right)\right\}}{DEN}\right] \tag{12.141}$$

where:

$$DEN = \left[z^3 + z^2\left\{-e^{L_pT} - 2 - \frac{KL_{\delta_a}}{L_p^2}\left(TL_p + 1 - e^{L_pT}\right)\right\}\right] +$$

$$+ z\left[2e^{L_pT} + 1 - \frac{KL_{\delta_a}}{L_p^2}\left\{-TL_p\left(1 + e^{L_pT}\right) - 2\left(1 - e^{L_pT}\right)\right\}\right] +$$

$$+ \left[-e^{L_pT} - \frac{KL_{\delta_a}}{L_p^2}\left\{TL_p e^{L_pT} + \left(1 - e^{L_pT}\right)\right\}\right] \tag{12.142}$$

Using the long hand division method (recurrence method) the following expressions are found for the coefficients A_i and B_i :

$$A_2 = -\left(\frac{KL_{\delta_a}}{L_p^2}\right)\left(TL_p + 1 - e^{L_pT}\right) \tag{12.143}$$

$$A_1 = -\left(\frac{KL_{\delta_a}}{L_p^2}\right)\left(-TL_p e^{L_pT} - 1 + e^{L_pT}\right) \qquad A_0 = 0$$

and:

$$B_3 = 1 \qquad B_2 = \left\{-e^{L_pT} - 2 - \left(\frac{KL_{\delta_a}}{L_p^2}\right)\left(TL_p + 1 - e^{L_pT}\right)\right\}$$

$$B_1 = \left[2e^{L_pT} + 1 - \left(\frac{KL_{\delta_a}}{L_p^2}\right)\left\{-TL_p\left(1 + e^{L_pT}\right) - 2\left(1 - e^{L_pT}\right)\right\}\right]$$

$$B_0 = \left[-e^{L_pT} - \left(\frac{KL_{\delta_a}}{L_p^2}\right)\left\{TL_p e^{L_pT} + \left(1 - e^{L_pT}\right)\right\}\right] \tag{12.144}$$

By "programming" the coefficients A_i and B_i as defined by Eqns (12.143) and (12.144) for ranges of values for the gain, K, and for the sampling period, T, the discrete time domain response of the system can be obtained. Figure 12.33 shows these responses as well as the response of the analog system. The solution for T=1.0 sec. was found to be unstable and was not plotted for that reason. The solution for T=0.5 sec. was found to be stable but very oscillatory up to t=8 sec. and was not plotted for that reason. Solutions for T=0.2 sec., T = 0.1 sec., T=0.01 sec. and T=0.001 sec. are shown. Note that the solution gets better for decreasing sampling period. Whether T=0.01 sec. or T=0.001 sec. does not seem to matter in this application: both solutions plot on top of each other and are virtually identical to the analog solution.

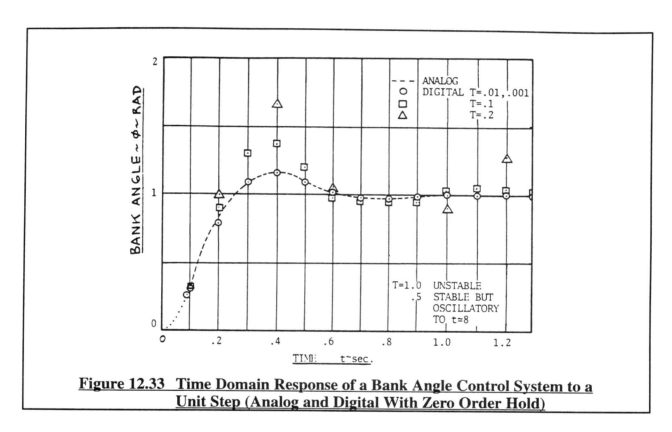

Figure 12.33 Time Domain Response of a Bank Angle Control System to a Unit Step (Analog and Digital With Zero Order Hold)

The beneficial effect of the A/D device is therefore obvious. It is also clear that for very high sampling frequencies (i.e. low sampling periods) the digital solution is practically identical to the analog solution. This means that as long as the sampling frequency of a digital system is high compared with the highest break frequencies in the s–domain of such a system, classical s–domain techniques for the analysis and synthesis of such systems will probably work.

Nevertheless, the discussions so far seem to indicate that in certain cases there is a question about the stability of a digital solution. The purpose of the next section is to shed some light on the stability issue.

12.6 EFFECT OF SAMPLING FREQUENCY ON THE STABILITY OF DIGITAL SYSTEMS

The following definition of stability will be used for the output of a digital system:

Definition: The output of a system is called stable if for any bounded input, the output is also bounded.

It was already observed that because a discrete system possesses information only for $\varepsilon^*(t)$ and not for $\varepsilon(t)$ several functions $\varepsilon(t)$ can have the same $\varepsilon^*(t)$. An extreme case was illustrated in Figure 12.4. The so–called "hidden" oscillations of Figure 12.4 are normally not a problem in practical systems, certainly not when the sampling frequency, ω_n , is large (i.e. the sampling period, T is small).

By analogy to what was learned in the s–plane, to assure system output stability it is necessary in the z– domain that the roots of the characteristic system equation are inside the unit circle. For example, in the case of the system of Figure 12.27, the roots of:

$$1 + KG(z)H(z) = 0 \tag{12.145}$$

must be located inside the unit circle in the z–plane. Another way of saying this is that:

$$|z_i| < 1.0 \tag{12.146}$$

must be satisfied for all roots.

Three methods for determining digital system stability will be briefly discussed:

12.6.1 Jury's Test
12.6.2 Routh–Hurwitz Criterion
12.6.3 Root Locus Method

12.6.1 JURY'S TEST

To determine the stability of the roots of the characteristic equation, the latter is written in polynomial form:

$$F(z) = a_n z^n + a_{n-1} z^{n-1} + \ldots + a_1 z + a_0 = 0 \tag{12.147}$$

For stability, the coefficient a_n must satisfy $a_n > 0$ in applying the following stability test which is due to Jury (Reference 14.1).

In Jury's Test the following matrix is constructed:

Row	z^0	z^1	z^2	......	z^{n-k}	......	z^{n-1}	z^n
1	a_0	a_1	a_2	......	a_{n-k}	......	a_{n-1}	a_n
2	a_n	a_{n-1}	a_{n-2}	......	a_k	......	a_1	a_0
3	b_0	b_1	b_2	......	b_{n-k}	......	b_{n-1}	
4	b_{n-1}	b_{n-2}	b_{n-3}	......	b_k	......	b_0	
5	c_0	c_1	c_2	......	c_{n-k}	......	c_{n-2}	
6	c_{n-2}	c_{n-3}	c_{n-4}	......	c_k	......	c_0	
7	etc. $\longrightarrow$							
$\downarrow$ etc.								

The coefficients in this matrix are defined as follows:

$$b_k = \begin{vmatrix} a_0 & a_{n-k} \\ a_n & a_k \end{vmatrix} \qquad \text{which yields:}$$

$$b_0 = \begin{vmatrix} a_0 & a_n \\ a_n & a_0 \end{vmatrix} \qquad b_1 = \begin{vmatrix} a_0 & a_{n-1} \\ a_n & a_1 \end{vmatrix} \qquad \text{etc.}$$

$$c_k = \begin{vmatrix} b_0 & b_{n-k-1} \\ b_{n-1} & b_k \end{vmatrix} \qquad \text{which yields:}$$

$$c_0 = \begin{vmatrix} b_0 & b_{n-1} \\ b_{n-1} & b_0 \end{vmatrix} \qquad c_1 = \begin{vmatrix} b_0 & b_{n-2} \\ b_{n-1} & b_1 \end{vmatrix} \qquad \text{etc.}$$

(12.148)

For stability, no roots may be on or outside the unit circle in the z–plane. According to Jury's test this is satisfied if ALL of the following conditions are simultaneously satisfied:

$$F(1) > 0 \qquad\qquad\qquad |a_0| < a_n$$

$$F(-1) < 0 \text{ if n is odd} \qquad |b_0| > |b_{n-1}| \qquad (12.149)$$

$$F(-1) > 0 \text{ if n is even} \qquad |c_0| > |c_{n-2}| \qquad \text{etc.}$$

As an example consider Equations (12.127) and (12.128). The characteristic equation is:

$$(z - 1)(z - e^{L_pT}) + \left(\frac{L_{\delta_a}}{- L_p}\right)K\left(1 - e^{L_pT}\right)z = 0 \tag{12.150}$$

or:

$$z^2 + z\left\{- e^{L_pT} - 1 - \left(\frac{L_{\delta_a}}{L_p}\right)K\left(1 - e^{L_pT}\right)\right\} + e^{L_pT} = 0 \tag{12.151}$$

Using the same data as before, namely: $L_{\delta_a} = 60 \text{ sec}^{-2}$ and $L_p = -10 \text{ sec}^{-1}$, substitution into Eqn (12.151) yields:

$$z^2 + z\left\{- e^{-10T} - 1 + 6K\left(1 - e^{-10T}\right)\right\} + e^{-10T} = 0 \tag{12.152}$$

Applying Jury's test to this result produces:

$$A_n = 1 > 0 \tag{12.153}$$

$$F(1) = 1 - e^{-10T} - 1 + 6K - 6Ke^{-10T} + e^{-10T} = 6K(1 - e^{-10T})$$

Observe, that for K=0, $F(1) = 0$ which indicates a stability violation. This occurs because of the s=0 (z=1) root in the forward path transfer function. Note also that for K>0, $F(1) > 0$. Continuing the application of Jury's test:

$$F(-1) = 1 + e^{-10T} + 1 - 6K(1 - e^{-10T}) + e^{-10T} = \tag{12.154}$$

$$= 2 + 2e^{-10T} - 6K(1 - e^{-10T})$$

Because the polynomial in Eqn (12.151) is "even", F(–1)>0 is the condition for stability. This results in the stability boundary sketched in Figure 12.34. It is also possible to construct Jury's matrix from Eqn (12.151). This results in:

Row	z^0	z^1	z^2
1	C	B	1
2	1	B	C
3	$C^2 - 1$	$CB - B$	0
4	$CB - B$	$C^2 - 1$	0
5	$(CB - B)^2 - (C^2 - 1)^2$	0	0
6	0	$(CB - B)^2 - (C^2 - 1)^2$	0

Note : $B = \left\{- e^{-10T} - 1 + 6K(1 - e^{-10T})\right\}$ $C = e^{-10T}$

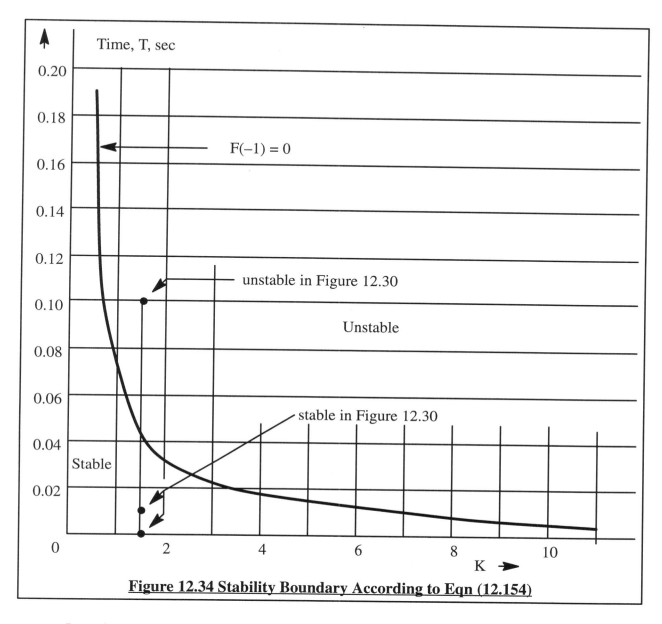

Figure 12.34 Stability Boundary According to Eqn (12.154)

It can be shown that application of Jury's test will result in a repetition of the F(−1)>0 requirement. Therefore, Figure 12.34 represents all necessary and sufficient conditions for which the system represented by Eqn (12.128) is stable. Note that this agrees with the findings of Figure 12.30.

12.6.2 ROUTH–HURWITZ CRITERION

It is not possible to apply the Routh–Hurwitz criterion directly to functions defined in the z–plane. By using the so–called w' transformation from the z–plane to the w'–plane the Routh–Hurwitz criterion can be applied in the w'–plane. The z– to w'– transformation is defined as follows:

$$z = \frac{1 + \frac{T}{2}w'}{1 - \frac{T}{2}w'}$$ (12.155)

Figure 12.35 shows how the s–plane is mapped into the z–plane and also how the z–plane is mapped into the w'–plane.

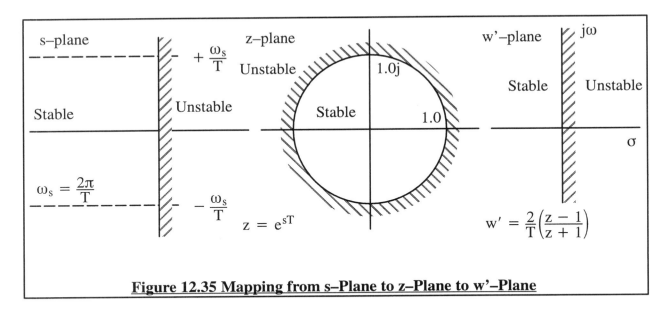

Figure 12.35 Mapping from s–Plane to z–Plane to w'–Plane

The transformation of Eqn (12.155) is applied to the characteristic equation (12.152) with the coefficients B and C defined as in the table at the bottom of page 924:

$$z^2 + Bz + C = 0 \tag{12.156}$$

Application of the w'–transformation yields:

$$\frac{\left(1 + \frac{T}{2}w'\right)^2}{\left(1 - \frac{T}{2}w'\right)^2} + B\frac{\left(1 + \frac{T}{2}w'\right)}{\left(1 - \frac{T}{2}w'\right)} + C = 0 \tag{12.157}$$

Slight rearrangement produces:

$$w'^2(1 - B + C)\frac{T^2}{4} + w'(1 - C)T + (1 + B + C) = 0 \tag{12.158}$$

Application of the Routh–Hurwitz stability criterion yields the following conditions:

$$1 - B + C > 0 \tag{12.159}$$

$$1 - C > 0 \quad \text{or :}$$

$$1 + B + C > 0$$

Because clearly: $1 - C > 0$ with $C = e^{-10T}$ is satisfied for T>0 it follows that 1–B+C>0 is the critical condition for stability. The reader is asked to show (upon substitution of the equations for B and C at the bottom of page 427) that the latter condition is the same as that expressed by F(–1)>0 with F(–1) given by Eqn (12.154).

12.6.3 THE ROOT–LOCUS METHOD

It should be recognized from the mapping characteristics defined in Figure 12.35 that all s–plane root–loci rules apply directly in the w'–plane. The interpretation of stability in the w'–plane is also identical to that in the s–plane. Finally, the Bode method as used in the s–plane also applies directly in the w'–plane.

For further applications of the w'–transformation the reader should consult Reference 12.2

12.7   RELATIONS BETWEEN THE S–, Z– AND TIME DOMAINS

Since much of the synthesis work on flight control systems involves knowing the relationship between time–domain phenomena and pole locations in the s– and z–domains respectively it is of interest to review some of these relations. Figures 12.36 through 12.38 provide this review. The reader is encouraged to study these three figures.

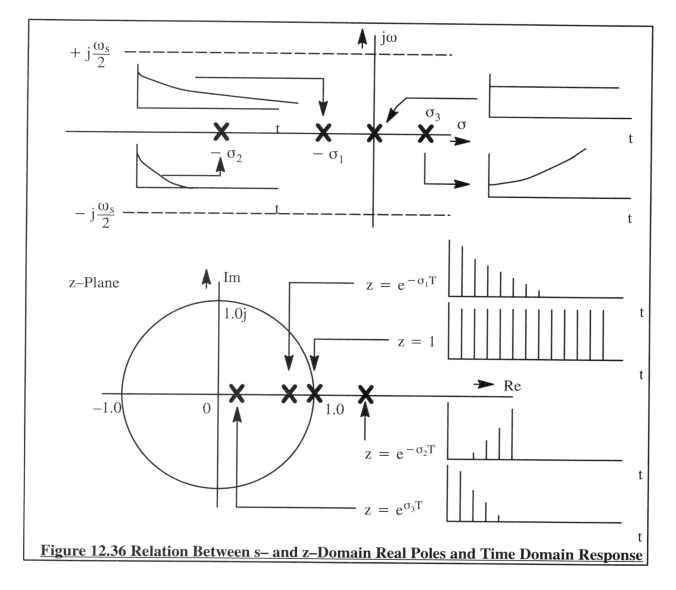

Figure 12.36 Relation Between s– and z–Domain Real Poles and Time Domain Response

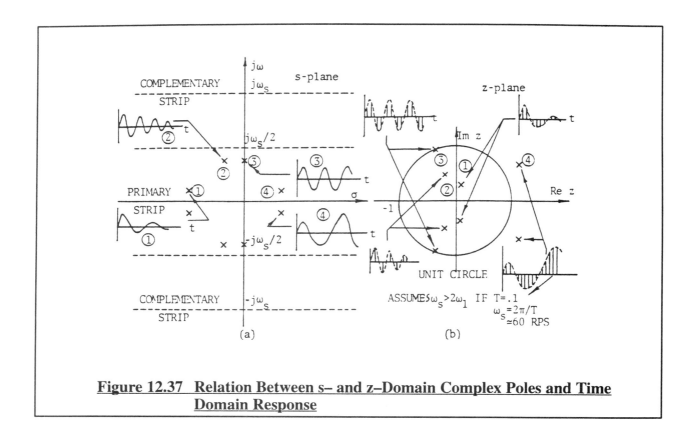

Figure 12.37   Relation Between s– and z–Domain Complex Poles and Time Domain Response

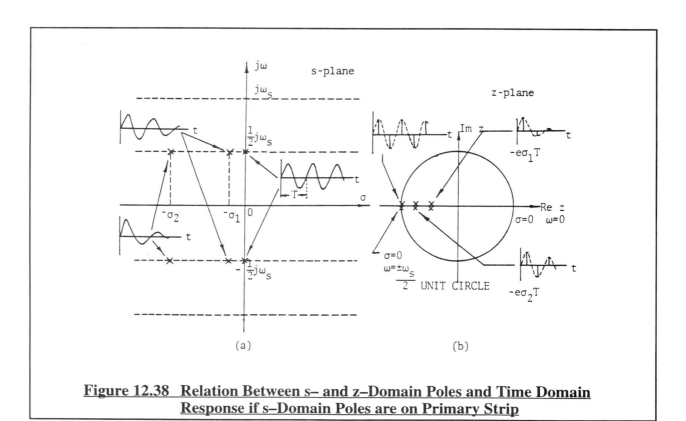

Figure 12.38   Relation Between s– and z–Domain Poles and Time Domain Response if s–Domain Poles are on Primary Strip

12.8 SUMMARY FOR CHAPTER 12

It has been shown in this chapter that by using the z–transform technique many of the conventional methods used in analyzing closed loop analog control systems can be applied to digital systems. An important feature of the analysis of digital control systems is that the location of the samplers must be accounted for and can lead to results which are different for different sampler locations. For high sampling rates digital systems behave almost like analog systems. This suggests that the methods of Chapters 9, 10 and 11 are still useful for the initial analysis of digital control systems.

12.9 PROBLEMS FOR CHAPTER 12

12.1 The characteristic equation for a sampled data system is found to be:

$$z^3 + 5z^2 + 3z + 2 = 0 \tag{12.160}$$

Determine the stability of the system.

12.2 The characteristic equation of a sampled data system is given by:

$$z^3 + Kz^2 + 1.5Kz - (K + 1) = 0 \tag{12.161}$$

Sketch the root loci of the system and determine the range of K values for which the system is stable.

12.3 A digital control system has the following configuration:

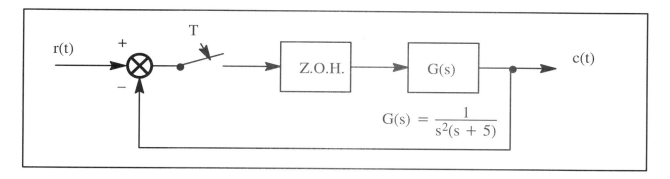

If r(t) is a unit step, find the following quantities:

a) C(z) b) $C^*(t)$ c) $\lim_{t \to \infty} C^*(t)$

12.4 Consider the system of problem 12.3 but now for the case where:

$$G(s) = \frac{K}{s(1 + 0.2s)} \tag{12.162}$$

a) Determine the system z–plane root loci for T=0.1 sec as well as for T=1.0 sec.
b) Repeat a) for the same system but **without** the Z.O.H.
c) In each case find the range of K values for which the system is stable.

12.5   Consider the following sampled data system:

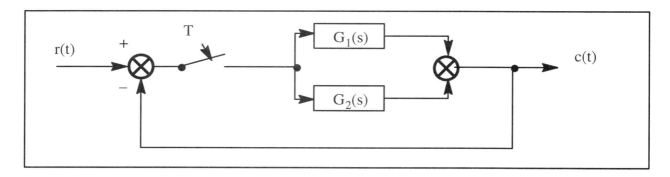

   a)   Derive an expression for C(z)/R(z)
   b)   If $G_1(s) = 1/(s + 1)$ and $G_2(s) = 3.14/(s^2 - 0.81s + 13.16)$ and

          T=1 sec., determine $C^*(t)$ for the case that r(t) is a unit step.

12.6   An airplane has a bank angle control system as sketched below:

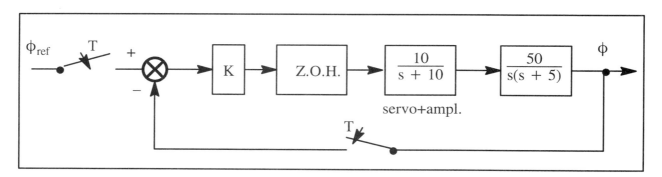

   a)   If this were a pure analog system (no samplers and no Z.O.H) sketch the s–plane root
          locus and find the range of K values for stable operation
   b)   For the system sketched above find the range of K values for stable operation for the
          case where T=0.001, T=0.01, T=0.1 and T=0.5 sec.
   c)   For a step input of ϕ_{ref} find the final value of $\phi(t)$ for cases a) and b).
   d)   Let the servo–ampl. be represented by a/s+a and discuss the effect of the break
          frequency, a on system stability by drawing K–T stability contours for a=2.5,
          a=5, a=10 and a=20 sec.

12.10 REFERENCES FOR CHAPTER 12

12.1   Kuo, B.C.; Analysis and Synthesis of Sampled Data Control Systems; Prentice–Hall,
        Englewood Cliffs, N.J.; 1963.

12.2   Whitbeck, R.F. and Kofmann, L.C.; Digital Control Law Synthesis in the w'–Domain;
        Journal of Guidance and Control; Vol.1, No.5, Sept.–Oct. 1978.

APPENDIX E: HARDWARE ASPECTS OF AUTOPILOT SYSTEMS

In this appendix several hardware aspects of autopilot systems are briefly discussed. The objective is to give readers without an exposure to autopilot system installations and their functions an idea of what such hardware is like. The author is grateful to Century Flight Systems, Inc. for contributing some of their autopilot systems data to this text with permission to publish.

Figure 11.21 (see page 803) shows a ghost view of a typical autopilot installation in a light twin. When an autopilot system is matched to an airplane, several issues of system safety must be resolved before FAA certification of such an installation can be obtained. When more and more automation is integrated into the flight control system of an airplane a formal fault tree analysis with associated probability–of–occurrence estimates must be made. References E1 through E8 may be helpful to readers without a background in fault tree analysis. Also, reliability and redundancy issues are important in any automatic systems where failure could compromise safety. References E9 and E10 contain information on these subjects.

E 1   AUTOPILOT AND SENSOR FUNDAMENTALS

It was shown in Chapter 11 that each autopilot and/or stability augmentation loop relies for feedback on certain sensor signals. In this Section some of the most common autopilot sensors are briefly discussed.

E 1.1   Pitch Attitude Angle, θ and Bank Angle, ϕ.

Figure E1 shows a typical arrangement for an artificial horizon instrument (attitude gyro) which measures both angles θ and ϕ. Reference E11 contains explanations of how mechanical attitude gyros work. Many modern gyros use lasers instead of mechanical (spinning) elements. Reference E12 contains explanations of how various gyros work in conjunction with one another. With this type of installation the Euler angles θ and ϕ are measured. Figures 11.23 and 11.60 respectively show how these angles are used in attitude feedback systems. The angles θ and ϕ are displayed to the pilot on his instrument panel. An example of such a display is shown in Figure E2.

It is foreseen that in the future, GPS (Global Positioning System) receivers will be used to sense pitch attitude and bank angle signals for use in feedback systems. This will eliminate two gyros and replace them by four GPS receivers and a computational network. The receivers would be installed at the airplane nose and tail (for pitch attitude) and at the airplane left and right wing tip (for bank angle). In large airplanes, elastic distortions will have to be accounted for.

E 1.2   Heading angle, ψ.

Heading angle information is normally supplied by a magnetic compass, a remote–indicating compass, a directional gyro and/or a flight director system. Reference E11 contains explanations of how such heading sensing systems work. Figure 11.65 shows how the angle ψ is used in a heading angle feedback systems. The heading angle is usually displayed to the pilot on his instrument panel. An example of such a display is shown in Figure E3 (see page 837).

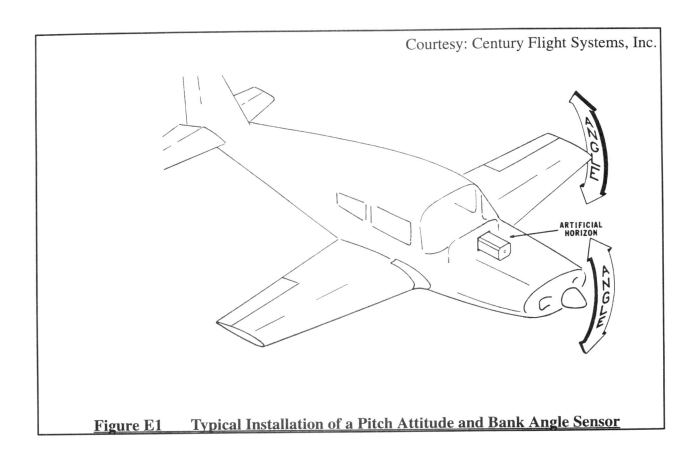

Courtesy: Century Flight Systems, Inc.

Figure E1   Typical Installation of a Pitch Attitude and Bank Angle Sensor

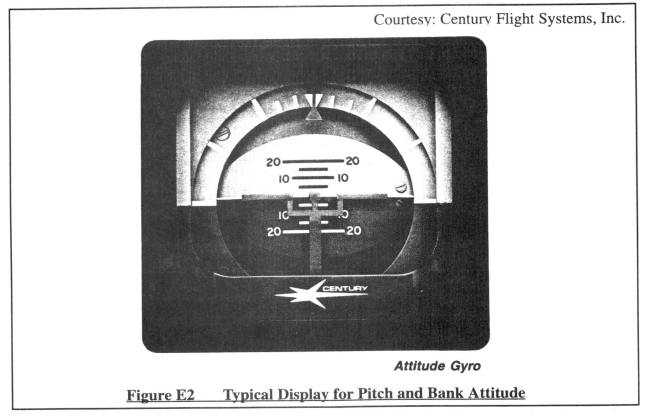

Courtesy: Century Flight Systems, Inc.

Attitude Gyro

Figure E2   Typical Display for Pitch and Bank Attitude

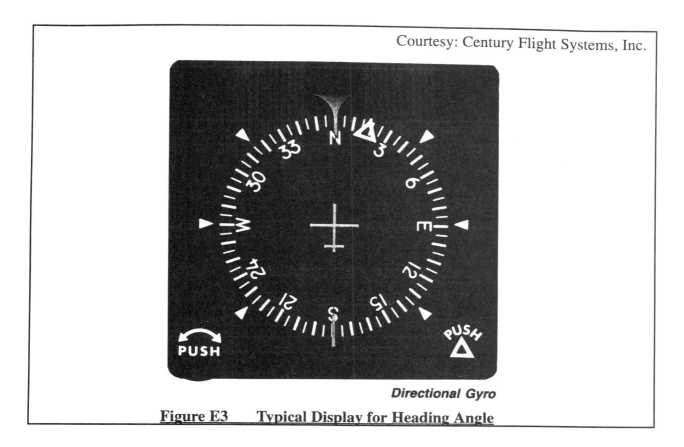

Figure E3   Typical Display for Heading Angle

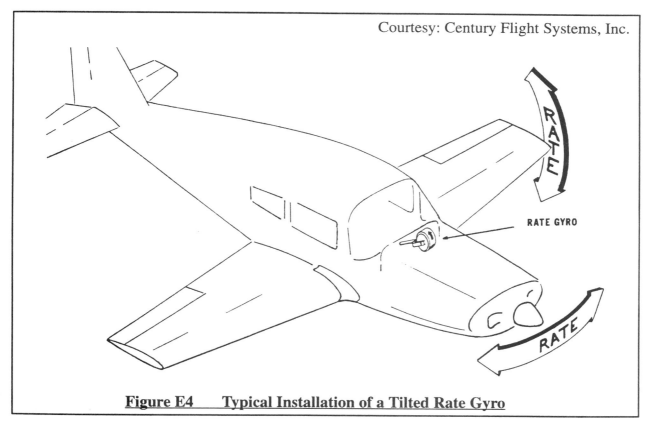

Figure E4   Typical Installation of a Tilted Rate Gyro

E 1.3   Angular Rates Such As: dψ/dt, dθ/dt and dφ/dt

Angular rates are normally sensed with rate gyros. How such gyros function is discussed in Reference E11. Figure E4 (see page 935) shows how a rate gyro can be "tilted" in an airplane to measure a combination of yaw rate and roll rate. Such tilted rate gyros are common in yaw damper and turn rate systems. In many systems it has been found acceptable to compute these angular rates by differentiation of the output of the gyro sensors of the primary attitude angles: ψ, θ and ϕ. Whether or not this is acceptable depends on the levels of system noise which can be accepted as a result of the differentiation process.

E 2   AUTOPILOT MODES

Autopilots are available with many different modes. Synthesis procedures for several example autopilot modes are discussed in Chapter 11 . The pilot has to determine which mode is to be used in any given flight situation. Figure E5 shows an example of the mode select and mode annunciator panel of a Century 2000 autopilot.

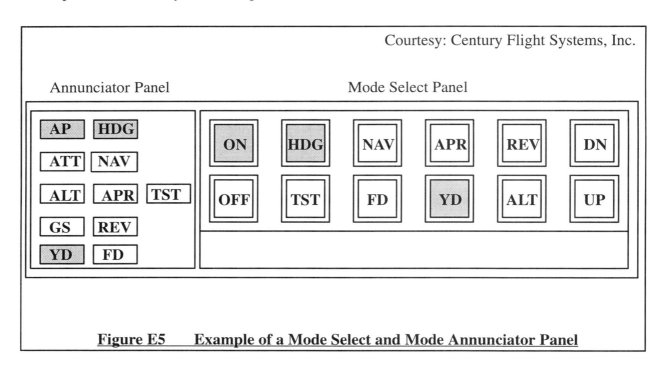

Figure E5   Example of a Mode Select and Mode Annunciator Panel

The acronyms in Figure E5 have the following meanings:

AP	stands for: Autopilot	HDG	stands for: Heading
ATT	stands for: Autotrim	NAV	stands for: Navigation
ALT	stands for: Altitude	APR	stands for: Approach
GS	stands for: Glideslope	REV	stands for: Reversed
YD	stands for: Yaw damper	FD	stands for: Flight director
TST	stands for: Test	ON	stands for: On
OFF	stands for: Off	DN	stands for: Down
UP	stands for: Up		

Autopilot manufacturers provide detailed operating manuals for their equipment. After performing the recommended ground test procedures the pilot can switch the autopilot on and engage one or more modes by depressing the corresponding buttons. The annunciator panel will highlight the modes selected. In the case of Figure E5 the pilot has switched the autopilot on and selected the heading hold mode (HDG) with the yaw damper (YD) on. The airplane will maintain the heading angle selected by the pilot on his directional gyro or on his horizontal situation indicator.

Autopilots also contain logic which prevents selection of conflicting modes.

It must be possible to disconnect an autopilot system by more than one means. Typical disconnect methods in use are:

- Off switch on the autopilot interface panel (see Figure E5)

- Autopilot disconnect switch on the cockpit control wheel or stick (see Figure E6a)

- Automatic disconnect when the pilot exceeds a given force level on the cockpit controls. This is done with a force transducer.

- Switching off all electrical power to the autopilot

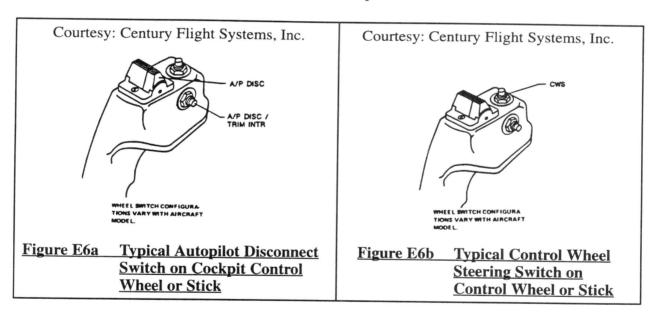

Courtesy: Century Flight Systems, Inc.

Courtesy: Century Flight Systems, Inc.

Figure E6a   Typical Autopilot Disconnect Switch on Cockpit Control Wheel or Stick

Figure E6b   Typical Control Wheel Steering Switch on Control Wheel or Stick

Pilots also prefer to be able to maneuver the airplane through the autopilot. That way it is not necessary to disengage the autopilot while flying the airplane. One method to accomplish this is through control–wheel (or control stick) steering, also known as CWS (or CSS). Figure E6b shows the engagement switch for a CSS mode. With that switch depressed the airplane can be maneuvered through the autopilot when moving the stick. Controlwheel steering was discussed in Sub–section 11.5.4 (see page 828).

In many modern installations the function of the autopilot is more that of a flight management system. In a flight management system the autopilot will, at the option of the pilot, fly the airplane over predetermined vertical, longitudinal and lateral flight paths. These flight paths can cover the total flight profile of an airplane in the most sophisticated of such systems.

Reference E13 is a convenient source for data on various autopilot types, costs, weights and power requirements.

E 3   REFERENCES

E1   Anon.; ARP 1834 Fault/Failure Analysis for Digital Systems and Equipment; SAE Aerospace Recommended Practice; Society of Automotive Engineers, 400 Common-wealth Drive, Warrendale, PA 15096.

E2   Anon.; Military Standard, Reliability Modeling and Prediction; MIL–STD–756B, 18 November 1981, Department of Defense, Washington, D C 20301.

E3   Anon.; Military Standard, Procedures for Performing a Failure Mode, Effects and Criticality Analysis; MIL–STD–1629A, 24 Nov. 1980, D.O.D, Washington, D C 20301.

E4   Anon.; Military Specification, Flight Control Systems–Design, Installation and Test of Piloted Aircraft, General Specification for; MIL–F–9490D (USAF), 6 June 1975.

E5   Anon.; FAA Advisory Circular, AC No: 25.1309–1A, System Design and Analysis, 6/21/88, FAA, U.S. Department of Transportation, Washington DC.

E6   Anon.; FAA Advisory Circular, AC No: 25.1329–1A, Automatic Pilot Systems Approval, 7/8/68, FAA, U.S. Department of Transportation, Washington DC.

E7   Garrick, B.J.; Principles of Unified Systems Safety Analysis; Nuclear Engineering and Design, Vol. 13, No. 2, pp 245–321, August 1970.

E8   Lambert, H.E.; Fault Trees for Decision Making in Systems Analysis; Lawrence Livermore Laboratories, DCRL–51829, 1975.

E9   Lloyd, D.K. and Lipow, M.; Reliability: Management, Methods and Mathematics; Prentice–Hall, Inc., Englewood Cliffs, N.J., 1962.

E10   Olmos, J. and Wolf, L.; A Modular Approach to Fault Tree and Reliability Analysis; Department of Nuclear Engineering, MIT, MITNE–209, August 1977.

E11   Pallett, E.H.J.; Automatic Flight Control; Granada Publishing Ltd., London, 1979.

E12   Curran, Jim; Trends in Advanced Avionics; Iowa State University Press, Ames, Iowa, 1992.

E13   Business and Commercial Aviation Magazine: Planning and Purchasing Handbook, May issue (published annually), Mc Graw Hill, N.Y.

INDEX TO PARTS I AND II

Acceleration error (constant) — 733
Acceleration feedback — 690, 688
Acceleration of gravity — 9, 3
Additional lift distribution — 40
Adverse aileron yaw — 117
Advanced Aircraft Analysis — 461, 45
Aerodynamic center (airfoil, wing, airplane) — 191, 89, 84, 47, 45, 38, 37
Aerodynamic characteristics of planforms and fuselage — 45
Aerodynamic force — 10, 9, 6
Aerodynamic force and moment derivatives w.r.t. angle of attack — 137
Aerodynamic force and moment derivatives w.r.t. lateral–directional
    control surface deflections — 160
Aerodynamic force and moment derivatives w.r.t. longitudinal control surface
    and flap deflections — 145
Aerodynamic force and moment derivatives w.r.t. angle of attack rate — 140
Aerodynamic force and moment derivatives w.r.t. pitch rate — 143
Aerodynamic force and moment derivatives w.r.t. roll rate — 149
Aerodynamic force and moment derivatives w.r.t. sideslip — 148
Aerodynamic force and moment derivatives w.r.t. sideslip rate — 148
Aerodynamic force and moment derivatives w.r.t. speed — 132
Aerodynamic force and moment derivatives w.r.t. yaw rate — 157
Aerodynamic fundamentals — 35
Aerodynamic hinge moment — 240
Aerodynamic influence coefficient matrix — 597, 592, 589, 587, 586
Aerodynamic moment — 10, 9, 6
Aerodynamic and thrust forces and moments — 65
Aerodynamic and thrust force per unit area — 3
Aeroelastic effect on control power — 273, 204
Aeroelastic equilibrium — 6, 4
Aeroelasticity — 579
Aileron floatation — 273
Aileron gearing ratio — 271
Aileron hingemoment derivatives — 271
Aileron reversal — 582, 580, 579
Aileron rolling moment coefficient derivative — 103
Ailerons — 102
Aileron wheel (or stick) force — 270
Airfoil — 35
Airfoil aerodynamic characteristics — 35
Airplane class — 418, 417

Airplane mass density 3
Airspeed hold mode (throttles) 816
Airspeed hold mode (speedbrakes) 819
Airworthiness code 422, 421
Altitude hold mode 813
Amplitude ratio 636, 632, 631, 630
Analog–to–digital converter 881
Angle of attack 186, 66
Angle of attack effectiveness 61
Angle of attack feedback 793, 395
Angle of attack perturbation 186
Angle of attack stability 191
Angle of attack–to–canard feedback gain 399
Angle of attack–to–elevator transfer function 321
Angle of attack to elevator Bode plot 665, 664
Angle of sideslip 186, 66
Angle of sideslip feedback 395
Angle of sideslip perturbation 186
Angle of sideslip stability 192
Angle requirement 698
Angular acceleration 7
Angular acceleration about the main gear 291
Angular momentum 13, 6, 3
Angular momentum equations (scalar format) 11
Angular momentum equations with spinning rotors (scalar format) 14
Angular rotation 7
Angular velocities 17, 10
Angular velocity perturbation(s) 186
Anhedral 96
Apparent static longitudinal stability 252
Apparent time constant 730
Applied forces 3
Approach categories 841
Approach guidance 841
Area 42
Artificial stability 260
Artificial stick force (feel) 294, 278
Aspect ratio 42
Asymptotic approximation 645, 644
Authority limit 397, 396
Automatic flare (landing) mode 852
Automatic flight control system 779
Autopilot disconnect 937
Autopilot hardware 933
Autopilot installation 803
Autopilot interface panel 802

Autopilot mode	936, 779
Autopilot systems	933, 801
Automatic landing	801
Automatic navigation	779
Axis systems	3

Balance tab	259, 257
Bandwidth	727
Bank angle	17, 14
Bank angle effect on engine out flight	222
Bank angle gyro	933
Bank angle hold mode	833
Bank angle response	369
Bank angle response requirements	442, 441, 440, 439
Bank angle to aileron Bode plot	670, 661
Bank angle to rudder Bode plot	673
Basic lift distribution	40
Blow–down tab	261, 260, 257
Bob–weight	266, 255
Bode method	711, 695
Bode plot	686, 631, 630, 647, 341
Bode plot inverse application	678
Body axis rates	20, 19
Body fixed axis system	3
Breakaway angle	744, 706
Break–out force requirements	444, 443
Break frequency	641, 634

Camber	211, 35
Camber/twist distribution	590, 587
Canard (configuration)	234
Cancellation compensation	750
Center of gravity of the root locus diagram	705
Center of gravity root loci	378
Center of mass	5
Center of pressure	40, 38
Characteristic equation	696, 311
Characteristic equation roots	332
Characteristics of the flight control system	443
Chord plane	52
Chord ratio	242
Civilian flying quality requirements	415
Classical control theory	685
Climb	25

Closed loop sampled data systems	915
Closed loop transfer function	694
Cockpit control forces	267, 240, 183
Compensatory system	764
Complex conjugates	326
Complex root	313, 311
Computational methods	65
Computed pitch rate	789
Computed yaw rate	781
Constant mass assumption	5
Constant mass distribution assumption	5
Control anticipation parameter and requirements	433, 432, 431
Control characteristics	183
Control forces	183
Controllability	47
Control power	183
Control power derivative	85
Control power matrix	320
Control power required	457
Control surface deflection	59
Control surface distribution matrix	587
Control surface effectiveness	59
Control surface perturbations	129
Control wheel steering mode	828
Convergence	305
Cooper–Harper pilot rating scale	765, 416, 415
Coupled roll–spiral requirements	437
Cruise	25
Cruise shape	622, 608, 579
Cutoff rate	728

Damping ratio	309
Delay time	729, 727
De Moivre's Theorem	889, 704, 313
Dependent variables	11
Derivative root loci	378
Design driver	198
Design for augmented stability in pitch	451, 445
Design for spiral and dutch roll stability	446, 445
Design for roll control effectiveness	445
Differential equations of motion	11
Differentially deflected ailerons	117
Differential stabilizer	102
Differential stabilizer rolling moment coefficient derivative	104
Differentiator	645

Digital computer 881
Digital control system analysis 881
Digital–to–analog converter 887, 882
Dihedral effect 196, 96
Dimensional stability derivative 347, 318
Directional stability derivative for an elastic airplane 613
Directional stability 192
Directional stability, pedal free 269, 268
Direct thrust effects 90
Distance measuring equipment (D.M.E.) 846
Dive 25
Dive angle 23
Divergence 305
Dorsal fin 270
Down spring 266, 264, 257
Downward velocity 9
Downward velocity perturbation 127
Downwash 214, 51, 45
Downwash gradient 214, 55, 52
Drag coefficient 72, 44
Drag coefficient at zero angle of attack 74
Drag coefficient at zero lift coefficient 74
Drag (force) 71, 9
Drag induced yawing moment 216
Drag polar 74
Drag rise 195
Drag rudder 120
Dutch roll   approximate transfer functions 363
             approximation 363
             damping ratio 364
             frequency and damping requirements 436
             mode 357
             mode shape 377, 376
             undamped natural frequency 364
Dynamic pressure 22
Dynamic pressure for airplane divergence 595
Dynamic pressure at divergence 583
Dynamic pressure at reversal 581
Dynamic pressure ratio 101, 78, 51
Dynamic instability 304
Dynamic longitudinal stability derivatives 319
Dynamic neutral stability 304
Dynamic stability 304
Dynamic stability (definition) 303
Dynamic stability (criterion) 315, 303

Earth fixed axis system	3
Effect of free controls on dynamic stability	555
Eigen values	311
Elastic airplane	4
Elastic airplane aerodynamic force distribution matrix	594
Elastic airplane stability derivatives	615, 603, 602, 601
Elastic axis	582, 581, 580
Elastic deflection angle	591
Elastic equilibrium shape	587, 586
Elastic twist angle	580
Electrical signalling	294
Electro–hydraulically powered elevator system	627
Electro–magnetic pulse	294
Electro–mechanical jackscrew	260
Elevator	84
Elevator control power reduction due to aft fuselage bending	584, 583, 579
Elevator floatation	251
Elevator–per–'g'	229
Elevator trim tab	250
Elevator–versus–load–factor gradient	233, 229
Elevator–versus–speed gradient	280, 202
Empirical methods	65
Engine inoperative flight	25
Elevator hingemoment derivatives	242
Equations of motion	3
Equations of motion (review)	21
Equilibrium angle of attack distribution	609
Equivalent elastic airplane	600
Equivalent elastic airplane derivative	607, 605
Equivalent longitudinal stability derivative	398
Equivalent parasite area	74
Equivalent pitch damping derivative	395
Equivalent stability derivatives	395, 308
Equivalent static margin	263
Equivalent yaw damping derivative	397
Error characteristics (system)	734
Error constant	730
Error (signal)	694
Error specifications	730, 725
Etkin	129
Euler angles	32, 22, 19, 15, 14
Experimental methods	65

Failure probability	421, 417
Failure state	421
Feedback control	685
Feedback gain	398, 396
Feedback path compensator	692
Feedback path transfer function	693
Feedback system design applications	738
Final value theorem	908, 552, 310
Finite angular rotation	16
First order hold	890, 888
First order lead and lag transfer functions	648
Flaperons	102
Flapped wing area	44
Flare before landing	801
Flare control law	854
Flat earth assumption	20, 3
Flight control surface	70
Flight control system effects	238
Flight control system types	298, 296
Flight envelope	413, 200
Flight envelope protection	294
Flight path angle	23, 22
Flight path relative to earth	19, 15
Flight path stability requirements	427
Flight phase (see: mission flight phase)	
Flight phase category	420, 417
Flying qualities	413, 303, 183, 10
Flying qualities and relation to design	445
Flying quality levels	421, 417, 416
Flying quality requirements	434, 423, 415
Force equations	21
Forward path transfer function	693
Forward path compensator	692
Forward speed perturbation	127
Forward speed stability	186
Forward velocity	9
Fourier series	628
Fowler flap	81
Frequency domain	715
Frequency domain (connection with time domain)	715
Frequency domain specifications	725
Frequency response	631, 629, 628, 627
Frequency response for first order lag	640
Frequency response for first order lead–lag	642
Frequency response for second order lag	643
Frequency response from open loop transfer function	637, 636

Friction (bandwidth) — 249
Friction coefficient — 290
Friction in flight control system — 555, 249
Frise ailerons — 117
Fuel sloshing — 5
Fuselage bending — 583, 579
Fuselage effect on wing aerodynamic center — 56

Gain margin — 725, 712, 711
Gap (open or closed) — 242, 59
Geared tab — 259, 257
Gearing (of controls) — 106
Gearing ratio — 271, 267, 241
Geometric dihedral — 96
Glide — 25
Glideslope coupler — 844
Glideslope hold mode — 843
Glideslope intercept and hold — 851, 801
Glideslope receiver — 842
Glideslope transmitter — 843
Gravitational acceleration — 20, 3
Gravitational force (and components) — 20
Ground adjustable tab — 257
Ground effect — 288
Gyros — 933
Gyro tilt angle — 784

Handling qualities (see: flying qualities)
Heading angle — 17, 14
Heading angle gyro — 933
Heading angle hold mode — 836, 833
Heading angle to aileron Bode plot — 670
Heading angle to rudder Bode plot — 676
Hinge moment — 242, 240
Hinge moment coefficient (elevator) — 242
Hinge moment derivatives — 267, 242
Horizontal tail angle of attack — 79
Horn (geometry) — 242
Human pilot transfer function — 763

I.L.S. (Instrument Landing System) — 857
Independent variable — 11
Indirect thrust effects — 90

Inertial coupling   400
Inertial coupling due to pitch rate   407
Inertial coupling due to roll rate   400
Inertial derivatives   603, 600
Inertia transformation from body to stability axes   346
Influence coefficient matrix   586, 579
Initial conditions   310
Initial value theorem   908, 552
Inner loop   738
Instantaneous forces and moments   184
Instantaneous perturbations   184
Integrator   647, 646
Inverse application of Bode method   678
Inverse z-transforms   906
Irreversible flight control system   297, 293, 238, 183

Jackscrew   260
Jig shape   622, 609, 608, 595, 587, 586, 579
Jury's test   924

Kinematic equations   31, 30, 25, 21, 19
Kirchhoff's law   633
Krueger flap   81

Lag   628
Lag compensator   744
Lag network   635, 633
Lagging tab   260
Lag of downwash   140
Lags in actuator response   443
Lags in the displays   443
Lags in the flight control system   444, 443
Laplace transform   893, 551, 310, 308
Lateral-directional aerodynamic forces and moments   94
Lateral-directional autopilot modes   833, 801
Lateral-directional characteristic equation roots   355
Lateral-directional cockpit control forces   267
Lateral-directional control force requirements   434
Lateral-directional dimensional stability derivatives   348
Lateral-directional dynamic stability and response   346
Lateral-directional flying quality requirements   434
Lateral-directional mode shapes   372
Lateral-directional navigation modes   857, 801

Lateral–directional stability and control characteristics
    for steady state, straight line flight   216
Lateral–directional thrust forces and moments   122
Lateral–directional transfer functions   350, 346
Lateral–directional trim   283
Lateral phugoid   391
Lateral phugoid stability requirements   437
Lateral speed perturbation   127
Leading edge blowing   212
Leading edge radius   35
Leading edge shape parameter   35
Leading tab   260
Lead–lag compensator   815, 746
Level of flying qualities   421
Lift coefficient   77, 44
Lift curve slope (airplane)   80, 45, 41, 37
Lift (force)   77, 9
Lift–to–drag ratio   339
Linear momentum   6, 3
Linear momentum equations (scalar format)   8
Linear range of angle of attack   37
Linear velocities   17, 10
Linear velocity perturbation(s)   186
Load factor   226, 190
Load factor derivatives   603
Load factor feedback   794
Localizer hold mode   857
Localizer intercept and hold   857, 801
Localizer receiver   842
Longitudinal aerodynamic forces and moments   71
Longitudinal autopilot modes   804, 801
Longitudinal characteristic equation roots   325
Longitudinal coefficients for an elastic airplane   596
Longitudinal control force requirements   423
Longitudinal dimensional stability derivatives   319
Longitudinal dynamic stability and response   318
Longitudinal flying quality requirements   423
Longitudinal mode shapes   341
Longitudinal navigation modes   841, 801
Longitudinal stability and control characteristics for
    steady state, straight line flight   198
Longitudinal thrust forces and moments   90
Longitudinal transfer functions   329, 318
Longitudinal trim   275
Loop radius   232

Mach number — 38
Mach number hold mode — 816
Mach number hold mode (using elevator) — 823
Mach tuck control (Mach trim) — 824
Magnitude cross–over frequency — 711, 641
Magnitude requirement — 698
Main gear rotation point — 288
Maneuvering flight — 224
Maneuver margin — 433, 231
Maneuver point, stick fixed — 336, 233, 231, 230
Maneuver point, stick free — 256
Mapping of s–plane into z–plane — 899
Mass balance — 557, 555
Mass density (airplane) — 3
Mass symmetry — 11
Matrix format for perturbed lateral–directional equations of motion — 349
Matrix format for perturbed longitudinal equations of motion — 320
Matrix format for perturbed state, lateral–directional forces and moments — 162
Matrix format for perturbed state, longitudinal forces and moments — 147
Matrix format for perturbed state, longitudinal and
    lateral–directional thrust forces and moments — 174
Matrix format for steady state, lateral–directional forces and moments — 123
Matrix format for steady state, longitudinal forces and moments — 93
Matrix solution to lateral–directional trim — 283
Matrix solution to longitudinal trim — 275
Maximum allowable control forces — 247
Maximum lift coefficient — 37
Maximum rudder deflection — 220
Maximum steady state roll rate — 369
Maximum trimmable lift coefficient — 200
Mean geometric chord — 42
Mean line — 35
Military flying quality requirements — 415
Minimum control speed — 220
Minimum drag coefficient — 37
Mission flight phase — 417, 415
Mission profile — 419, 417
Modern control theory — 687
Mode shape — 341
Moment equations — 21
Moment equilibrium — 199
Moment of inertia — 11, 8
Moment trim — 199
Momentum, angular — 6, 3
Momentum, linear — 6, 3
Monte Carlo scheme — 855

Multhopp   57
Multiple feedback loop system   868, 738
Multiple variable control system   868
Munk effect   115, 57

NACA   35
NASA   35
Nichols chart method   686
Negative camber   211
Neutral point, stick free   253, 252
Neutral point, stick fixed   253, 233, 230, 202
Neutral stability   184
Neutrally stable equilibrium   185
Newton's second law   3
Non–linear terms   28
Non–rotating axis system   4
Non–symmetrical airplane   12
Non–terminal flight phase   420
Non–uniqueness property   894
Nose shape   242
Nyquist diagram method   686

Oblique all–flying wing   12
One engine inoperative (OEI) flight   218
One–fifth–one–five rule   649
One–three–one rule   649
Open loop poles   696
Open loop transfer function   695, 310
Open loop zeros   696
Optical signalling   294
Orientation of airplane relative to earth–fixed coordinate system   14
Oswald's efficiency factor   74
Outer loop   738
Overhang   242
Overshoot   729

Pade approximation   766
Parabolic error constant   736
Partial fraction expansion   634
Payload   33
Peak magnitude   644
Pedal force   267
Pedal–free directional stability   268

Perturbed aerodynamic force distribution matrix		599
Perturbed elastic airplane derivatives		603
Perturbed elastic deformation		598
Perturbed equations of motion		29
Perturbed gravitational forces		598
Perturbed inertial force distribution		598
Perturbed kinematic equations		31
Perturbed state		65
Perturbed state definition		22
Perturbed state flight		27, 24, 22
Perturbed state forces and moments		597, 125
Perturbed state lateral–directional forces and moments		148
Perturbed state longitudinal forces and moments		131
Perturbation substitution		27
Phase angle		636
Phase cross–over frequency		711
Phase margin		727, 711
Phase shift		632, 630
Phugoid	approximate transfer functions	338
	approximation	338
	damping ratio	339, 332
	damping requirements	427
	mode	332
	mode shape	345, 344
	undamped natural frequency	339, 332
Pilot bandwidth		659
Pilot compensation		414
Pilot control of bank angle		768
Pilot control of pitch attitude angle		774
Pilot effort		414
Pilot equalization		765
Pilot gain		765
Pilot induced oscillations (P.I.O.)		771
Pilot lead		414
Pilot neuromuscular lag		765
Pilot rating		413
Pilot reaction time delay		765
Pilot transfer function		763
P.I.O.		771
Pitch attitude angle		17, 14
Pitch attitude angle gyro		933
Pitch attitude command system		846
Pitch attitude hold mode		804
Pitch attitude hold mode (effect of flight condition)		810
Pitch attitude hold mode (effect of servo break frequency)		810
Pitch attitude to elevator Bode plot		667, 666

Pitch–attitude–to–elevator transfer function	321
Pitch damper	789, 395
Pitch damping derivative	194, 145
Pitch rate	9
Pitch rate perturbation	128
Pitch rate stability	194
Pitch–rate–to–elevator feedback gain	396
Pitching moment (airplane)	80, 9
Pitching moment coefficient	80, 44, 37
Pitching moment coefficient about the aerodynamic center	45, 40
Pitching moment coefficient at zero lift coefficient	37
Pitching moment due to speed stability	195
Planform parameters	42
Pole assignment	738
Poles	696, 637
Pole–zero plot	715, 643, 642, 640
Porpoising	557
Position error (constant)	736, 731
Position feedback	690, 688
Position vector	5
Potential flow	57
Prandtl–Glauert transformation	61, 47, 41
Pressure	3
Pressure distributions responsible for hingemoments	243
Product of inertia	11, 8
Prolonged control force application	247
Proverse spoiler yaw	117
Pull force	241
Pull–up	23
Pulsed Laplace transform	893
Pulse train	882, 881
Pulse transfer function of sampled data systems	911
Pure gain pilot	769
Pursuit system	764
Push force	241
Radius of gyration	433
Ramp error constant	736
Ramp function	715
Rate of change of angle of attack	128
Rate of change of angle of sideslip	129
Rate feedback	690, 688
Rate gyro	936
Rate of turn	226, 224
Real root	312, 311

Rectilinear flight		23
Redundancy		294
Regulations		413
Relative stability		686
Residue		638
Resonance frequency		728, 644
Resonance peak		728
Response (definition)		306
Response to an elevator input		340
Response to aileron or rudder input		371, 369, 353
Response to control inputs		353, 324
Response to gust input		354, 325
Return–to–trimspeed–stability		249
Reversal speed		580
Reversible flight control system		297, 238, 183
Reynolds number		37
Ride		190
Rigid airplane		4
Rigid airplane stability derivatives		601
Rise time		729
Robust		686
Rodden		129
Roll angle		14
Roll control derivatives		102
Roll damper		395
Roll damping derivative		193, 152
Roll damping derivative for an elastic airplane		611
Roll	approximate transfer function	367
	approximation	365
	control effectiveness requirements	442, 441, 440, 439
	mode	367, 357
	mode shape	377, 376
	mode time constant requirements	438
	time constant	369
Roll mode		357
Roll rate		9
Roll rate perturbation		128
Roll rate stability		193
Rolling moment (airplane)		95, 9
Rolling moment coefficient		95, 44
Rolling moment coefficient derivatives		106, 104, 103
Rolling moment due to sideslip stability		196, 195
Rolling moment in steady sideslip requirements		442
Root breakdown		327, 326
Root (chord)		51
Root contours		756, 753

Root loci 378
Root locus asymptotes 703, 702
Root locus center of gravity 705
Root locus diagram (step–by–step construction) 707
Root locus method 696, 695, 686
Roots of the characteristic equation 325, 311
Routh–Hurwitz stability criteria 927, 355, 326
Routh's discriminant 355, 326
Rudder–aileron spring 284
Rudder control power derivative 114
Rudder float angle 268
Rudder hingemoment derivatives 267
Rudder lock 270, 269, 268
Rudder pedal force 285, 267, 247
Rudder–pedal–force–versus–sideslip–gradient 269
Rudder side force coefficient derivative 113
Rudder yawing moment coefficient derivative 120
Rotating axis system 7, 4

Sampled unit step 885
Sampler 882
Sampling frequency 924
Sampling period 884
Sampling rate 881
Scalar component form 11
Scalar format 32, 8
Second order lead and lag transfer functions 653
Second order system response 317
Sensitivity analysis 378, 326
Sensors 933
Separate control surface system 780
Separate surface control system 874, 873
Servo break frequency 809
Servo tab 257
Settling time 730
Short period   approximate transfer functions 334
          approximation 333
          damping ratio 335, 332
          frequency and damping requirements 428
          mode 332
          mode shape 345, 344
          undamped natural frequency 334, 332
Side force (aerodynamic) 109
Side force coefficient 110, 109, 44
Side force coefficient due to control deflection derivative 160, 113

Side force coefficient due to sideslip derivative 110
Side force in steady sideslip requirements 442
Sideslip 65
Sideslip angle 95
Sideslip angle to aileron Bode plot 669
Sideslip angle to rudder Bode plot 673
Sideslip feedback 797
Side speed stability 189
Side–step maneuver 189
Side–stick controller 294
Side velocity perturbation 127
Sidewash 100
Sidewash derivative 101
Sign review for aerodynamic coefficients and derivatives 175
Signal sampling 881
Skidding turn 189
Slant range 863, 857, 843
Slot 212
Small perturbation assumption 30, 28
Small perturbation equations 307, 20
Small perturbation lateral–directional equations 308
Small perturbation longitudinal equations 308
Snaking 558
Soft field 291
Speed damping derivative 133
Speed of (system) response 686
Speed stability 188, 186
Speed to elevator Bode plot 662
Speed–to–elevator transfer function 321
Speed–to–speedbrake transfer function 821
Speed–to–thrust transfer function 818
Spillage drag 216
Spinning rotor 13, 11, 7
Spiral approximate transfer functions 367
        approximation 365
        mode 357
        mode shape 377, 376
        stability requirements 437
        time constant 367
Spoiler rolling moment coefficient derivative 104
Spoilers 102
Spring–mass–damper system 309
Stability and control during perturbed state flight 303
Stability and control during steady state, straight line flight 197, 183
Stability and control during steady state, maneuvering flight 224
Stability and control during steady state, pull–up (push–over) flight 231

Stability and control during steady state, turning flight   224
Stability augmentation   793, 395
Stability augmentation system   779, 399, 397, 395
Stability axes (definition)   346, 125, 67, 65
Stability boundary   191
Stability characteristics   183
Stability criteria   315, 184
Stability derivatives for an elastic airplane   596
Stability derivatives using aerodynamic influence coefficients   592
Stability of digital systems   924
Stabilizer   84
Stable break (pitching moment coefficient)   212, 86, 85
Stable equilibrium   185
Standard format for lateral–directional transfer functions   372
Standard format for longitudinal transfer functions   341
Static directional stability derivative   114
Static longitudinal stability   191
Static longitudinal stability derivative   85
Static margin   263, 205
Static margin, stick fixed   253
Static margin, stick free   263, 253
Static stability augmentation   793
Static stability (criteria)   184, 183
Steady level turn   276, 26, 23
Steady rectilinear flight   25, 23
Steady state (flight)   183, 65
Steady state forces and moments   67
Steady state equations of motion   24
Steady state definition   22
Steady state flight   25, 24, 23, 22
Steady state output   638, 629
Steady state turning flight   26
Steady state roll rate   272
Steady symmetrical pull–up   276, 26, 23
Stick force   278, 240
Stick–force–speed–gradient   280, 265, 259, 258, 253, 249, 248, 240
Stick–force–per–'g'   256, 254
Stiffness feedback   690, 688
Structural influence coefficient matrix   591, 590, 586
Subsonic cruise   23
Subsonic speed range   45
Supersonic cruise   23
Supersonic speed range   45
Surface integral   4
Sweep angle   43
Sweep effect on dihedral   98

Symmetrical airfoil ... 35
Symmetry assumption ... 11
System accuracy ... 686
System matrix ... 320
System performance specifications ... 725
System sensitivity ... 737

Tab (geometry) ... 242
Tab effect on trim ... 257
Tab hinge moment derivative about elevator hingeline ... 242
Tab hinge moment derivative about tab hingeline ... 262
Tail size required for rotation ... 291
Tail stall ... 210
Tail stall locus ... 210
Takeoff rotation ... 288
Taper ratio ... 42
Taylor series ... 110, 95, 80, 77, 72
Temporary control force application ... 247
Terminal flight phase ... 420
Theorem of residues ... 635, 634, 311
Thickness ratio ... 35
Third oscillatory mode ... 332
Three surface configuration ... 234
Thrust coefficient ... 92
Thrust effect on trim diagram ... 214
Thrust force ... 70, 10, 9, 6
Thrust force and moment derivatives w.r.t. angle of attack ... 168
Thrust force and moment derivatives w.r.t. angle of sideslip ... 172
Thrust force and moment derivatives w.r.t. forward speed ... 163
Thrust moment ... 10, 9, 6
Tilted rate gyro ... 786
Time constant ... 730, 332
Time domain ... 715
Time domain (connection with frequency domain) ... 715
Time domain response method ... 686
Time domain specifications ... 728, 725
Time history ... 11, 7
Tip (chord) ... 51
Toe–in angle (of engines) ... 123, 107
Torsional stiffness ... 582, 581
Trailing edge angle ... 242, 35
Transcendental ... 123
Transfer function ... 310
Transfer function matrix ... 320
Transformation matrices ... 18

Transient output (response)   638, 630
Transonic speed range   45
Trim   206, 199, 183
Trim diagram   214, 205
Trim (effect of tail area on)   457
Trim of a canard configuration   235
Trim of a conventional configuration   234
Trim of a three–surface configuration   236
Trimmable stabilizer   250
Trim speed   265, 258, 254, 249
Trim tab   266, 257
Trim tab system   250
Trim triangle   206
Tuck   328, 204, 195, 137, 85
Tuck derivative   195
Turbulence   190
Turn   224, 23
Turn coordination   839
Turn radius   226, 224
Turn rate   226
Turn rate mode   838, 833
Twist angle   49

Undamped natural frequency   644, 309
Unit impulse function   894, 715
Unit step   310
Unit vector   8
Unity negative feedback system   731, 695
Uniqueness of sampled data   884
Unstable break (pitching moment coefficient)   212, 86, 85
Unstable equilibrium   185
Upwash   51, 45

Velocity components   21, 9
Velocity error (constant)   732
Velocity feedback   690, 688
Velocity of the center of mass   6
Vertical acceleration feedback   815
Vertical speed stability   190
Volume integral   4
V.O.R. hold mode   866
V.O.R.–hold (Very high frequency Omnidirectional Range)   857, 779
Vortex sheet   52

Washout circuit   789, 781
Waypoint   857
Wetted area   74
Wing divergence   582, 579
Wheel force   247
Wheel–to–ground friction coefficient   290
Wind–milling drag   216
Wing lift vector tilting   154
Wing position effect on dihedral   98
Wing tip suction   154
W–transform method   927, 881

Yaw damper   780, 692, 395
Yaw damping derivative   194, 160
Yawing moment (airplane)   114, 9
Yawing moment coefficient   44
Yawing moment in steady sideslip requirements   439
Yaw rate   9
Yaw rate perturbation   128
Yaw rate stability   194
Yaw–rate–to–rudder feedback gain   398

Zero–frequency gain   341
Zero–lift angle of attack   49, 45, 37
Zero–lift plane   52
Zero–mass derivatives   603, 600
Zero order hold   888
Zeros   696, 637
Z–transform method   893, 881

Notes

Notes

Notes

Notes

Notes

Notes

Notes

Airplane Design & Analysis Textbook Descriptions

All textbooks can be ordered from our on-line store at www.darcorp.com.

Airplane Aerodynamics & Performance
C.T. Lan & Jan Roskam

The atmosphere • basic aerodynamic principles and applications • airfoil theory • wing theory • airplane drag • airplane propulsion systems • propeller theory • fundamentals of flight mechanics for steady symmetrical flight • climb performance and speed • take-off and landing performance • range and endurance • maneuvers and flight

• **ISBN 1-884885-44-6** • **Softcover** • **Reprint: 2003**

Airplane Flight Dynamics & Automatic Flight Controls Part I
Jan Roskam

General steady and perturbed state equations of motion for a rigid airplane • concepts and use of stability & control derivatives • physical and mathematical explanations of stability & control derivatives • solutions and applications of the steady state equations of motion from a viewpoint of airplane analysis and design • emphasis on airplane trim, take-off rotation and engine-out control • open loop transfer functions • analysis of fundamental dynamic modes: phugoid, short period, roll, spiral and dutch roll • equivalent stability derivatives and the relation to automatic control of unstable airplanes • flying qualities and the Cooper-Harper scale: civil and military regulations • extensive numerical data on stability, control and hingemoment derivatives

• **ISBN 1-884885-17-9** • **Softcover** • **Reprint: 2001**

Airplane Flight Dynamics & Automatic Flight Controls Part II
Jan Roskam

Elastic airplane stability and control coefficients and derivatives • method for determining the equilibrium and manufacturing shape of an elastic airplane • subsonic and supersonic numerical examples of aeroelasticity effects on stability & control derivatives • bode and root-locus plots with open and closed loop airplane applications, and coverage of inverse applications • stability augmentation systems: pitch dampers, yaw dampers and roll dampers • synthesis concepts of automatic flight control modes: control-stick steering, auto-pilot hold, speed control, navigation and automatic landing • digital control systems using classical control theory applications with Z-transforms • applications of classical control theory • human pilot transfer functions

• **ISBN 1-884885-18-7** • **Softcover** • **Reprint: 2003**

Airplane Design Part I
Preliminary Sizing of Airplanes
Jan Roskam

Estimating take-off gross weight, empty weight and mission fuel weight • sensitivity studies and growth factors • estimating wing area • take-off thrust and maximum clean, take-off and landing lift • sizing to stall speed, take-off distance, landing distance, climb, maneuvering and cruise speed requirements • matching of all performance requirements via performance matching diagrams

• **ISBN 1-884885-42-X** • **Softcover** • **Reprint: 2003**

Airplane Design Part II
Preliminary Configuration Design and Integration of the Propulsion System
Jan Roskam

Selection of the overall configuration • design of cockpit and fuselage layouts • selection and integration of the propulsion system • Class I method for wing planform design • Class I method for verifying clean airplane maximum lift coefficient and for sizing high lift devices • Class I method for empennage sizing and disposition, control surface sizing and disposition, landing gear sizing and disposition, weight and balance analysis, stability and control analysis and drag polar determination

• **ISBN 1-884885-43-8** • **Softcover** • **Reprint: 1999**

DARcorporation

Design • Analysis • Research

1440 Wakarusa Drive, Suite 500, Lawrence, Kansas 66049, USA - Tel: (785) 832-0434 - Fax: (785) 832-0524

info@darcorp.com – www.darcorp.com

Airplane Design & Analysis Textbook Descriptions

All textbooks can be ordered from our on-line store at www.darcorp.com.

Airplane Design Part III
Layout Design of Cockpit, Fuselage, Wing and Empennage: Cutaways and Inboard Profiles
Jan Roskam

Cockpit (or flight deck) layout design • aerodynamic design considerations for the fuselage layout • interior layout design of the fuselage • fuselage structural design considerations • wing aerodynamic and operational design considerations • wing structural design considerations • empennage aerodynamic and operational design considerations • empennage structural and integration design consideration • integration of propulsion system • preliminary structural arrangement, material selection and manufacturing breakdown
• **ISBN 1-884885-56-X** • **Softcover** • **Reprint: 2002**

Airplane Design Part IV
Layout Design of Landing Gear and Systems
Jan Roskam

Landing gear layout design • weapons integration and weapons data • flight control system layout data • fuel system layout design • hydraulic system design • electrical system layout design • environmental control system layout design • cockpit instrumentation, flight management and avionics system layout design • de-icing and anti-icing system layout design • escape system layout design • water and waste systems layout design • safety and survivability considerations
• **ISBN 1-884885-53-5** • **Softcover** • **Reprint: 2000**

Airplane Design Part V
Component Weight Estimation
Jan Roskam

Class I methods for estimating airplane component weights and airplane inertias • Class II methods for estimating airplane component weights, structure weight, powerplant weight, fixed equipment weight and airplane inertias • methods for constructing v-n diagrams • Class II weight and balance analysis • locating component centers of gravity
• **ISBN 1-884885-50-0** • **Softcover** • **Reprint: 2003**

Airplane Design Part VI
Preliminary Calculation of Aerodynamic, Thrust, and Power Characteristics
Jan Roskam

Summary of drag causes and drag modeling • Class II drag polar prediction methods •airplane drag data • installed power and thrust prediction methods • installed power and thrust data • lift and pitching moment prediction methods • airplane high lift data • methods for estimating stability, control and hingemoment derivatives • stability and control derivative data
• **ISBN 1-884885-52-7** • **Softcover** • **Reprint: 2000**

Airplane Design Part VII
Determination of Stability, Control, and Performance Characteristics: FAR and Military Requirements
Jan Roskam

Controllability, maneuverability and trim • static and dynamic stability • ride and comfort characteristics • performance prediction methods • civil and military airworthiness regulations for airplane performance and stability and control • the airworthiness code and the relationship between failure states, levels of performance and levels of flying qualities
• **ISBN 1-884885-54-3** • **Softcover** • **Reprint: 2002**

Airplane Design Part VIII
Airplane Cost Estimation: Design, Development, Manufacturing, and Operating
Jan Roskam

Cost definitions and concepts • method for estimating research, development, test and evaluation cost • method for estimating prototyping cost • method for estimating manufacturing and acquisition cost • method for estimating operating cost • example of life cycle cost calculation for a military airplane • airplane design optimization and design-to-cost considerations • factors in airplane program decision making
• **ISBN 1-884885-55-1** • **Softcover** • **Reprint: 2002**

DARcorporation

Design • Analysis • Research

1440 Wakarusa Drive, Suite 500, Lawrence, Kansas 66049, USA - Tel: (785) 832-0434 - Fax: (785) 832-0524

info@darcorp.com – www.darcorp.com